HOW TO AVOID
THE FUTURE

HOW TO AVOID
THE FUTURE

Gordon Rattray Taylor

Secker & Warburg

London

First published in England 1975 by
Martin Secker & Warburg Limited
14 Carlisle Street, London W1V 6NN

SBN: 436 51637 3

PRINTED AND BOUND IN GREAT BRITAIN BY
MORRISON AND GIBB LTD, LONDON AND EDINBURGH

Affectionately dedicated to
Frank and Ivy

CONTENTS

V: Practical Problems

VI: Suggestions

ACKNOWLEDGEMENTS

My sincere thanks are due to the following for permission to quote from their work: Lord Ashby, Dr Patricia Elton Mayo, Dr Earl Cook, Professor Eibl-Eibesfeldt, Mr T. E. Geddes and J. O. Long, Dr Theodore Gordon, Mr Tony Parker, Mr Colin Ward, and Sir George Young; and to the editor of *Technology Review*, who, with Dr Cook also gave permission for the use of the diagram on page 218.

I also warmly thank the following for providing unpublished material or other information: Dr J. I. W. Anderson, Mr W. Blake and BOAC, Professor Harrison Brown, Mr Peter Cadogan, Professor John Calhoun, Mr Colin Crouch, Dr Byrd Curtis, Mr J. L. Davidson, Mr Freeman A. Ford, Dr John Fulkerson, Mr E. J. Gibson, Professor T. R. Gerholm, Mr Edward Goldsmith, Mr J. N. Haresnape, Dr James G. Horsfall, Mr D. A. Horner, Dr N. J. Keen, Dr J. W. King, Professor Hubert Lamb, Professor Gordon Manley, Mrs F. M. Paxton, Mr Leonard Pearce, Professor Norman Pirie, Mr S. Redman, Mr Gordon Rose, Mr Stig Siegers, Professor Roberto Vacca and Mr R. H. Wilby; together with the Association of Chief Police Officers, the *Farmer's Weekly*, the National Association for the Care and Resettlement of Offenders, the National Research Development Council, the Officer in charge of Sahelian Relief, the Population Reference Bureau, the United Nations Library and others too numerous to mention individually. My warm thanks also to Mr and Mrs Al Toffler for help in obtaining materials from America.

I should also like to give credit to Mrs Hope Malik, who did much of the research, to my secretary, Mrs Elizabeth Kurn, and to Miss Pamela Avis who typed the fair copies.

G. RATTRAY TAYLOR
Freshford—St Jacques—St Cèzaire

FOREWORD

For people who bury their heads in the sand Robert Graves coined the adjective 'struthious', from the Greek *struthe*, an ostrich, and now we need a noun for them too: Arthur Koestler has suggested Old Struthonian. This book is not for alumni of that school.

In order to avoid the future it is first necessary to take a good look at it. But while many people feel obscurely that it needs avoiding they prefer not to think about it if they can get out of doing so. As every psychiatrist knows, some people avoid problems by denying them, others by ignoring them. Neither method is effective.

Attempting to predict the future is a dangerous occupation. People can forgive failure but to be right is quite intolerable. Optimism is a precious commodity and those who find their optimism threatened quickly deny the validity of warnings. 'Doomster' has become a recognised term of abuse. Some of my biological speculations, dismissed at the time as far-fetched, are already coming true. The famine which I foresaw five years ago is here.

The future, not to put too fine a point on it, promises to be dire: more violent than anything we can remember, more unstable socially, and more insecure. Life will be more inconvenient and frustrating, the material standard of living will fall, there will be financial disasters and whole classes will be wiped out. Food and resources will be in short supply, noise and pollution will be worse. There will be famines and no doubt wars, both civil and uncivil. It will also be much colder. Unless, of course, we all take drastic action to avoid this, starting *now*.

At the moment there is no great sign of any such effort, and it is in the bold hope of triggering a response which might prevent, or at least minimise, some of these developments that I have written this book. It is not, however, just intended as a block-buster or time bomb. It has developed logically from all the thinking I have done about how societies develop over the past thirty years and which I have reported on from time to time in previous books—including one which no one wanted to publish, written about 1950 and called *The Theory of Social Collapse*. This is the sixth in the group of books I call *The Social Imperative*.

By and large the courses which we should be following are plain, though often inconvenient. In every problem area there are experts who are feeling frustrated because the policies, obvious to anyone who has studied the problem, are not being pursued. This is mainly because governments do not understand or do not care or think it will not prove popular or are beholden to interest-groups. So it is only by developing public opinion that change can be brought about. And to develop public opinion you have to look realistically at the problems and at what it will mean for everyone if we neglect them. Which brings us back to this book, and the need to evaluate various alarming current trends.

A modern technological society cannot function without a high degree of social cohesion. That cohesion is being rapidly eroded. Where social structure will crack first is a rash thing to prophesy. Possibly in Italy? My guess is that it will be in Great Britain just because Britain was the first country to attempt democracy, the first to industrialise, the first to develop labour unions and the first in other social fields. It is thus reasonable to suppose she may be further along the road to anarchy than other countries. Certainly, there are signs of a most disquieting sort, as I shall describe in due course. It is for this reason that a great many of my examples and statistics are taken from Britain, rather than because I live there.

PART I

Future Imperfect

I

POSSIBLE FUTURES

The future is not what it used to be.—Arthur Clarke

1 A Sense of Malaise

'The hottest socio-economic story of the moment,' according to a recent *New York Times* editorial, 'is the coming crash and the end of civilisation as we have known it.'

True, the end of Western civilisation has been announced before, but the fact that these announcements proved premature does not mean that such a forecast will not one day prove correct. It is a matter of urgency to examine how society is held together and how such crashes occur—not only in order to see whether such a disaster is imminent but, more importantly, to see what we could do about it. The evidence suggests, as I shall show, that a crash of some kind is highly probable unless an almost miraculous effort to readjust is made.

Even if things are not as bad as the Jeremiahs say, there are certainly serious problems ahead. The question: what does the future hold? has never been asked more widely and urgently than today. The primary reason for this is the rapid pace of change in technological society, which makes life more uncertain than ever before. A century ago a man could expect to plant a tree and see it mature; buy a house and expect to die in it; return to the haunts of his youth and expect to recognise them. Today, his house may be swept aside to make way for a motorway or a government project; the surroundings may be torn down and replaced; the very language itself alters confusingly; the conventions and methods of yesterday prove obsolete tomorrow.

Hence the numerous institutes of futures research, the periodicals devoted to prediction and the technological forecasting sections of big industrial firms. Despite all this activity, it remains difficult for the ordinary man to read the message. Doomsters are at once con-

3

tradicted by boomsters. What is one to believe? How can one make plans?

Yet, despite all this, I believe one central problem has been largely neglected: the maintenance of social cooperation and cohesion. The problems of energy, of pollution, of famine and population growth, of inflation and so on, are serious enough. But at least they are well recognised and are being thought about. But if society itself does not run smoothly—if people withdraw their efforts, or smash and destroy, or terrorise one another—then our chances of solving the more obvious problems become minimal and the survival of society itself is thrown into doubt.

It hardly needs emphasising that cohesion is ebbing away. To be sure, the main body of citizens continues to cooperate and display a sense of social responsibility, but the numbers of those who defy social regulations are rising sharply. In Italy, kidnapping has become almost routine. Bomb explosions occur at frequent intervals in Britain, France, Italy, Germany, Japan and elsewhere. Hijackings are no longer news. The rate of violent crime has doubled within a generation in several countries. Violence on the current scale has hardly been seen since the Renaissance. In the conditions of the past, it was perhaps understandable; but today, with higher living standards, education, social security, and police forces, it is far less easily comprehensible. The argument 'we have always had violence' does not hold water. And the violence takes on an ever more sinister character. When we read that burglars hanged a 72-year-old man and cut off his ears to force him to disclose where his tiny savings were hidden—and then started on his wife—we seem to be back in the Middle Ages. Worse still, we observe that governments of nominally civilised countries torture their captives and blandly disregard the international conventions they have signed.

Apart from the stream of extraordinary and arresting forms of misbehaviour which the Press daily reports—from the crude mass rapes known as 'gang bangs' to subtly ingenious computer frauds— there is a mass of less serious anti-social behaviour, from shoplifting to motoring offences, which from very familiarity we have come to condone, but which shows, nevertheless, which way the wind is blowing. More significant still, theft and violence now find their advocates. Philosophers write books glorifying violence, and burglary is justified on the grounds that property is theft. Not only defiance of authority but intolerance of free speech are openly advocated.

These phenomena represent quite evidently a major failure to integrate men into their society, to obtain acceptance for a social contract which prescribes duties as well as rights. We can also identify a disastrous failure of social cooperation in our massive industrial disputes, and in the obstinate refusal of those who ask for more money to adopt the improved technologies which could raise the living standards of everyone, themselves included.

While the individual seems less and less willing to play the game by the rules, the rule-book itself gets longer and longer. Central control creeps into more and more areas of life; the power of regulating one's own life slowly seeps away.

Precisely because people do not behave cooperatively laws are passed in an attempt to make them do so. The end of this process is totalitarianism. As life becomes intolerably insecure and unstable, people begin to look for a strong man to restore order. There are alarming signs that the West is on the verge of abandoning democracy. Herr Willy Brandt, the former West German Chancellor, has said that he gives democracy in Europe another twenty years at most, and his is not the only voice to issue such a warning.

REFLECTIONS ON DOOM

My first point is that this is not a crisis. It is a climacteric. Not just until 1980, or AD 2000, shall we have to be concerned with the dizzy unbalance of industrial societies; the vulnerability of great cities to disruption by minorities in pursuit of their own—sometimes legitimate—interests; the recurring anxieties about supplies of raw materials to sustain consumption; the indefensible, and unbridgeable, gap between standards of living in affluent nations and in the Third World. Population, consumption, pollution: these spectres will brood over mankind for the rest of his time on earth.

. . . But this [recovery] is not likely to happen in a nation whose equilibrium is disintegrating from causes within its own system; the likelihood is an exacerbation of internecine conflict, an uncontrollable growth of distrust and disillusion, an invitation to anarchy.

> Lord Ashby, Master of Clare College, Cambridge. Chairman, Royal Commission on Environmental Pollution (The David Owen Lecture, 1975, University College, Cardiff)

Behind the growth of violence and protest we can detect a growing sense of envy and resentment, a feeling that life is not what it should be. Paradoxically, that feeling is coupled with an almost schizophrenic indifference to the plight of others. It is this rising pressure which could eventually blow the system apart. I fear a phase of anarchy resolving into a dictatorship.

This sense of deep alarm is not confined to a few pessimists. Men of great reputation have begun to issue warnings. Lord Ashby, the eminent scientist, has told us that we are approaching not a crisis, merely, but a climacteric. Maurice Strong, executive director of the UN Environment Programme, says that, on a realistic assessment of the evidence, 'we will have to acknowledge that if Doomsday is not inevitable it is possible—perhaps even probable—if we continue on the present course.' Alexander King, until recently Director General for Scientific Affairs of the OECD (Organisation for European Co-operation and Development), believes: 'Personally I do not think we have yet reached the flash-point of social chaos, but there are many signs that we have embarked on a course which could easily lead to world crisis.'

Of course there are others who pooh-pooh such fears. 'We are invited,' says the London *Times*, 'to compare our situation with, say, that of the Romans when Heliogabalus wore the purple and the Goths were beginning to muster on the Danube; or the inhabitants of Ur, when the Euphrates changed its course, withdrawing the basis of their inflexible economy.' Comfortingly, *The Times* concludes that such admonitions 'do seem to run rather far ahead of the evidence', and that current problems 'do not amount to grounds for prophecy that the props are about to be knocked from under Western industrial society. . . .' The point seems too important to leave to the complacency of a leader-writer. This is the question I therefore chiefly propose to explore.

Faced with such titanic issues, it is natural for the ordinary man or woman to feel a sense of helplessness. 'There's nothing I can do, so I refuse to worry,' is a frequent response. But the situation is not past repair: there *are* things we can do. Only if public opinion is aroused will governments take action. The remarkable change in official attitudes to pollution and ecological problems was generated entirely by the growth of an informed public opinion.

The first thing to grasp is that the growth of social pathology is not a mysterious development over which we have no control. At least in outline, the causes are understood, and the general character of the necessary remedies is clear. If we ignore the slick political explanations and drive through to the basic sociology, the dynamics of what is happening become reasonably plain. True, the reforms which such an analysis suggest are not easy or even agreeable: major changes in the way we run our society are called for.

The cutting edge of the problem, however, is the failure of governments to respond or even to show signs of having understood the true seriousness of the position. This is why the public must itself take up the issue. The central issue is: can our society respond to the challenge with the necessary conviction and enthusiasm? If it cannot, Western society will indeed decline into chaos and insignificance.

While the decline of social cohesion is the core issue—and the most neglected one—we must place it in a wider perspective. Let us start, therefore, by looking at the future in a general way. What do the experts foresee? Then let us look more closely at such current problems as violence and ask how far these trends might go, and what a further escalation of violence could mean for us. A glance at the comparable situation during the collapse of the Roman Empire will give us the necessary aesthetic distance for an overall analysis of our own social problem. This clears the way for an analysis of specific threats and for proposals and policies of action to deal with them and with the core situation.

First, then, let us take a look at what the professional forecasters predict for us in the next twenty years or so. Is the picture in their crystal balls gloomy or encouraging?

2 The Future Surveyed

Many professional forecasters are comparatively optimistic. One who is not is Dr Theodore J. Gordon, one of the founders of the Institute for the Future in Middletown, Conn. He reckons that at least five major crises await us over the next twenty years. All five are unavoidable, he says.

First, the 'balance of terror' is becoming less stable. The situation in which no great power dared to initiate a war for fear of massive and disastrous retaliation is dissolving under the impact of new weapons: mininukes guided precisely to their target; chemical and bacterial weapons whose very nature is unknown to the general public; techniques of economic and even meteorological harassment which cannot, for a long while, even be identified as aggression. Limited warfare becomes more and more 'thinkable'.

Second, food shortages may increase to dangerous proportions as the population continues to expand and agriculture lags. Meanwhile natural climate changes, especially a general cooling trend with the possibility of a new ice age, seem to be conspiring with the degradation of the environment to make farming more difficult. Gordon thinks it may be necessary to manufacture synthetic soils to replace our eroded and leached-out ones, and that 'artificial farming environments' may be commonplace by the 1990s. Meanwhile, galloping inflation will continue. The growth of multinational corporations will help to widen the gap between the rich and poor nations. Simultaneously, the formation of international cartels, on the lines of the oil-producing states, will, while making things awkward for the rich countries, bring many poor countries to the brink of disaster.

Each one of these problems, taken separately 'presents enormous and unique difficulties,' he said, in an address to the American Association for the Advancement of Science in 1974; 'together they form an unholy fabric which challenges our credulity'. I am entirely in agreement with his general position, and I shall discuss these problems later in the book.

What is remarkable about Gordon's paper is his willingness to take a negative view. Most futurologists concentrate on the trends they consider encouraging, or see the discouraging ones as minor nuisances rather than disasters. They do not allow at all for them reaching intolerable limits, as a result of which society radically reorients itself. Nor do they allow for trends reversing themselves, or for strong reactions developing. We have only to think of the position barely ten years ago, when the trend to polluting the environment, which had run for more than a century, seemed to be accelerating rather than otherwise. No one forecast the emergence of determined public opposition forcing a modification, maybe even a reversal, of the trend.

Another pessimist, Hasan Ozbekhan, then with the Rand Corporation, stuck his neck out in 1969 and named the dates by which certain world problems would have reached 'explosive proportions'. Let us see how well his predictions are making out:

Balance of nuclear deterrence becomes unstable:	5–15 years	1974–84
Institutions become inadequate to tasks:	3–30 years	1972–99
Demand for participation in decision-making:	1–5 years	1970–74
Race crises:	1–5 years	1970–74
Political impatience of the young:	1–5 years	1970–74
Catastrophic famine:	3–15 years	1972–84
Urban maladjustment:	20 years	1989
Administrative illegitimacy in the US:	3–8 years	1972–77

The last I take to mean a general withdrawal of backing from the government and senior civil service; I have tried to clarify the wording of some of the other items. So far, there seem to be two hits: famine is becoming serious (especially in Africa) and institutions are proving unable to cope with inflation. But the youthquake has subsided, at least for the time being, as has racial tension. The nuclear stalemate, as we have seen, may be breaking up. The demand for participation, though certainly present, is not clamant. Score to date: 3 out of 8.

Professor Harrison Brown, of the National Academy of Sciences in Washington, and co-author of a technologically optimistic book of forecasts, revealed his pessimism on the political level at the Nobel Conference in Stockholm in 1969. He sketched three alternative futures:

1 The affluent nations become more affluent; the gap between them and the third world widens. The latter are stripped of resources. Nuclear war eliminates the affluent nations. The third world lives unhappily ever after.

2 Here the disruption takes place before all the resources are consumed, so that the poor world eventually becomes a rich world and repeats the fiasco.

3 A rational programme is developed to eliminate injustice and inequity and to outlaw nuclear war.

This last, he conceded, is 'the least probable . . . indeed it verges on the miraculous'.

John Platt, a biophysicist who is also an associate director of the University of Michigan's Mental Health Research Center, and who has thought extensively about future dangers, takes an almost equally gloomy view. He fears the emergence of a nuclear dictatorship, 'in which some dictator holds the world in his grip by nuclear blackmail, perhaps after a first exchange of nuclear weapons. . . . Today the human race has no adequate checks and balances against such a possibility.' Another possibility is a '*1984*-type situation' in which two or three great powers maintain an unstable peace, based on totalitarian repression. But he hopes for an "open pluralism" and believes that satellite TV, computer diagnosis of ill-health and group-living will serve to bring this about.

That was in 1972. In 1969 he had been still less optimistic, forecasting 'a storm of crisis problems from every direction'. To solve them 'nothing less than the application of the full intelligence of our society is likely to be adequate.' He made a courageous attempt to classify world problems by the estimated time to crisis and by intensity—the number of people affected multiplied by the degree of effect. He concluded that the least serious problems were the ones receiving the most attention from scientists, and vice versa. At the bottom of his list were problems like water supplies, development design, economic problems and exploiting space, which were being studied—in some cases overstudied. At the top was total annihilation, followed by major physical, biological or political changes, such as the rich–poor gap, famine and ecological balance, all likely to become crucial in less than 20 years. Third on the list was 'widespread almost unbearable tension' represented by such problems as poverty, pollution, racial wars, and the need for participation. These problems are already here.

To solve them we need, among other things, new social indicators, similar to the cost-of-living index, which could enable us to measure welfare. Encouragingly, a start has been made in this direction.

However, Platt's optimism returned and in 1973 he saw, in the publication of a number of books dealing with world problems, signs that '1973 may be the year when a world survival movement actually develops'. The fact that so many authors are converging on a shared image of the global future from many different points of view he found 'astonishing and heartening'. If these books and the groups they represent, could generate a real movement of this kind, it could create a focus of hope, a sense of community, and a mobilisation of personal and political resources for the long haul on a scale that would in fact transform these global problems. 'It would be not merely a human organisational event, but a scientific and biological event that could change the slope of all those Doomsday curves.'

For my part, I suspect that it will take more than a few books to create a sense of community and that getting the politicians to change their spots is going to be even more difficult. But perhaps it constitutes a gleam of light at the end of the tunnel.

I fear that predictions of this kind, oriented towards certain 'problems' taken out of any kind of social context, are all but useless for several reasons. First, they ignore the interaction of problems, and especially of problems not listed. Thus the above writers say nothing whatever about such practical problems as shortage of energy and resources, or the possible effects of a cooling climate. Equally, they make no attempt to integrate social problems (like famine) and demands (like the demand for equality) into the picture. Still less do they consider such tenuous matters as the search for identity or a sense of style. Other questions I should like to see treated include the following. Is irrationality, religiosity, superstition, milleniarism going to increase? Does 'educated incapacity' (Herman Kahn's phrase for 'acquired inability to see or understand a problem, much less a solution') affect our chances of survival?

3 The Optimists

In sharp contrast with the apocalyptic futurologists are those who see current trends developing ever further—the same-only-more-so school—and who are perfectly happy about it.

Typical of this euphoric, trend-bound futurology is Burnham Beckwith's *The Next 500 Years*, according to which everything will just go on getting more so indefinitely. Beckwith lists 31 major trends he expects to continue: for example, more industrialisation, more urbanisation, more specialisation, more leisure, more research, more education, more knowledge, more people, more paternalism, more feminism, more permissiveness, more cultural uniformity, more monopoly and ever higher incomes. And somehow, despite all this, more personal freedom!

Most of this, he says firmly, will continue not merely for five hundred years but for a thousand years. All is for the best. 'The world of AD 2500 will not be ruled by brutal dictators who exploit and terrorise their subjects, as Orwell and Wells feared, but by benevolent and highly-educated professional administrators.' Apparently most of them will be women, since as early as AD 2100, 30 to 40 per cent of all legislators will be women; while Britain, the USA and the USSR will have female chief executives by AD 2000.

The only trend that sounds at all discouraging is that the variety of goods on offer will become progressively more restricted. And despite the steady growth in permissiveness—and of pornography— no country will permit polygamy by AD 2100. Divorce, however, will continue to flourish so that Europe will have American rates of divorce by 2060. Work will occupy 3 to 4 hours a day, for only 200 days a year, and the income of the richest will not be more than double that of the lowest-paid workers.

Nuclear war will not slow down these trends but speed them up. By 2200 there will be a world government, relying heavily on public opinion polls. World population will have reached 8.6 billion (600 million in the US) and will still be growing at 11 billion (1200 million in the US) by 2500.

I don't believe a word of it.

The same-only-more-so is also the general message which emerges from the labours of the Hudson Institute, as far as one can gather from the ambiguous prose of Mr Herman Kahn, but there are so many alternatives and contradictions that it is not always possible to be sure what he thinks. I particularly enjoyed his prediction: 'Some acceleration, some continuation, but also some selective topping off of *multifold trend* (and perhaps some temporary reversals).' That just about covers all the possibilities.

Ignoring all the qualifications and double-talk, he seems to foresee more population, urbanisation, industrialisation and centralisation of power. 'My picture of the long-term future is where the better-off people, and this is likely to be half the world, have 2–3 houses, every adult has a car, they have access to air transportation—maybe they have their own helicopters—they have two boats, a submarine . . . and I'm beginning to wonder whether this is really a good thing.' American culture patterns will prevail everywhere and the world will become more 'Westernistic'. This appears to mean more pragmatic, philistine, anarchic and devoted to the pleasures of this world. (Rather oddly, he thinks this will be a world resembling 'Hellenistic Greece' though I should have thought nothing could be much further from it.) Despite being anarchic, it will be relatively orderly and unified, although there will be, by 1980, a serious problem of unauthorised violence. (What these contradictory statements add up to is baffling: your guess is as good as mine.) Moreover, a key issue for the Western nations will be a choice between anarchy and coercion. Kahn does however come down fairly firmly on the Caribbean as a danger-spot. 'In practically every one of the Caribbean nations there is strong potential for an irrational, ferocious, anti-white, anti-foreign, anti-capitalist revolutionary regime.... The effect of such governments would be terrible in material terms but could conceivably infuse pride into the masses.'

However, he does not see famine adding to our troubles. As a result of US policies, 'we can confidently predict a world food surplus rather than shortage for the mid-seventies,' he wrote as recently as 1972. Already in 1975 famine is widespread.

The danger which looms largest, in Mr Kahn's thinking, is due in 1985, when industry begins to produce more goods than anyone wants, and has to be cut back in some way. He calls this a 'technological crisis'—though in reality it is an economic one.

Apart from this, and some violence in South America, which won't affect the rest of the world, the outlook is cosy. We can 'react to the future positively,' because such horrors as nuclear war, eco-catastrophe or the 'Vandals at the gates' should not materialise before 1985.

Like the other forecasters mentioned, Kahn takes it as certain that there will be no change in value-systems in the immediate future. The 'counter-culture' has peaked: the new values espoused by youth will spread no further. Incompetent and hysterical, their leaders can exert no political effect. Perhaps there may be a religious 'counter-reformation' but more probably the values of 'Middle America' will prevail.

4 The Reformists

Another approach to the future, commoner in Europe than in America, is to visualise the world as you would like it to be and then consider what you could do to realise your vision. Futurology here melts into politics. This is, naturally, the only kind of futurology permitted behind the Iron Curtain, where they already know what the future holds—the dictatorship of the proletariat—and wish only to hasten that inevitable outcome.

The kind of future seen by futurologists of this sort varies, but is in any case widely different from the same-only-more-so prospect which the Hudson Institute takes for granted. Almost invariably, European thinking anticipates a major social shake-up.

A particularly thorough attempt to crystallise this kind of thinking was made a year or so back under the auspices of the European Cultural Foundation as part of the project known as 'Europe 2000'. In 1971, as a preliminary step towards drawing up plans for the development of agriculture, of cities, of education and of industry, the four main areas studied, member countries established 'workshops' at which people drawn from widely different walks of life were asked to consider what kind of future they wished to see, and to name the obstacles to be overcome and the changes required. Eventually, at a general meeting attended by representatives from each of these national groups, their ideas were subsumed into various alternative images of the future.

There were four patterns, which, in words for which I alone am responsible, I will attempt to summarise thus:

1 *Competitive self-development* The economic system is entrepreneurial; the state confines itself to supervision. Private property is respected and income is related to performance. This leads to increasing affluence, growing populations, more leisure and some decentralisation. Broadly, the continuation of the present trend in industrial Europe.

2 *Quality of life* To be achieved by planning of resource use. Ecological harmony is the dominant idea: thus competition for resources is checked by a planned reduction of affluence. Agriculture is seen as having a twofold function: food production and the rational use of land and water resources. Science is directed towards maintaining the earth's resources. Cooperation is taught to children and some regional autonomy is possible.

3 *Self-Realisation* Here the stress is on human dignity and personality; creative freedom and social responsibility are the prime values. There is a trend towards equalising incomes, with everyone guaranteed a basic minimum. All participate in decision-making, so that bureaucracy and coercion are eliminated. Individuals are free to choose different life-styles. The disparity between urban and rural ways of life, and between manual and intellectual work, disappears. Work is both a duty and a means of fulfilment. Cooperative farming and communal living are realised.

4 *Communism* A radical transformation of the class society brings about a single community of egalitarian type. There is no private property and the community decides which goods and services to produce. Agriculture is no longer subordinated to industry. Work is

a moral stimulus, a right and a duty. Each individual must contribute according to his abilities and is provided for according to his needs. Large-scale economic planning means that money is no longer a source of power. The key values are solidarity and integration into the group.

It would be valuable to quantify this material, to find out what proportion of the public, in each country, would seriously prefer each type of society. It is a mark of our backwardness that such an essential area has never been investigated.

Interestingly enough, all four of the above conceptions of society aim to abolish the split between agriculture and industry. Actually, the Ecoists and the Egoists have a good deal in common, visualising a gentle, cooperative world based on harmony between man and man and man and Nature, fundamentally in contrast with the puritanical ego-suppression of the communists and the inegalitarian ruthlessness of capitalism. Unfortunately, in a world dominated by considerations of political and military power, the realist patterns seem more likely to predominate than the idealist.

5 Is Prediction Possible?

It has been said that the future is either already determined according to some divine scenario, in which case it is possible to predict it but impossible to alter it; or it is fluid and undetermined, in which case it is possible to alter it, but impossible to predict it.

Fortunately, matters are not quite so bleak as this paradox suggests. The future, while not determined, is not wholly free: it is constrained by the fact that it has to develop out of the present. The process of history has a certain momentum. We can therefore predict the future with a degree of confidence which declines the further ahead we look. It is the fact that our prediction may help to mobilise the forces which will alter the trend and render it untrue which makes prediction chancy. In plainer words, we ought to distinguish warnings from predictions. The man who cries 'Fire!' is not predicting that the house will inevitably burn down; he is attempting to prevent that happening by pointing out the implications of a trend *if* nothing is done about it.

Futurologists, nevertheless, tend to project trends without committing themselves as to how far people will react against them. Recognising this the French group known as Credoc drew a picture of a France crowded into large cities with empty agricultural land between, and emphasised the provisional nature of this projection by calling it a 'Scenario of the Unacceptable'.

Trend projection, however, is an inadequate device for another reason. Anyone examining the coach and carriage business in the nineteenth century might have extrapolated it to an enormous size by now; but the emergence of the motor-car meant the downturn of coach-building. Changing economic conditions can reverse trends; for instance the employment of personal servants and gardeners rose in the nineteenth century but has been declining in recent times.

But the kind of predictions we have been surveying are of very limited usefulness, even if they turn out correct. In the long view, it is not very important to be told that nuclear power will account for a quarter of our electricity needs or that liberal arts graduates will be preferred to science graduates in business.

The statement 'Ever since the Renaissance man has been looking for a new sense of identity' tried to pin down an aspect of society which is much more to the point, but which forecasters are quite blind to. It is new ways of thinking, new demands and expectations, new attitudes to society and each other which change life significantly. The most interesting thing one could have forecast in the Middle Ages was the break-up of the mediaeval world-view and the emergence of rationalism. Probably the most useful and interesting forecast anyone could have made in 1950 would have been the development of the permissive society in all its detail: the untidy clothing as well as the sexual freedom, the exasperation as well as the vanishing of distinctions between the sexes. Hardly anybody made such a forecast, however.

If prophets at the Peace Conference after World War I had forecast the rise of Nazism, it would have been even more à propos.

Is the world going to become less unjust? Is violence going to increase? Is there going to be a religious revival? Or a new totalitarianism? Are the arts dying out? Is mankind going to be any happier? These are the questions to which we all want answers. And our guides remain silent.

If futurology is to become a useful discipline, it will have to explore the dynamics of social change and base its forecast on some body of theory about the redistribution of power between social groups and changes in human aspirations and limits of toleration.

It seems therefore that we need a method of treating social change as a whole. Just as we describe processes of growth and development in the biological field in holistic terms—'the bud opened into a flower'—so we must describe social development holistically. Afterwards, we can break the totality down into sub-processes, and then analyse these still further. We cannot work from small to large unless we have an exhaustive knowledge of the nature and potentialities of every element. We do not have such knowledge for biological systems; much less for social ones.

Trend-line predictions are also liable to be upset by unexpected events, some favourable others disastrous. The Black Death changed the course of Europe, making labour scarce, raising the price of corn and provoking wars. The invention of steam power also changed the course of history, possibly for the better. But the favourable events are usually slow to take effect, while the disasters strike quickly—for just the same reason that it takes much longer to make something than to destroy it.

In the next few decades, what could happen that would change all our forecasts in a positive sense? The invention of a lightweight and compact means of storing electricity, perhaps, or the simulation of photosynthesis, the process by which plants lock up the energy of sunlight; this would give us a cheap energy source and an energy store at the same time. The food position would be transformed if we could discover how to make nitrifying bacteria attach themselves to non-leguminous plants (as they already do to legumes) since this would greatly reduce the need for fertiliser. A means of enhancing human intelligence would be even more useful. But all such discoveries take decades to come into general use. The internal combustion engine was invented in the nineteenth century, but did not really change the pattern of life for fifty years. Today things move faster, but it would still take a generation to get new electricity stores or nitrifying bacteria into general use. Factories have to be built and bugs ironed out: much worse, people have to be persuaded to play.

It is disasters, not blessings, that could falsify all predictions for the next twenty-five years or so; let us try to imagine some of them.

II

EXPECTING
THE UNEXPECTED

*The fecundity of the unexpected far exceeds
the statesman's prudence.—P. J. Proudhon*

1 Plagues and Ills

The possibility that a new and disastrous plague, compared with
which the Black Death would be small beer, may shortly be launched
upon the world must now be taken quite seriously. Scientists have
issued their warnings and governments are now debating what
precautions they could take.

The risk arises because biologists are becoming able to modify
bacteria, to reconstruct viruses and even to manufacture *de novo*
viruses which never existed before. The danger was foreseen as long
ago as 1960 by the Australian Nobel prize-winner Sir Macfarlane
Burnet. He pointed out that the techniques, then being developed,
for culturing viruses and looking for new mutants, involved the risk
that a dangerous new mutant might escape and set off an epidemic
against which the population of the world, possibly including animals,
would be helpless, since the body's natural defence systems would be
unprepared to cope with it. The appearance of 'a serologically
unique virus of great virulence . . . is a very serious danger,' he wrote.
If it escaped into circulation without being immediately dealt with,
the consequence might be 'an almost unimaginable catastrophe . . .
involving all the populous regions of the world'. Now this danger
has suddenly come nearer.

The basis of his concern was his theory, now generally accepted,
that the body contains a 'library' of patterns on which it draws to
manufacture antibodies to defeat invading viruses and bacteria.
Hence if an invader which carried markings not in the library (or

17

no markings at all) were to enter the system, the body would fail to recognise it and to set defences into action.

Since Macfarlane Burnet issued his warning, biological technique has become far more sophisticated. Currently, the great area of excitement in biology is the technique known as hybridisation, in which genetic material (DNA) from two different sources is brought together to create an entirely new combination. The hybrid gene can then be used to create an unprecedented organism. At present such work, known as plasmid engineering, is confined to viruses and bacteria. Thus, whereas Burnet only feared an accidental mutation, now we can make them to order.

In the summer of 1973 a conference was held in the US to discuss these rapidly developing methods and to exchange wrinkles and findings. This was the Gordon Conference, held in New Hampton, New Hampshire. At this meeting 130 scientists were so concerned by what they learned that they instructed their secretary and president to draft a 'letter of concern' and to send it to Philip Handler, then the President of the National Academy of Sciences, and John R. Hugness, President of the National Institute of Medicine of the USA. It was also sent to *Science*, the leading US scientific weekly.

Commenting that certain of these hybrid molecules 'may prove hazardous to laboratory workers and to the public', the letter urged that the Academy should set up a study committee to recommend guidelines for such work and added (hinting, one assumes, at the possible military applications) 'the risks involved in current large-scale preparations of animal viruses might also be considered.' The committee subsequently set up urged that a moratorium be placed on (i) introducing into a bacterium resistance to antibiotics or toxin-making properties, and (ii) the introduction of virus genes into bacteria. The fact that scientists commonly use for experiments a normally harmless bacterium found universally in the human gut enable the risk that an explosive multiplication of some new germ might occur in someone's intestines and, as has happened with anti-biotic resistance, be spread round the world. It could even cause a cancer explosion. Such work is now 'almost unthinkable' said a member of the committee. British workers, while scouting the danger of the first of the above experiments, saw a real risk in introducing cancer-genes into such bacteria. The bacteriological warfare departments have so far maintained an ice-cold silence.

Perhaps because I myself originally set out to be a biologist, I regard this as the most realistic of the serious risks which will be hanging over our heads in the next quarter century. So does Professor Joshua Lederberg, of the University of California at Los Angeles, who says that modern developments in molecular studies 'undoubtedly point to the development of agents against which no reasonable defence can be mounted'. We can hardly rely on more than a ten-year delay between important discoveries in biological warfare research laboratories and their availability to hostile and irresponsible forces outside. It is not so much the use of these agents by the great powers that is the danger as their possible use by small nations, by insurgents and terrorists, or the occurrence of accidents. Crowded, underfed human populations provide the best possible situation for the spread of new viruses. 'Bacteriological warfare agents for use against man can be expected to be far more capricious than any other form of weapon,' says Lederberg. It is not so much the dangers associated with research which matter but that of containing infectious agents which are being manufactured and stockpiled in large quantities and are being tested in the open air.

GERMAN POLICE CONTINUE HUNT FOR MAD SCIENTIST

The 'mad scientist', as the West German news media has dubbed him, is reported to have sent four extortion letters to Chancellor Will Brandt's office demanding $8,200,000. If the ransom is not paid, he has threatened to spread the bacilli of anthrax and botulism through the post, plant them in factories, shopping centres and infect water supplies of several large cities in which synagogues are situated.

The extortion letters were also reported to have warned that Government members would be kidnapped and public buildings bombed. The $8,200,000 demanded would be 'atonement money' for the five Arab guerrillas killed in a battle with police after they had kidnapped a group of Israeli athletes at the 1972 Munich Olympics.

Japan Times 19 November 1973

Note: Botulinus toxin is the most deadly substance known: a teaspoonful would be sufficient to kill all living things in the world.

This process is encumbered with even more secrecy than the laboratory work. 'The main effect of security has not been to deny information to an enemy,' say Lederberg, 'but to protect an establishment from both constructive and destructive criticism at home.'

The refusal of public-health bureaucracies to give sufficient thought to the possibility of major pandemics of human disease occurring, whether spontaneously or as a result of human activity, is disgraceful. Can it be that they are pessimistic about global health anyway? Lederberg recommends extensive monitoring to detect any misuse, a free flow of information, more research on coping with these risks, and above all, the establishment of agreed sanctions against any persons or nations which make use of them.

Of course, the prolific efforts of chemists, who synthesise thousands of new substances a year, and our habit of putting many different additives in food without adequate tests (often without any) also holds out the risk of massive poisoning or even genetic damage. Recently workers in the US Department of Agriculture analysing various agricultural chemicals were thunderstruck to find that some of them—a group known as PCPS—broke down in the environment into incredibly toxic substances known as dioxins. A millionth of a gram—a mere speck—will kill a guinea-pig. This fact was discovered when millions of commercially raised chickens were poisoned in 1957. PCP also contains as contaminants substances known as furans, likewise highly toxic.

Apart from the wonders of science, the appalling problems of sewage disposal in the overcrowded areas of South-East Asia pose a serious threat of plague. 'It is probable that at least one major global outbreak of disease will occur before the year 2000,' says John Vallentyne, a Canadian expert on water-purity. '. . . the focus will almost certainly be somewhere in Asia, probably in South Central Asia . . .' Such a viral epidemic could have 'disastrous consequences round the world'. It could happen tomorrow.

If I were asked to make an off-the-cuff guess about the kind of unexpected disaster most likely to strike the developed world in the next twenty years or so, I think I should pick the prospect of a Thalidomide-type tragedy—but on a far larger scale—caused by food additives. More than 2,000 different substances, it is reckoned, are being added to foodstuffs today: anti-caking agents, enzymes, binders, firming agents, buffers, sequestrants, texturisers, flavourings, preservatives, moisturisers, colourings, antioxidants, thickeners, stabilisers, extenders and many others. Only a few of these have been tested for their long-term biological effects and the rules for rejection are far from strict. (Thus Britain allows the addition of a dozen colouring additives which are entirely prohibited in the USA and has no regulations controlling the use of flavourings. Many of the colouring agents are coal-tar derivatives, a chemical group many members of which cause cancer. For instance, the xanthines, which give some foodstuffs a yellow colour, are often mutagenic.)

And while we know much too little of the biological effects of these additives taken singly, we know nothing of what they may do in combination. My guess is that some enterprising manufacturer will one day unwittingly bring together two additives—say, an extender and a colouring agent—which react chemically to produce a really toxic or mutagenic end-product. But whereas Thalidomide was taken only by pregnant women, and then by only a proportion of them, foodstuffs are in general eaten by all and sundry. If the effects are immediate, a widespread epidemic of illness and death might occur, but within weeks the cause would be identified. If, however, the effects are long-term—as is usually the case with cancer-causing compounds—twenty years may pass before a sudden rise in cancer, or maybe in deformed births, warns us that something is wrong. And by then millions of people may have eaten the stuff and be carrying the seeds of their destruction. Identification of the guilty substances may be as difficult and fraught with controversy as was the case with tobacco and cancer. Years could pass before the situation is put right. Our slap-happy attitude to food sophistication (as it is called, 'adulteration' having unpleasant associations) is, to a biologist, almost unbelievable.

2 Eco-catastrophes

Biologists of many persuasions have already warned us of the danger of an eco-catastrophe—the upsetting of the balance of nature. A vivid scenario for such a disaster has been drawn by Paul Ehrlich, the Stanford University geneticist, and I described some other possibilities in *The Doomsday Book* (1970). Since then scientists have been busy turning over the possibilities, in the hope of avoiding being taken unawares, and several eerie possibilities have come up. The difficulty, of course, is that we do not know enough about the balance of nature to be able to predict with any confidence.

One such eventuality was recently pointed out by Dr A. W. Fairhall of the New Zealand Institute of Nuclear Sciences, in a communication to *Nature*. It is a possibility that the coral reefs of the Pacific are about to vanish: perhaps also the shells and skeletons of oysters, crabs and various other sea-creatures may dissolve away. These organisms derive the calcium from which their shells and bones are made from calcite and aragonite, with which the oceans are supersaturated: that is, the water contains so much that the calcium tends to dissolve out. Whereas, if the water were undersaturated with respect to these substances, they would tend to dissolve *out of* the reefs and shells and *into* the water, since nature tries to achieve a balance of concentrations. So much depends on maintaining this supersaturation.

If carbon dioxide gas is absorbed by the sea, its content of aragonite declines; in fact at 41 parts per million, the aragonite would be reduced to one-quarter of its present level. Now man has greatly increased the output of carbon dioxide as a result of burning coal, oil and natural gas. Fairhall calculates that, if fossil fuel use continues to expand as it has done in the past century, the oceans will reach the 41 ppm level by AD 2008. Indeed, to hold them on the verge of saturation we should have to limit future fossil fuel consumption indefinitely to the level it was at in 1969.

Fairhall's mathematical model of the chemical and physical processes involved predicts that the carbon dioxide present in the upper layer of the sea should increase by 1.4 per cent in the next decade. If it is so increasing it ought to be possible to detect the trend within the next three to five years. 'If it is detected,' observes Fairhall wryly, 'there will be very little time left to consider what, if anything, could be done about it.'

In the meantime, we might do some research. We know nothing about whether sea-creatures can build shells in these unsatisfactory conditions nor if, once built, the shells will persist.

Some of the disasters which scientists have speculated about are now thought, on the basis of experimental studies, to be unlikely—for instance, the possibility that the earth might run out of oxygen. But one which is still being taken very seriously, and which experimental work seems to confirm rather than otherwise, is the possibility that fleets of stratospheric aircraft might destroy the layer of ozone which shields the earth from the sun's ultra-violet radiation. Following Congressional concern at this idea, a committee was appointed to consider what the biological effects of such a reduction might be. In 1972 it reported that, if the ozone at these high altitudes were reduced by 5 per cent only, this would cause a 26 per cent increase in the harmful radiation at the earth's surface. This might be expected to cause an additional 8,000 cases of skin cancer a year in the US alone, as well as causing genetic damage which could not be calculated.

What makes SSTS a potential threat to the ozone layer is not the fact that they emit water vapour, but that they emit oxides of nitrogen, which combine with the ozone, in a number of different ways, to convert it to oxygen. Defenders of the SST argued that the explosion of atomic bombs in the period to 1963 had released nitrogen oxides, but that only a slight reduction of ozone had resulted. Unfortunately no one really knew how much of these oxides had actually been formed by the bomb, and little was known about the amount of ozone normally present. Taking the most favourable view—namely, that the bomb had released a lot of oxides, and that normal ozone was present in large quantities, it looked as if the ozone might be cut by 10 per cent. Taking the least favourable view, it might be cut by a factor of ten times, which would certainly be disastrous. Experiments were therefore continued and in 1974 a Harvard team concluded that the ozone reduction might be only 1 per cent. Meanwhile the National Ocean and Atmosphere Authority (NOAA) was making measurements of the actual ozone levels about 13 miles up with balloon-borne sensors. This showed that natural levels of nitrogen oxides were much smaller than had been thought. Thus, if theory was reliable, the addition of more oxide 'might cause significant damage to the ozone layer'.

Another factor which may confuse the issue is the rate at which air mixing occurs, and Britain's Lord Rothschild, then heading the government's think-tank, declared that their studies showed that the climatic effects of Concorde would be insignificant.

When a panel of the US Department of Commerce arrived at the view that SSTs might raise the levels of nitrogen oxides from 3 to 70 parts per billion, Professor Harold Johnstone of the University of California realised this could mean disaster. Making the necessary calculations he showed that the possibility of a serious effect was too great to be dismissed. Later, Professor Dr Paul Crutzen of Oxford, assuming a different sequence of chemical reactions, arrived at even more alarming figures. The US Department of Commerce projection is now accepted as being much too high, but even on the revised figure the possibility of causing dangerously low levels of ozone, at least in areas where SST traffic is intense, cannot be excluded.

In September 1974, MIT scientists announced, on the basis of a new computer model of the atmosphere, that 500 SSTs of the kind the US hopes to build would probably cut the ozone by 10–15 per cent and urged the setting of world limits to the production of oxides of nitrogen to keep the ozone loss below 1 per cent. A few days later, a Russian scientific journal expressed similar misgivings in connection with Russia's Tu144 supersonic transport. The last straw was the discovery by University of Michigan scientists that the inert gases used as propellants in aerosol sprays were accumulating in detectable amounts high in the atmosphere and can break down into substances which destroy the protective ozone layer. Though they do not constitute a threat at the moment, Ralph J. Ciccione and his co-workers think they could have a significant effect by 1985 or 1990. Studies to check this have been put in hand.

Unfortunately, people do not react very strongly to pollution they cannot see or even smell. Cancer rates could rise for some years, and genetic effects could be produced for even longer, before people would begin to take the matter seriously, as the history of tobacco-smoking and cancer demonstrates.

The fact is, the biosphere is not so undamageably tough as we tend to suppose, and man may yet inadvertently disturb it, despite all the warnings. One particularly likely effect would be the production of unintended climatic change.

3 Ice Surge

'No matter how deeply disturbing the thought of using the environment to manipulate climate for national advantage is to some, the technology permitting such use will very probably develop within the next few decades.' Thus Dr Gordon J. F. Macdonald, Executive Vice-President of the Institute for Defense Analyses and chairman of a special panel appointed to study weather control.

In Cambodia, the American air force made attempts to cause rainfall and flooding by cloud-seeding, and no doubt more sophisticated attempts to alter climate will be made long before the end of the century. Russia, for instance, would like to free her northern ports of ice and it would be much easier for her to extract oil from the Siberian oilfields in warmer conditions. Gordon Macdonald has suggested that one way this might be done is by creating an 'ice-surge' in the Antarctic. Since ice melts under pressure, scientists believe that, at the bottom of great ice-sheets, the ice may be near its melting point. Any increase in pressure would then cause melting, freeing the ice-mass from rocky projections and enabling it to slide down the slope into the sea. The friction would generate heat, causing further melting and so propagating the flow. Such surges occur naturally. The reduction in Antarctic ice would heat the atmosphere, causing a corresponding melting of Arctic ice to match, thus freeing northern ports. The largest natural ice-surge yet reported is probably the one which occurred in Spitzbergen between 1935 and 1938. The ice advanced on a front of 30 km for distances up to 21 km. Some surges are said to have advanced 100 metres a day. Small glaciers can move as fast as 5 miles an hour.

Macdonald reckons that, since a one-megaton bomb would melt 100 million tons of ice, the use of 100 megatons would certainly be enough to start such an ice-slip. However, the immediate effect would be a tidal wave which 'would completely wreck coastal regions, even in the northern hemisphere'. So, he argues, it is unlikely to be tried except as an offensive method of war, and then only by a mainly landlocked country.

However, J. T. Hollin of Yale thinks that the point may be near at which such an ice-surge may occur naturally, and that we should begin to look for signs. He agrees it might well inundate the world's coasts, so any reports of unstable ice-conditions in the Antarctic would justify the reader in coastal areas in moving on to higher ground, and everyone in buying warm clothing.

If and when the wave of ice reaches the sea it will form an ice-shelf which will reflect the sun's rays, reducing the earth's average temperature by 6 degrees Centigrade. As the bergs break up the sea level will rise from 60 to 100 feet, drowning most of the world's major cities.

A distinction should be drawn between such sudden catastrophes and the possibility of a slow degradation of the environment which finally reaches the point at which an irreversible breakdown occurs. Here the slowness with which the crisis develops allows more time to recognise the problem and attempt to take avoiding action.

However, let us assume for the moment that no such sweeping disasters occur. What kind of future could we reasonably expect? In my view, for reasons I shall give in detail later, the overriding problems will not be physical but social: violence, terrorism, industrial militancy, inflation, governmental incompetence, and perhaps attempts to impose totalitarian systems on democratic countries. Depending on how seriously one takes these possibilities a number of alternative futures can be foreseen. Perhaps the best way to present them is in the form of brief alternative scenarios. Afterwards, we consider which seems most probable.

4 Alternative Scenarios

Five possible types of future emerge: two apocalyptic, two quite depressing, one rather optimistic. Let us start with the most disastrous of all, nuclear war, since if this occurs no other speculation is worth considering.

1 *Nuclear War* Johan Galtung, Director of the International Peace Research Institute in Oslo, believes that a major war is unlikely in the next twenty years or so. He pins his optimism on the fact that a web of international organisations is slowly binding the whole world together, plus the growth of cross-national marriage, foreign travel and working abroad. He foresees multiple citizenship and the obsolescence of national borders, which will finally offer no more obstacle than does the frontier between Norway and Sweden today. In view of current difficulties in leaving the USSR and its satellite countries, this seems optimistic, to say the least. In any case, the decision to go to war does not depend on such matters. However, Professor Bernard Feld, secretary general of the Pugwash Conference on Science and World Affairs, puts the odds on a nuclear weapon being used before 1984 at three to one, and thinks the chance of avoiding war before the end of the century is even slimmer. Chinese leaders are convinced that a third world war is unavoidable, and will start in Europe within the next generation, according to a report from Peking by David Bonavia of *The Times*. Deputy Foreign

Minister Teng-hsai-ping told visiting European industrialists that
he believes Russia will attack Europe, not China.

CHINESE LEADERS SURE THAT THIRD WORLD WAR IS UNAVOIDABLE

The Chinese leadership is convinced that a world war,
starting in Europe, cannot be avoided in the next generation
[said] Mr Teng Hsiao-ping, a deputy Prime Minister.

Mr Teng's thinking seems to be in line with Chinese
pronouncements of the past year, to the effect that the
Soviet Union's military strength is being massed against
Europe in the first instance and the apparent threat to
China is a feint to distract attention from Moscow's true
aims . . . Peking believed that Europe would be the real
target.

The Times 16 October 1974

I am more alarmed by the fact that a dozen nations now possess
the resources necessary to build a hydrogen bomb: thus the risk of
'button errors' is increased—for minor nations may not employ such
elaborate precautions and interlocks as have been devised by Russia
and America. I follow a hint of Galtung's in the following scenario.

Scenario A

In the late seventies, Brazil, under a hard-driving military government, was emerging as a major economic force. The population was
rising, thanks to a policy of encouraging immigration, and the
opening up of the Amazon basin had created a frontier situation
resembling that in the United States during the nineteenth century.
Anxious to exert more leverage in world affairs, as well as to become
the leader of the Latin-American sub-continent, Brazil covertly
sought the help of India and soon became possessed of atomic
weapons. By this time Israel, Egypt and South Africa had become
members of the nuclear club. Sweden and Switzerland, relying on
the three-months clause, had withdrawn from the non-proliferation
treaty. What was going on in Japan, some of whose off-lying islands
were closed to visitors, was anyone's guess.

By this date, mininukes of various sizes were available capable of
knocking out a single industrial estate or flattening a large government office without putting the city out of action, and there was talk
of a 'channelled blast' blockbuster which would take out a single
skyscraper as neatly as a tooth. Several attempts at nuclear blackmail
had kept the world poised in front of its colour television sets until
the ransom demanded was paid. Robbed in this way, each country

simply recouped by robbing another. A vast game of Monopoly developed.

But while the rich nations played Monopoly, the poor nations fell further and further behind in the race; a new generation, acutely aware of economic differences, was now adult and taking over the reins of power. Tension between the poor world and the rich world was becoming acute. The class war had become international.

At this point, China suddenly announced herself the leader and protector of the poor, offering to send nuclear teams wherever they were wanted, and summoning a conference of the leaders of developing nations. An ultimatum was issued calling on the rich nations to scale down their consumption to the planetary average, to dismantle factories and send them abroad, and to supply oil, cotton, timber, wool and manufactured goods to their poorer cousins. Russia, in sight of affluence for the first time, was even more appalled than America, but it is not known which of them pressed the button first.

2   *Eco-catastrophe*   We have already looked at some possible but rather extreme eco-catastrophes. But there are others so relatively likely that we should make room for them in any realistic assessment of the future. 'I confess I am more worried, looking at the next thirty years, about possible ecological instabilities in developed agriculture, dependent as it is on fuel, fertilisers, monoculture and constant genetic innovation,' says the economist Kenneth Boulding, 'than I am about possible curtailments of energy input into private transportation or even manufacturing. The latter does not seem to threaten more than inconvenience. A collapse of developed agriculture, however remote the possibility seems today, threatens major disaster for the human race . . .'

Here is another possibility.

Scenario B

By the eighties, the short-lived oil crisis was a thing of the past. An energetic search for oil, plus the development of the more brittle shales, had restored the tempo of industrial growth. Indeed, a cooling climate and some shortage of raw materials, which necessitated working lower-grade ores, had caused the rate of oil consumption to advance even faster than the most generous forecasts.

There had been some mishaps of course, notably the loss of the North Sea in 1980, following the snapping of several oil pipelines as a result of a shift in the sea-bed. Experts judged that the rapid removal of so much oil had left a cavity, into which the sea bed collapsed, taking most of the oil-rigs with it. The North Sea was now devoid of fish, and the various coastal resorts round it had been badly hit. Indeed, Knocke, Skegness and some of the Swedish islands had actually had to be abandoned, but desperate efforts had prevented more than a fraction of the oil from seeping out into the Atlantic. Permanently strike-bound, Britain herself had in any case gone back to candles and donkeys.

As a result, people had become blasé about the danger of oil spills, and not much concern was felt when it was reported that two half-million ton tankers, powered by atomic energy, had collided in the Beaufort Sea. (The pipeline from the North Slope across the Alaskan tundra had proved so vulnerable to the interference of the eco-bombers that it had been abandoned in 1978.)

In the Beaufort Sea, the waters sweep slowly round in a vast movement known as a gyre, for a lip of rock prevents much interchange with the Bering Sea. Several years passed, therefore, before it was realised that a million tons of spilt oil was slowly being spread over the whole Arctic, seeping under the ice, emerging through the long fissures which thread it, and finally running over the surface of the ice-sheet. In the sub-zero conditions of the Arctic, oil is very persistent. Few bacteria exist to break it up.

As the surface darkened, it began to absorb the sun's heat more readily and thus began to melt. This revealed more oil, and the process speeded up. Satellite observatories reported the rapid shrinking of the polar ice-sheet. Scientists hastily calculated that, if the reflectivity was reduced 20 per cent all the ice would go in two years and would never return owing to the warming of the atmosphere. Actually it took three years. By a meteorological quirk, the heating of the Arctic caused cooling in the middle latitudes. Not only agriculture but fisheries were disrupted. But this was insignificant compared to the rise in sea-level. As New York, London, Paris, Stockholm, Oslo, Leningrad, Montevideo, Sydney, Melbourne, Calcutta, San Francisco, Cape Town and Tokyo sank beneath the waves, civilised life as it had been known up to that time came to an end.

3 *Orwellian Future* Turning now to less than catastrophic futures, one inevitably thinks of Orwell's *1984*. The great powers, armed to the teeth, and holding their dissatisfied peoples in check by a reign of terror, maintain an uneasy peace. Rumours of impending attack are used to justify every injustice and to quell every revolt. The party, with a quasi-religious enthusiasm, holds all noses to the grindstone, much as the medieval church applied its ascetic codes. All resistance was heresy, to be destroyed by fire, sword or torture.

George Orwell having described the prospect with a brilliance I cannot attempt to equal, I can only say:

Scenario C

Read *1984*.

**4   *Ultimate Technology* ** Many science fiction writers have foreseen the probability of a future in which war is avoided, but all the trends of current society are pushed to a horrible extreme.

Scenario D

Thursday was not my best day. To start with, there was no water in the taps when I went to wash and as I plugged my shaver in, there was a power cut. That meant no coffee either and no air-conditioning. It was so hot I nearly left off my bullet-proof vest. Just as well I didn't. That sniper was on the building opposite again, and as I dashed from the front door to the garage, he got me. The impact of the bullet hurled me into the garage real fast. I knew I would be safe once I was in the car, because the new plastic armour can stand up to anything smaller than a heavy machine gun. I checked the boot and engine for possible bombs and got in. That's the worst moment, I think: you can never be sure that one of the pressure-sensitive explosives has not been concealed in the seat or under the floor mats.

At the office, I had to walk up eleven flights and was too out of breath to return the guard's greeting as he checked my pass. (Normally we use the magnetic checks, of course, but the machine was not working owing to the power cut.) There wasn't much work, with all the voice-writers and miniputers out of action, and there wasn't any mail. No doubt it had been stolen again. Ever since the paper shortage began to bite, there'd been a racket of selling undelivered letters for recycling.

After tidying my desk and emptying the trash-basket (office-cleaners being a thing of the past) I began to think about the weekend. On Friday, there would be meat for dinner, with luck. Marie had found a little shop which would sell you hamburgers when they got to know you. They had a rather odd taste, and Marie said she thought they were made of rat, but dog seemed to me more likely.

And after dinner, a shot of Euphorium and then two blissful hours in the new Pseudosex we've just acquired. Boy, that machine is really something! It's like the first time I ever laid Marie, all over again. Without it, life would hardly be worth living. Marie agrees; she says it makes up for everything.

**5   *Optimistic Scenario* ** When we begin to think what would constitute an optimistic view, we at once see that, by some means or other, governments are going to have to stop thinking about the next election or their national prestige and attend to the ever-widening gap between the rich nations and the poor. Failing which, as several prophets have foretold, the affluent society will be brought down in ruin. Nations at each others' throats, like Israel and Egypt, India and Pakistan, the USA and the USSR, are going to have to forget their national paranoia and find the goodwill to work out a mode of cooperation. How such a conversion is going to be achieved is hard to foresee.

Scenario E

Rumours began to spread among the senior officers of the Pentagon that a new and powerful agent of chemical or bacteriological warfare had been discovered at the Porton Research Establishment in England. Hastily obtaining some through the mutual aid agreement, they mounted a battle exercise and sprayed two companies of men with the agent. The results were extraordinary. Within a few minutes the men simply refused to fight. They were not doped; they were not hallucinated. In fact, their competence was increased if anything, and when a man fell from one of the half-tracks and was injured, his companions rescued him and conveyed him to a dressing station with the greatest care and solicitude.

The agent was, in fact, not a chemical, but a fungus normally growing on cereals and resembling a wheat rust. But by genetic intervention, the Porton biologists had altered its chemistry so that it produced, as a breakdown product, a powerful pharmacologic agent with an effect similar to that of nitrous oxide. That is to say, it opened the mind to a sense of kinship with all other creatures and also with Nature. Anyone who absorbed it not only became kind and thoughtful to others, but felt impelled to live in harmony with the environment.

Of course the Pentagon at once realised, as had the British, that such a drug, if once its existence became known, would make war impossible and so make their profession useless. Stringent efforts were made to suppress all knowledge of its existence. But in vain: an accidental spill in the laboratory had already converted a scientist, who at once saw that only good could come of passing the formula to the Russians and Chinese. They were already far advanced with plans to spray all European crops from the air, so that it would enter the system of anyone who ate bread or even porridge. Being a fungus it flourished in the gut, continually providing the organism it infested with the illuminating chemical. The only course open to the Pentagon, naturally, was to spray the Russian and Chinese fields with equal thoroughness.

War being thus abolished, and a spirit of harmony prevailing, it was possible to abolish armaments and it became possible, indeed essential, to transfer thousands of scientists and technologists to useful work. Before long, new strains of rice and soya were produced, and a way was found to make cows calve twice a year. Birth-control pills were combined with a harmless addictive substance, so that people felt impelled to go on taking them. Before long, the population began to drop. The next advance was a drug which increased intelligence, as a result all outstanding problems were soon solved. Industry, released from arms-making, turned its attention to reconstructing the cities, and the golden age dawned.

Surveying these five possibilities, one cannot help feeling that the last—the optimistic one—seems rather less probable than the other four. It is something on the lines of the former which we should be planning to avoid.

However, let us put aside such general speculation and turn to facts. The most important single factor affecting the immediate future, I suggest, is the steady loss of social cohesion which is occurring, especially in Western societies, though also in India and elsewhere. This manifests itself most noticeably in the form of anti-social behaviour, crime and violence. Just as high temperature warns us that all is not well in the body, so violence is an indication that something is wrong in society. So let us look rather closely at this trend to estimate its importance and try to understand its origins. For if society breaks up this will outweigh all other considerations and will render any forecasts which ignore it nugatory.

PART II

Internal Weakness

III

GROWING ANARCHY

The practice of violence changes the world but the most probable change is to a more violent world.—Hannah Arendt, On Violence

1 Three-party Crimes

In 1974 the mayor of St Tropez, the fashionable Mediterranean resort, received a threat that bombs would be planted in the town if he allowed nude bathing to continue! Whether this was a genuine threat or an attempt to satirise the current vogue for achieving one's ends by threatening the innocent with death did not emerge. Either way, the incident spotlights the new readiness of individuals—as distinct from political minorities—to resort to ruthless violence to attain their ends by sacrificing innocent third parties.

Most of these threats have no such comic element, and we must face the fact that they are growing steadily worse and more numerous. As I write, there are reports from London, Tokyo, New York, Paris, and Rome, to say nothing of Belfast. The technique of bombing has become an open book. Prevention is almost impossible. I see no forces which can prevent an appalling escalation of this crime. We must lay our plans on the assumption that violence will continue to get worse.

Not only bombings, but assassinations and mass slaughters such as that at Lydda Airport, and the shooting down of passenger aircraft must be expected. The weapons are easily obtained: a rocket launcher and seven mortar cases were found in the room of a student —a student!—at East Anglia University recently.

Also mushrooming is the taking of hostages—it is happening in the Hague as I write—kidnapping and abduction. There have been over 300 abductions in Italy since 1960, involving over $30m. in ransom money—to take but one country as an example. The us State

35

Department now issues businessmen going to South America with a booklet on how to cope with terrorist attacks. Police forces are forming squads of sharpshooters to pick off hostage-takers.

Yet very little serious effort to meet the situation has been made. The world's governments have not even found it possible to agree on a system of bringing plane hijackers to justice—despite the fact that they own the costly planes in most cases. Of 28 Palestinian terrorists surrendered to various Arab governments in 1973 none has been punished. Of some 80 such over five years, about a dozen were sentenced, most of whom were subsequently freed. It is as if we wished to push these ugly facts out of our minds and hope that the trouble will subside if ignored.

I do not think that they will go away. I recall these painful events because I believe they represent an important strand in the general loss of social cohesion which we are trying to explore. They warn us that our civilisation is genuinely at risk and deserve our closer attention. On the one hand, they represent the rejection of demo-cracy and rational methods generally; above all, of disregard for majority opinion. Simultaneously they mark a lack of concern for others that is of psychotic character. Society cannot stand much more of this.

The characteristic feature of these crimes is not that they are political—some of them are not—but that they involve three parties: the criminal, an innocent party who is threatened, and a third party who is expected to be influenced by this threat. I therefore call them Three-Party Crimes (TPCS). Thus they constitute a moral blackmail of a most despicable kind, and growing familiarity should not dull our indignation at them. The terrorist exploits the better nature of others: the unwillingness of civilised people to let others die is what he trades upon. Hence, the more civilised his opponents, the weaker their situation. Authoritarian governments might refuse to give way at the pistol point; democratic governments naturally find it more difficult. Thus the terrorist pushes the world towards authori-tarianism while forcing it back to barbarism. Moreover, by operating internationally, he exploits the disunity of nations.

Of course, kidnapping for a ransom existed in the past, though it was never common, and the taking of hostages in time of war to protect a messenger was not unusual. But today technology has changed the scale of such operations and made them much easier to carry out. Firearms make it easier to capture unarmed citizens, and motor vehicles whisk them away before a hue-and-cry can be raised. Again, explosives make it possible to threaten indiscriminately great numbers of people, who cannot even be warned, which inten-sifies the pressure on the third parties, while transport and timing devices make it possible for the criminal to place such bombs with minimum risk to himself. As technology progresses, it must be expected that this kind of crime will become both easier still and more destructive, to the point where life becomes intolerable and society begins to crack.

However, it is not so much the efforts of common criminals which threaten us as those for which a political motive is claimed. Actually, as soon as we look at all closely at political terrorists, we see a strong strain of psychopathology, and begin to suspect that for many of them politics is only a convenient excuse for behaviour to which they are impelled anyway. Some are driven primarily by ego needs: the desire for notoriety is common in hijackers and assassins. But others are clearly nihilistic or even sadistic. The self-styled 'freedom fighter' Rose Dugdale used to pour lighter-fluid on her hands and set it alight, while her friends squirmed, which suggests both motives. She bites her nails to the quick, a classic sign of aggression. Sadism is evident in the carefully thought out 'punishments' of the IRA, such as shooting off a man's kneecaps or destroying his lower jaw, not to mention others even more horrible. Up to October 1974, 110 men and women had been given 'knee jobs'—for some of which not bullets but electric drills were used. Sadism is equally evident in the terroristic methods used by the Huks in the Philippines and elsewhere. 'So not kill only . . . but mutilate your adversaries. . . . Pierce their eyes . . . cut off their arms . . . and hang them,' urges the student paper *Ez-Zitouna* in Tunis. The Huks went in for tearing men apart with horses. And much more.

The suggestion that such terrorists are *not* politically motivated, however much they may persuade themselves they are, is confirmed by the fact that political experience has repeatedly shown that indiscriminate acts of terror do not advance a political cause. Many years back, the Vietcong engaged in random bombing but soon learned that it merely aroused opposition to them. They then forbade all such exploits though continuing to use the most savage terrorising methods selectively—for instance, to ensure the cooperation of village headmen. It is obvious that four years of bombings in Northern Ireland have failed in their aim, whereas a national strike altered government policy within a matter of days.

Nevertheless, there is a political angle, arising from the fact that terrorism is financed and encouraged by governments, which see it as promoting a general social breakdown from which an authoritarian government might arise.

2 The New Terrorists

Not only money but arms and training are provided on an international basis. When Ulrich Schmücker, the 22-year-old explosives
officer of a small German group known as the 'June 2 Movement'
was captured by police, he 'sang', revealing that even this small
gang was receiving steady Arab support, on a cash basis. (Rifles and
grenades cost DM 5,000.) Not only were weapons supplied but
members could hide out for a while in the Lebanon, for a fee of
DM 3,000 or receive military training for DM 10,000. (After his release
he was killed by gang members for his betrayal of their secrets.)

Russia, of course, supports subversive groups and Western intelligence agents have confirmed that the KGB and its army counterpart
the GRU, have trained, equipped and financed the Popular Front
for the Liberation of Palestine (General Command). This support
has gone on for five years and apparently includes the provision of
SAM-7 ground-to-air missiles. Yuri Ivanov Starchinov, assigned three
years ago as military attaché to the Soviet Embassy in the Lebanon,
is reported to be the master-mind of this group, which was brought
into existence by his predecessor.

According to Mr John Barron, a *Reader's Digest* editor, in his book
KGB, the KGB has armed and trained both wings of the IRA and
'sends representatives rather openly' into Ireland to sustain and
advise them. A *Pravda* correspondent, Mr Yuri Yasnev, is named as
one of the contact men, but the actual training was arranged through
Cuba. Certainly Russian rifles and rocket-launchers are in use by
the IRA. Colonel Qaddafi boasted in an interview in Paris in 1973
that his government had financed not only Palestinian guerrillas but
also the IRA and 'many other' rebel groups. 'The government of
Libya, and perhaps one or two other Arab governments have
certainly helped the Palestinian campaign. Less well known is the
evidence that some groups may be receiving support from Russia,'
says *The Economist*, noting that the Basque liberationists who held a
press conference were carrying Czech-made weapons, that Palestinians rely on the Russian-made Kalashnikov rifle, and that Russian
Strela anti-aircraft missiles were smuggled into Italy and Belgium.
This last, being very new, is unlikely to have come from international
arms dealers; the fact that some Palestinians have used East Berlin
as a starting-point for their raids is doubtless significant.

In addition to the support of governments, extremist movements
often help each other mutually, and form a kind of international
conspiracy. Thus, the Popular Front for the Liberation of Palestine
(PFLP) has enlisted help from extremists in Japan, Turkey, West

Germany and America. (Early in 1974, the French police broke
up a terrorist cell in Paris consisting of Turks and Palestinians.) At
London's Heathrow Airport, a few days later, a team consisting of a
Pakistani, a Moroccan and an American girl was arrested. Koreans
are said to have been active in Northern Ireland. The IRA has also
been in close touch with the Basque ETA and the Breton Liberation
Front. Members of the outlawed group, the Federation for a Free
Quebec, boasted that they had been trained for guerrilla warfare in
Jordan and Cuba.

It is technology which has made this internationalism possible,
both in the sense that rapid transport and communications enable
such groups to keep in touch, and in the wider sense that only
affluent societies provide the funds and leisure for such activities.
Funds for Black Power in Britain are reputed to have come from
Moscow, Peking, Dar-es-Salaam, Communist sources in Belgium
and, on at least one occasion, from Cuba, says Ian Greig in his book,
Today's Revolutionaries.

Terrorist techniques, once they proved successful in one country,
are speedily adopted in another. After Brazilian and Guatemalan
kidnappers abducted foreign diplomats, Argentine guerrillas likewise
grabbed foreign businessmen. Then their example was copied in
Belfast, where a German industrialist was seized. Similarly, the Arabs
borrowed the device of hijacking aircraft from adventurers heading
from the US to Cuba. The car-bomb, used occasionally by the Mafia
in America, was turned into a standard weapon by the IRA and then
copied by the Basque terrorist group Euzkadi ta Azkatasuna (ETA)
in Northern Spain.

In addition, terrorist techniques are increasingly copied by
criminals. Bank robbers take hostages; kidnappers have seen the
advantages of capturing prominent businessmen and demanding
money from the wealthy companies that employ them. Gangsters
netted a reputed $1m. from Amoco in return for Mr Willkie, an oil
executive, and a reported $3m. for a Peugeot executive, M. Boisset,
early in 1974. There were more than 400 kidnappings in Argentina
alone in 1973.

Many of these were by ERP, the People's Revolutionary Army,
which is said to have accumulated more than $30m. in this way,
including the record $14.2m. paid by Exxon for the general manager
of its Campana refinery, Mr Samuelson. In other cases, a sort of
blind revenge rather than cash seems to have been the motive:
offices of International Telephone and Telegraph have been bombed
in Nuremberg, Berlin, New York, Rome and Paris, following publication of a book about its political activities—mostly by the German
'Black Help' group and a French group calling itself frankly 'We

Must Do Something'. Palestinian groups, such as the Popular Front for the Liberation of Palestine have attacked prominent Jewish businessmen. Threats of sabotage can be effective, and the PLFP is said to have extorted protection money from four airlines flying to Lod in Israel. 'It seems probable that future variations . . . will include the threat of sabotage against extremely vulnerable but easily damaged installations, such as oil rigs, oil refineries and computer complexes . . .' says *The Economist*.

ONE KIDNAPPING EVERY FIVE DAYS IN ITALY

In Italy one person is kidnapped, on average, every five days, a bomb goes off every 67 hours and 26 minutes, someone is blackmailed every 16 hours and 54 minutes and a murder happens every eight hours and 56 minutes.

There is a robbery, usually armed, every two hours 40 minutes, someone has a handbag snatched or is defrauded every 57 minutes and a pocket picked every 42 minutes. There is a petty theft every 71 seconds.

The Times 18 September 1974

The ruthlessness and ingenuity to which such groups can aspire is shown by a training manual issued by California's Black Liberation Army during the Patty Hearst affair: '(1) If the ransom deadline is a week or less, the hostage should be buried in the ground with enough food and water to see him through. The terrorists can then either reveal his whereabouts without going near him, or, if the deal falls through, they can let him starve to death. (2) If the deadline is 24 hours, the victim should be drugged and left in the boot of a car. He can then be sprayed with armour-piercing bullets from a passing car if the ransom demand is not met.'

In reporting this, *The Economist* concludes with the comment: 'There will be an increasing tendency for terrorists who have failed in their own countries to seek easier targets abroad. Some of the exiled Latin-American revolutionaries may be among the first to move along these lines. Equally disturbing is the rise of would-be guerrilla groups among minority communities in western Europe. The activities of such groups constitute one of the everyday hazards that companies, as well as governments, must now take into account.'

Ruthless as kidnapping is, it lacks the purely sadistic elements displayed by advanced terrorists such as those which occurred in Algeria or among the Huks in the Philippines. These were not the excesses of men with adrenalin in their blood but were coolly advocated in print.

The largest group of terrorists appears to be the Arab one. Taking together Al Fatah, the Popular Front for the Liberation of Palestine, the Popular Democratic Front for the Liberation of Palestine, Sa'iqa (Syrian Ba'athist) and the Black September, we have a total of some 14,000 adherents in 1972, according to an estimate of the Institute for the Study of Conflict. The Japanese group which has cooperated with them, the United Red Army (URA), is estimated at 300 in Japan, where in fact it has made little mark.

Women have played prominent roles as terrorists, and the security expert Peter Hamilton claims that every terrorist gang has either a female leader or a female second-in-command. He adds that a school for training 'anti-men' women as guerrillas is operated in Switzerland.

Little work has been done (and less published) on the crucial question of what motivates these people who cheerfully destroy others. Those taking part in the Munich massacre were described as young, well-educated men speaking French, German and English. The Red Army members, certainly, come from middle-class families. Its original leaders were the son of a hotel proprietor and the daughter of a businessman.

When Japanese police pursued Red Army members into a lonely mountain area north of Tokyo they came across a dozen corpses, all members of the movement who had been tortured and strangled to death for 'deviationism'. Some, it turned out, had been guilty of lack of revolutionary dedication, others of 'bourgeois leanings' in that a boy had shown affection for a girl; another girl had been killed for the crime of becoming pregnant. A wife had been forced to kill her own husband, two boys to kill their own brother. The pathology bears a chilling resemblance to the Manson murders in California.

As long as a few hundred such people are produced by any society and left free to move about the world, we shall have an unacceptable situation. It must not be underrated. 'Already no air traveller is secure from attacks by politically motivated, or paranoiac, or simply criminal individuals; no letter can be opened in safety; diplomats can no longer go about their business without fear of being kidnapped or losing their lives; nobody can be sure he is not a potential hostage; no international gathering, like the Olympic Games, is free from threats of violence.' Thus Colin Legum in the *Observer* in 1972. 'Nor are the possible victims restricted to any particular or national group: 27 diplomats from 11 countries have been kidnapped (Arabs as well as Israelis are among the number) and three have been killed in the last five years; planes have been hijacked from Mexico, Turkey, Czechoslovakia, Russia and Japan, as well as from the US; parcel-bomb victims have died or been wounded in Tanzania, Libya, Egypt as well as in Britain and Israel; letter bombs travel in all directions from many parts of the world.' Today that list could be lengthened. Russian delegates warned the UN that the next step might be the use of bacteriological or atomic weapons to blackmail governments.

The obvious feature of political third-party crimes is that they represent an abandonment of the democratic process. The perpetrator has lost hope of any success by normal channels and resorts to force. Thus we are embarked on a long slope which leads to the dictatorship of the most ruthless. How can we avoid this? There are two cases. One is where a government is genuinely unresponsive to popular demand, if not indeed actually oppressive, and that the ensuing violence has a broad popular backing. In this case the government must either yield or risk being overthrown. But quite often the activists are a small minority, whose aims are not endorsed by the mass of the public—as in Northern Ireland, where repeated referenda have shown that the public as a whole wishes to remain within the United Kingdom. The same is true of the fascist groups in Italy and of the extreme left-wing groups in Britain—and of both in France. In such cases the only radical solution is to discover how such extremists were driven into these antisocial positions. How do they become so convinced of the rightness of their position that they can defend it despite overwhelming evidence to the contrary? One is reminded of the determination of the flat-earthers or the doctrinal rigidities of medieval heresies.

Neurosis has been defined as a response which, natural in itself, has become rigid and excessive. It is natural to wash your hands, but neurotic to wash them a hundred times a day. On this definition, most extremists are neurotic. At present little can be done for them, short of coagulation of certain brain centres, and no one would wish to grant governments the right to perform brain operations on their opponents. Nevertheless, neurotics can be given therapy and support, and those who are antisocial are often taken into care. Yet the employment by Russia of medical measures to silence critics of the regime shows that this policy too can be abused. In the long run the only acceptable course is to correct as far as possible the social conditions—that is, the family conditions—which give rise to neurosis. But this is a long-term solution.

However, the only sinister feature of the situation is the way in which elaborate justifications of violence (it is really flattering them to call them philosophies) have been put forward by left-wing 'intellectuals' and have been avidly swallowed by the young despite their obvious irrational components.

3 In Praise of Violence

German and French writers, notably Nietzsche and Sorel, have
been the main source of this line of thought. From them the line can
be traced through Fichte and Bismarck to Hitler and Lenin. Praise
of violence always goes with the symbolic revolt against a father-
figure, and his replacement by a son who is even more authoritarian
than the parent.

In the post-war world, Frantz Fanon, the black psychiatrist born
in Martinique, has been the main inspiration of this trend, probably
because of the mystical illogic of his pronouncements. For Fanon,
violence is not a disagreeable necessity, but actually desirable. The
'purifying flame of violence' enables the damned to be born again,
to become beautiful and holy, he says in his *Les Damnés de la Terre*.
Woman too should practise violence: 'by engaging in violence she
becomes fully human'.

During World War II, thousands of French sailors, refugees from
Hitler and the British, flooded into Martinique. As a Martiniquais,
Fanon knew only French culture, and knew none but a French
identity. So he was shocked to hear Martiniquais referred to as
'niggers' and became a fanatical exponent of colonial revolt. A
colony freed by violence becomes purged of all its defects, he claimed.
Violence creates a new spiritual unity; the act is 'consecrated in
blood'. But he lived to see what violence really created: weak,
corrupt and incompetent administrations, maintained by force,
injustice and terror.

Fanon's writings are not merely irrational but often flatly contradictory to fact. 'Decolonisation is always a violent phenomenon,'
he declares. 'The peasantry alone is revolutionary.' Peasants accept
modern medicine because it is a revolutionary weapon, he asserts.
Sexual deviations are unknown among black men: it is only Europeans who become sexually repressed in the process of striving for
achievement who become deviants, he says, wildly borrowing from
Freud in an attempt to provide a collective therapy for the black
race. After the revolution, all white institutions must be destroyed
utterly, lest they poison the new world. (He does not indicate what
institutions can be substituted.)

In France, the philosopher Jean-Paul Sartre, though now *démodé*,
became the main influence. While he dismissed Sorel's *Reflexions sur
la violence* as 'fascistic chatter' he went a good deal further himself,
distinguishing 'revolutionary violence' which was acceptable from
'reactionary violence' which was bad. Two of his plays (*Les Mains
sales* and *Le Diable et le Bon Dieu*) argue that one can achieve little

in politics unless one dirties one's hands with violence and terrorism.
'The essential problem,' he told a newspaper interviewer, is to over-
come the idea that the Left ought not to meet violence with violence.
In 1966 he begged Russia to intervene with (nuclear) missiles against
American bases in the Far East, even if it meant a third world war.

But it is perhaps the German writer Herbert Marcuse who has
written the bible and prayer-book of the movement. Indeed his
Critique of Pure Tolerance (1966) was actually published with a black
cover to look like a prayer-book or missal.

As a German Jew who fled from oppression to a democracy,
where he has been allowed to speak freely and has been supported
while doing so, he might perhaps have been expected to see some
good in democracy, and in freedom of speech. But no—democracy
is a fraud and its freedom of speech illusory. Indeed this tolerance
is itself a form of repression. Allowing people to blow off steam is a
subtle way of maintaining domination. Moreover, protest itself
simply 'serves to strengthen the repressive administrator'. The
solution, strange to say, is to have some good old-fashioned intolerance, provided it is exerted by the Left. The right of free speech and
free assembly is to be suspended, because the whole of society is in
an emergency situation. And the sooner the better. 'Intolerance even
toward thought, opinion and word' is the thing, because democracy
'has destroyed the basis for universal tolerance.' Marcuse, the critic
of Stalinism, calls not only for terror but for a reign of terror.

Marcuse's popularity with the young doubtless depends mainly
on his sexual theories, likewise based on turning Freud on his head.
Everything that is wrong in society is due to sexual repression. (The
supposed permissiveness of modern society is just another fraud.)
What we need is 'erotisation of the entire personality'. Work too
must become 'erotised'. The analogy, in Marcuse's mind, between
sexual repression and political repression is clear and perhaps helps
to explain his obsessive preoccupation with the topic.

More sinister than such lucubrations is his argument that biased
information can only be corrected by information equally biased.
Untruth shall set you free!

As Maurice Cranston observes in a perceptive essay, Marcuse's
attitude to the present world is often indistinguishable from that of
an elderly Blimp or Junker. 'The degree to which the population is
allowed to break the peace wherever there is still peace and silence,
to be ugly and to uglify things, to ooze familiarity, to offend against
good form, is frightening,' Marcuse complains, adding that it is most
disagreeable to be compelled to 'partake of their sounds, sights and
smells'. As Cranston rightly says, Marcuse, who is one of those who
introduced the word 'alienation' into the language, is himself

alienated. 'Marcuse has the stomach of a very high-class aesthete, queasy, fastidious and misanthropic.'*

A full account of these philosophies of violence would also have to include the English psychiatrists R. D. Laing and David Cooper, but the theme of the 'demystification of violence' would take us further into the controversies of psychiatry than most readers would care to go.

More extraordinary perhaps is the tendency of some Catholic priests and theologians to espouse violence, lamented by Jacques Ellul in his book, *Violence*.

Father Cardonnel, a French Catholic, is representative of the 'theologians of revolution'. How shall Lent be observed nowadays? he asks. 'By a well-planned general strike. Such is the Lent that pleases God, the Easter liturgy of today.' But his enthusiasm for revolution is outclassed by that of the Franciscan, Fr Maillard, who has declared: 'If I noticed that my faith separated me by however little from other men and diminished my revolutionary violence, I would not hesitate to sacrifice my faith.' Thus revolution becomes an end, not just a means, a view also propounded by the American Richard Shaull. As Jacques Ellul comments, this is sheer nonsense and makes revolution an absolute value. Shaull's position, in fact, is that Christians should participate in *all* revolutions, whether of the Right or the Left, nationalist, fascist or whatever.

Even the central Christian doctrine of love is put aside. Fr Maillard says: 'We must not impede the global revolution of our brothers by our scruples. We face a real choice. Love in the form of generosity must be rejected as too idyllic; authentic love comes through political, economic, sociological studies.'

But as Ellul points out, these revolutionary Christians are not really concerned with all oppressed people; they distinguish the 'interesting poor'—us Negroes, North Vietnamese, Palestinian Arabs and the poor of South America—from the 'uninteresting poor' who are not worth troubling about: 'the Biafrans, massacred by the federal troops of Nigeria, the monarchist Yemenites, burned by napalm and bombed into obliteration by the Egyptian air force from 1964 to 1967; the South Sudanese, destroyed *en masse* by the North Sudanese; the Tibetans, oppressed and deported by China; the Kurds, perhaps 500,000 of whom were massacred in Iraq and Iran between 1968 and today'. Nor, one might add, does the extermina-

---

* It is an amusing example of the way in which such ideologues always take a step at some point into the ridiculous, that Marcuse bitterly criticised the literary style of *Time* magazine, comparing it unfavourably with the crystal purity of—of all things—the *Communist Manifesto*. Marcuse's own style is involuted and ambiguous beyond all description.

tion of the Patacho Indians by the Brazilian Bureau of Indian Affairs arouse much fervour among Christians.

'The interesting poor are those the defence of whom is really an attack against Europe, against capitalism, against the USA,' Ellul comments. The uninteresting poor are those who are simply struggling to survive as a people, as a culture. The motivation has thus nothing to do with love of the poor—but much to do with hatred of the less poor.

Some will find a certain irony in the Christian revolutionary's desire to abolish poverty in the name of a teacher who preached poverty.

It is not enough, however, to dismiss these rationalisations of violence as trivial just because the writers are irrational, illogical or ambiguous. The appetite for such literature arises because the situation itself is deadlocked. How does one remove an entrenched regime if non-violent methods fail? The medieval church recognised the existence of a 'just war'. And when faced with fascist oppression many normally peaceable people felt themselves justified if not morally obliged to take violent action. The medieval church at least sought to limit war and insisted that all other possibilities should be exhausted before war was launched. The objection to the philosophers of violence is that they tend to glorify violence, making it almost an end in itself. This is an obscenity far more appropriate for censorship than the pornography which so upsets the sexually inhibited in our society.

Given this kind of preaching, it is hardly astonishing to hear Eldridge Cleaver, the Black Power leader, describe himself as 'ex-convict, rapist, advocate of violence', and declare: 'the niggers are going to come into the white suburbs and turn the white suburbs into shooting galleries.' Cleaver has called Fanon's *Les Damnés* the 'Bible' of the black liberation movement in America.

4 The Mystery of Nihilism

'So we'll start unrest, and there'll be havoc everywhere—havoc such as the world has never before witnessed.' The words are those of Peter Verkhovensky in Dostoevsky's *The Possessed*, a man whose greatest ambition was to 'cause such a mess that everything will go flying to hell' because 'the idea is so attractive for some reason'. Why is it attractive? We find the same idea advanced by D. H. Lawrence, who said: 'It would be fun to upset the apple-cart. Let's make a revolution for fun.' Why is this idea of universal destruction so attractive to some people? It is precisely the fact that many of today's extremists seem more concerned with destruction than with building anything better to replace our admittedly imperfect society that is so discouraging.

Modern extremists echo these ideas exactly, as the title of Abbie Hoffman's book, *Revolution for the Fun of It*, clearly reveals. The editor of an obscure protest publication *The Loving Couch Press*—one Steve Jones of Manitoba, Canada—announced his editorial policy thus: 'My personal aim is to destroy. To fuck up my readers for 25 cents.'

Richard Neville, the editor of *Oz*, provided a partial explanation when he remarked that the Provos of the 1960s sought to provoke official retaliation in order to have something to fight against 'as there was nothing to complain of'. But it is rather more than confrontationism, or even the drama of a holocaust. Vicious, rodent-like destruction is also satisfying to some, such as the lecturer at Vincennes University who explained to a British journalist the aims of the militant students there. 'It's hard work but we're making progress. With any luck there won't be any university to come back to in the autumn.'

The nihilist rationale was outlined with unconscious humour by Carl Ogleby, former president of the militant American organisation Students for a Democratic Society (SDS): 'The rebel is an incorrigible absolutist who has replaced all "problems" with the one grand claim that the entire system is in error, all "solutions" with the single irreducible demand that change shall be total, all diagnoses of disease with one final certificate of death.' However, he then reveals that his objective is not so much total change as the overthrow of authority, when he says: '. . . total change means only that those who now have all power shall no longer have any, and all those who now have none . . . shall have all.' Sons, in fact, shall supplant their fathers.

It follows that any idea of gradual reform is out. Gradualism is more objectionable to the extremist than reaction itself. 'We have to give up any illusions about "peaceful" or "legal" means of change . . .' says Tom Hayden in *Rebellion and Repression*. 'We are creating an America where it is necessary for the government to rule behind barbed wire, for the President to speak only at military bases, and where, finally, it will be necessary to fight back.'

Alarming as all this sounds, I suspect that it is not much more than the desire of many young people for a purpose, a mission, combined with the excitement of physical activity, danger and planning. The real danger lies elsewhere. Nevertheless, the growth of nihilistic and revolutionary movements is a trend of some importance in any evaluation of the future.

The nihilistic urge reaches its extremest ultimate expression in self-destruction. The Japanese who carried out the massacre at Lydda airport explained that they did not fear to die for their crime,

since afterwards they would 'shine like stars in the sky' along with
their victims. This can only be called psychosis. (The Japanese seem
especially prone to suicidal tactics, as the wartime kamikaze pilots
demonstrated.) When Samson pulled the temple down about his
ears it was presumably because he felt he was without hope and
revenge was the most he could manage. So today it is hopelessness
plus resentment which motivates the nihilist. Even though we
condemn, we must, if only in our own interests, study and try to
dissipate that sense of despair.

Though extremists constantly attack the ills of society and
proclaim their support for 'underdogs' in other countries, it is
noticeable that few of them make any real effort to help underdogs
in a direct manner, for instance by going to underdeveloped countries
and teaching better farming techniques. They attempt to adopt
black men as symbols of oppression (yellow men, who do not make
such good symbols, black being the natural opposite of white, get
practically no support, for which they are doubtless thankful). The
fact is that their motivation is not based on love for their fellow men,
or sympathy with their plight, but on hatred. Che Guevara put this
quite bluntly: 'Hatred is an element of the struggle—relentless
hatred of the enemy that impels him [the revolutionary] over and
beyond the natural limitations of man and transforms him into an
effective, violent, selective and cold killing machine.'

The supporting element in the extremist's personality is of course
rejection of authority, but carried to an ultimate extreme. This
explains why, to the young revolutionary, 'the burning struggle is
more important than dogma. . . . If there is any dogma at all it is
confrontationism.' Precisely: the revolution becomes an end in
itself, because it is the assertion of independence which is the sole
objective. This is why the revolutionaries have so few ideas about
what they propose to substitute for the system they wish to destroy.
It also explains why they are so scornful of liberalism and attack
tolerance and rationality. That is why they shout down speakers
with whom they disagree, why they seek to pull down, smear or
denigrate prominent figures. The truth or falsity of the smear does
not matter; all that matters is to pull down the idol.

Obscenity is valued as a means of annoying the older generation,
or as Professor Marcuse rather grandly puts it, the use of obscenity
is 'a methodical subversion of the linguistic universe of the establishment'. That makes it sound positively respectable! Calling the
President 'pig'—he solemnly explains—or making animal noises
during a political speech, together with the use of sexual epithets are
part of 'the great design of the desublimation of culture which, to
the radicals, is a vital aspect of liberation'.

The fact that these extreme positions are adopted principally by students is explained by their age, and the circumstance of being treated as an adult for the first time, coupled perhaps with the fact that many of those who now go to universities are unsuited for academic studies and are looking for action, not thought. It is a consequence of the 'higher education for all' movement which its proponents failed to foresee. Many of these rebels settle down after a year or two. The question therefore arises how far such behaviour represents a long-term threat to the stability of society. I suspect that some degree of radicalisation is produced: even those students who do not take part are forced to consider some of the issues raised, and this enhanced sensitivity to real social problems I can only regard as a very good thing. It is only the most extreme, and particularly those who are animated by permanent resentments, who will continue to be politically active. But this residue constitutes a serious threat.

5 Official Violence: Terror

Advocates of violent methods commonly argue that the state uses violent methods, and that this justifies their using violence in return. This is a verbal quibble. All societies, including the most unsophisticated, license the restrained use of force against persons regarded as a danger to society, such use of force being defined by law or convention and backed by public opinion. The use of minimum necessary force in self-defence is likewise permitted. Such measures in no way justify the unlimited use of force against innocent parties without public sanction: this is not force but violence.

Nevertheless, it is sadly true that many governments are resorting more and more to violence (as distinct from force) and as society becomes more disordered, ruling elites are increasingly tempted to resort to violence to restore order and to preserve their own existence. There seems to be a world-wide drift towards the use of torture, assassination, secret surveillance and subversive activity. Spreading out from the great dictatorships, which have always been unblushing in the use of violence and terror, this drift has affected, first, the military dictatorships which formerly recognised certain standards and now begins to affect the us, France and other democracies. Reigns of terror are maintained not only in Russia and China, but in places like Rhodesia and Korea. Pragmatism drives out principle, and any methods are acceptable, provided that they work and that they can be kept out of sight.

Regimes which can only maintain themselves by such extreme methods are evidently lacking in normal cohesiveness.

According to Amnesty International, more and more governments are turning to torture to retain their power and soldiers are taking over from the police as torturers. Furthermore, in a lengthy report issued in November 1973, this London-based organisation reported that 'the practice of torture is being internationalised. Experts and their training, as well as torture equipment, are provided by one government for use in another state.' The report listed sixty countries now known to be using torture for political purposes, including the Soviet Union, the Argentine, Brazil and Portugal. Tortures included sexual assault, suffocation, sensory deprivation and audio-visual techniques.

Governments tend to wrap such practices in secrecy, but in 1972 it become known that the Pakistan Military Attaché was buying instruments of torture and brain-washing equipment in the United States. The Pakistan government, denying responsibility for the army's action, permitted a debate on the matter in the National Assembly.

Even Britain, with a strong, if not very long-lived, tradition of rejecting torture as a political weapon, has allowed herself to employ the newer psychological techniques which are beginning to make physical torture obsolete. Russia has broken new ground with the use of haloperidol, dubbed by Russians 'the chemical strait-jacket' which, forcibly injected into the victim, reduces him to psychic impotence.

We can confidently expect the use of torture to spread more widely and take even more sophisticated forms. We can also expect it to be extended to children, since children are now systematically employed by terrorists to carry messages, and even bombs, to dispose of weapons, and to obstruct the police or soldiery. The use of violent methods by governments naturally makes ridiculous their appeals for peaceful behaviour on the home front.

Another significant development is the growing willingness of governments to foster, and even actually to arrange, subversion in other countries by violent as opposed to persuasive means. The leader here has been the United States, which has been behind right-wing putsches in several South American countries; the CIA was recently reported to be operating in Thailand where it occupied almost a whole floor in the American Embassy, and which, as everyone knows, attempted unsuccessfully to unseat the government of Cuba and did unseat President Jagan. American support also helped to install the recent military government in Greece, which has become infamous for its use of sadistic torture—sadistic because it is not devoted to some instrumental end, such as extracting information, but is employed as a technique of terror and for its own sake.

Agents of the Central Intelligence Agency have also trained and assisted in commanding South American police forces and are reliably reported to have supplied them with instruments of torture, notably devices for giving electric shocks to the testicles.

A further development of this trend is government-sponsored assassination for political purposes. It emerged in evidence to the US Senate that at least one CIA assassination team had been sent to Cuba with, presumably, the object of assassinating Fidel Castro, and mystery surrounds the death of President Allende in Chile, where CIA teams are known to have been fostering revolt. Israel has also made use of assassination, perhaps relying on the early Jewish doctrine of an eye for an eye. The last refinement, as usual, is Russian: the use of the intensely poisonous substance thallium in an attempt to kill a former Russian agent.

When police are given carte blanche to eliminate subversive organisations or individuals there are always some who are delighted to seize the opportunity for gratuitous violence, and policies often deliberately encourage the recruitment of butchers and sadists. This trend seems to have reached its furthest development in Brazil. In mid-1973 'conservative' estimates put their victims at 1,300.

Police violence is hardly less frightful in Turkey, as Jane Cousins has documented in *Turkey: Torture and Political Persecution.*

The use of illegal and uncivilised methods by governments is inevitably taken by its opponents as justifying them in using methods equally violent.

What is depressing is not simply that violence exists, but that, having climbed some way out of the pit of barbarism, the world now seems to be slipping back into it. The fact that the United States, supposedly a civilised country with a democratic system and a free press, can so ruthlessly sponsor violence bodes ill for the future of other allegedly civilised countries.

As the case of Belfast shows, even in conditions of high and unpredictable risk, life goes on. Just as in wartime, people struggle to preserve a semblance of normality. So in the future, we shall still travel by air, still open our mail, still go to cinemas and crowded stores. As technology advances, it will become harder and harder to avoid the sudden confrontation with death. Bombs will become as small as book-matches, small as an aspirin tablet. Interruptions to public services will become more frequent and longer-lasting. There will be unforeseen inconveniences as terrorists get at computer programmes.

So far, however, terrorists have concentrated on threatening people. There have been a few threats to destroy property, such as famous pictures. Threats to statuary, buildings of historic merit, the contents of museums and so on may be the next step. One day only duly authorised people will be permitted to enter museums and art collections. But the situation could become still more serious if extremists of a more genuinely political bent began to threaten the technological basis of society itself.

IV

VULNERABLE WORLD

A civilisation is as fragile as a life.—Paul Valéry

1 The New Balance of Power

In November 1972, three armed hijackers took over a Southern Airways DC-9 and demanded a ransom of $10m. for the thirty passengers and crew members on board. They also demanded a document, carrying a US Government seal, to say that the money was a 'Government grant'. If their conditions were not met, they said, they would crash the airliner into the 'atomic energy plant' at Oak Ridge. In point of fact, Oak Ridge is the experimental head-quarters of the Atomic Energy Commission and contains numerous buildings spread over a considerable area, most of which do not contain reactors, so it was not a particularly good choice. Even if they had chosen to fly their plane into a nuclear power station, probably the steel pressure vessel would have withstood the impact and, if not, the safety devices would have doused the reactor. Much more dangerous would have been the electric turbines. If the rapidly-spinning rotors had been brought to an abrupt halt, they would have hurled knife-sharp turbine blades in every direction, slicing through steam-lines, power-lines and people. Still, the idea was original.

This episode embodies many of the typical features of modern violence. First, there is the willingness to threaten third parties on a huge scale. There is also the suicidal desire to perish in a holocaust if one cannot have one's own way, which we have seen to underlie nihilism—but here in a non-political context.

But it also illustrates another aspect of our situation: the decisive change brought about by modern technology which enables the criminal to do vastly more harm than ever before and then to escape more easily. The bandit of old might take a couple of hostages; the hijacker can take 150. The terrorist of old might set fire to a building; the modern terrorist can blow up the homes of a thousand people.

In America, teenagers have made entire apartment blocks unin-habitable by wrecking the elevators.

The fact is that we have entered a new phase in the history of violence, one in which not only are the destructive weapons more powerful by factors of a thousand or even a million times, but at the same time society is more vulnerable than ever before.

A change has occurred in the balance of power. Just as in warfare there are periods when defence is more effective than attack—as in the murderous trench-warfare of World War I—and others when attack is superior to defence—as in the tank-battles of World War II —so the balance has shifted in favour of the mobile, well-armed terrorist and against his victims. In fifty years or so it may shift back again, probably because methods of brain-washing or anti-aggression drugs will be invented. But for the moment the terrorist and the wrecker hold all the aces.

2 Our Fragile Technology

Technological society is highly specialised and hence mutually inter-dependent: whenever one function is knocked out, the effect is soon felt throughout society. We get a glimpse of this whenever a strike paralyses a basic industrial activity, such as the supply of electricity or the functioning of communications. In the days of windmills and watermills, it was totally impossible for any organised group to knock out the whole of an industry. Nor could such a group bring communications to a halt. Today it is all too easy. To take just one example, much of the air traffic of northern Europe is controlled from two or three air traffic control centres, such as the South of England centre at West Drayton, Middlesex. A guerrilla with a bomb or even a machine-gun could, if he could get into one, bring half the aircraft in northern Europe to a halt, probably causing several fatal crashes besides. From Heathrow alone between 900 and 1,000 aircraft arrive or leave every day, while some American centres handle ten times as many as this.

Communications channels are also brittle. Most countries now depend fairly heavily on microwave links, established by mounting dish-like aerials on high towers. (These short waves travel in straight lines, consequently each tower must have a straight line-of-sight to the next, with no intervening hills or structures.) Britain has over 100 such towers, spread 25 to 30 miles apart: those at London, Bristol, Birmingham, Manchester and Carlisle are important junction points in the network. Such towers are obviously open to destruction by explosive; it would be equally effective to sever the multi-core cables entering and leaving transmitter towers. These systems have some redundancy: traffic can be rerouted through cables buried in the earth, and no doubt the links reserved for defence matters are so duplicated. As sabotage increases, it will be necessary to increase this redundancy to the point at which sabotage ceases to be effective.

National electric transmission grids represent an even more fragile feature. In Britain, at 1 April 1973, there were 174 power stations linked together by some 4,268 km (1,900 miles) of 'super grid' operating at 400,000 volts, and lesser networks at 275,000 and 132,000 volts. The various stations are brought into use, as demand rises during the day, in order of efficiency by means of a control system of great complexity located at seven area control centres, plus a national centre in London. The National Centre receives, by means of telephone cables, more than 1,100 meter-readings from subsidiary stations and 9,000 indications of whether switches are open or closed in other centres. As the Chairman of the Central Electricity Generating Board, Mr Arthur Hawkins, recently explained, 'To be frank, we deliberately sail close to the wind, because this is in the best financial interests of our customers, and, thanks to the skill of our operators, we seldom get our feet wet. This "balancing act" is known in the trade as "playing fine tunes on the system". It calls for split-second decisions and nerves of steel.' It also calls for something more. A man with a gun or a bomb could easily prevent the staff of these centres from taking the necessary steps to balance power with demand, and this would cause large sections of the system to shut down automatically. Disruption of the telecommunications system, depriving the staff of the necessary data on which to base decisions, would of course have even more widespread effects.

It would not be necessary to plant a bomb: simply to throw a few switches into the wrong position, unbalancing power-supply and demand, would be enough to trigger a wave of imbalance throughout the system.

Ground transport systems are also easily put out of action. Motorways can be jammed solid by the breakdown of a vehicle on an overpass or bridge—or for longer periods by wrecking the structure with explosives. Railways are thrown into chaos if a single train breaks down, blocking all others on the line, while the signal boxes outside busy junctions are especially sensitive points. Underground railways are obviously especially at risk, since passengers cannot escape easily. It is not really necessary to damage the track, vehicles or signalling, since subways are dependent on ventilating systems. Before the last war, German agents tested the possibility of disseminating poison gas throughout London's subway system by releasing harmless bacteria near the air-intakes of the ventilating system and checking whether the bacteria arrived at other stations in the system. They did.

> I could pick three to five ex-Underwater Demolition, Marine Reconnaissance or Green Beret men at random and sabotage virtually any nuclear reactor in the country. . . . There is no way to stop such activity other than to maintain a system of civil surveillance more strict than that maintained during the last world war. . . .
>
> Testimony of Bruce L. Welch, former US Navy demolition officer and present Associate Professor of Environmental Health, Johns Hopkins School of Medicine, before the Joint Congressional Committee on Atomic Energy, 15 March 1974.

Almost any channel by which supplies arrive or leave provides an opportunity for the terrorist or wrecker. Water, milk, oil, electricity, sewage. . . . Every pipe, wire, moving belt or radio-channel offers a risk. The Channel tunnel (on which work has now stopped) would be an attractive target, points out Professor Richard Clutterbuck, of Exeter University, an expert on urban guerrilla methods. A single bomb could bring much of Britain's trade with the Continent to an indefinite standstill and cause unbelievable traffic jams for a hundred miles behind each exit. Another very obvious target are the 40 oil rigs and 23 gas pumping platforms in the North Sea, equally accessible to international and home-based terrorists, not to mention the pipelines on the ocean bed. The Royal Navy is toying with the idea of buying some armed trawlers to act as a patrol fleet—not a very reliable defence against aircraft or miniature submarines.

In certain industries, like paper-making, steel and some chemical processes, a whole industry may depend on two or three vast integrated plants. The Flixborough explosion handicapped the entire British plastics industry. The possibilities of large-scale industrial sabotage are now so frightening that it is strange that we have not seen more of it.

It is true that wartime bombing failed to bring industry to a halt, but the situation is not really comparable. Aerial bombing is a blunt weapon and, thirty years ago, industry was much less closely integrated than it is now. Moreover, in a state of war various precautions are taken which are not in operation in peacetime, or not as yet. So far we have only seen the occasional bomb directed at the industrial structure, perhaps because terrorists are basically more interested in hurting people than in winning political victories. If ever a political group should launch a concerted wrecking programme they could certainly bring about chaos long enough for their purposes.

But the most vulnerable points of all are society's control systems, including the systems of financial control. When banks are on strike, economies run into trouble. Today all our control systems—whether for energy, money, police, local administration or whatever—are being made dependent on that easily damaged device the computer, and it is no coincidence that in America students have several times attacked the computer. It is not really necessary to wreck the machine; enough trouble can be caused by erasing the memories or destroying the instruction tapes. Computers are apt to go wrong at the best of times. Recently one bank found that a week's entries were missing and was forced to write to its customers to ask them how much money they reckoned they had! Police data banks, now increasingly computerised, are an obvious target; in Britain the Angry Brigade tried to blow up the police computer at Tintagel House. But if social havoc were the objective, it would be better to erase the records of the Inland Revenue or disable the Stock Exchange computer.

COMPUTERS FIND BUG AND SLEEP LATE

On July 19th 1973 dozens of computers all over the world refused to start. After several days of frantic work by the suppliers of the computer and the software it emerged that July 19th, being the 200th day of the year, was the day on which a change of routine was automatically introduced to prevent software piracy. It so happened that all computers using a software package called Grasp plus a subordinate group of instructions known as PTO were in trouble. The computers were re-started by telling them that it wasn't July 19th. (This particular 'bug' must have been in the system for several years and no-one knows why it suddenly operated in 1973. No doubt there are hundreds of similar bugs lurking in obscure corners of programmes, just waiting to be disturbed and each new incident like this will give the computernics a fresh set of nightmares.)

New Scientist (9 August 1973) *59*: 325

Computer control of traffic systems is gradually becoming the thing, so that splendid opportunities of bringing traffic into dead-locked confusion are opened up. Airline booking arrangements are heavily computerised; the cost of any breakdown would be so high that they are usually duplicated. Computers offer a further possibility: a disgruntled programmer could feed in inaccurate facts or un-suitable instructions which could cause more havoc than simple obliteration of the data. ('Divide the amount in all bank accounts

containing more than £5,000 by ten; multiply the amount in all
bank accounts containing less than £1,000 by ten,' would lead to
some fun.)

Our society has chosen to reduce its safety margins. For instance
bridges are built to carry a load forty or fifty per cent greater than
the heaviest load that is likely to cross them—instead of being twenty
times as strong as necessary as in the past. The modern engineer
prides himself on economising by fining down safety margins. Sky-
scrapers are designed to withstand the strongest probable gale but
have little in hand for storms which thumb their noses at meteorological statistics. School roofs collapse because an unexpected loss of
strength in the beams cannot be absorbed. Aeroplane wings don't
quite break off. Power stations can just meet the load demand. Trains
don't quite run into the back of the train in front. Food is just
eatable, despite the questionable preservatives. Water is just drinkable. We have built an uncommonly fragile society.

3 More Powerful Weapons

In his remarkable book *The Jagged Orbit*, John Brunner imagines
many new possibilities of wilful murder and social disruption. Since
we already have bacteria which feed on petroleum and even plastics,
we can imagine bacteria may be bred which can feed on metal. Thus
a small smear of bacterial paste could grow by what it feeds on.
Rubbed on a bridge it might eventually destroy the bridge.

And since we now have extremely fine but strong fibres, which at
present are used to strengthen plastics, it is reasonable to suppose
we may one day have fibres so fine as to be invisible, yet strong
enough to stretch across a road and thereby slice vehicles and their
occupants into neat halves: as was done during the last war with
piano wire, which accounted for a few German motor cyclists, but
was only usable at dusk.

While society becomes steadily more vulnerable to disruption, the
weapons available become steadily more powerful. If a man was
seized with murderous rage in pretechnological society, he might
murder three or four people before he was overcome. Today with a
machine-gun, he can kill ten times as many; with a bomb, perhaps
a hundred times as many. There is no reason to think that this
progression will now stop. The next step is clearly nuclear bombs,
whether stolen from military arsenals, supplied to terrorists by
friendly governments (after all, terrorists have already been supplied
with guided missiles) or even manufactured in makeshift laboratories.

Undercurrents, an underground paper published in London, recently
printed instructions on how to make your own atom bomb, together

with advice on where to set it off. The point chosen was Charing Cross, in the belief that this would destroy the houses of Parliament, the royal palaces, and at least one railway station together with a key part of the subway system. In point of fact, it is a good deal harder to produce an effective atom bomb than the writer imagined. The resulting explosion would probably have been a relatively weak one—in terms of what we now expect from nuclear bombs—but lethal to a few hundred people in any event, apart from the radio-activity likely to be released.

But even if the basement-bomb is not to be taken too seriously, it is certainly the case that a Middle Eastern country (say) could bring together the necessary materials and sufficiently skilled scientists and technicians to make something much nastier: and it could provide all the time and money needed. And while such a bomb could not be fitted into a suitcase, it could be concealed in a railway container or giant truck. The Arab commentator, Mr Muhammad Hassanein Meykal, has urged the Arab states to make atomic bombs to counter the three the Israelis are alleged to have.

As Jon Tinker has noted in the *New Scientist*: 'Making an atomic bomb is technologically a simple exercise. All one needs is a com-petent nuclear physicist trained to first-degree level, a dozen good technicians, perhaps £50,000 worth of easily purchased equipment (some say £10,000 would do) and six months or a year of privacy. And some fissile material: U-235 or Pu-239.' And as we shall see in Chapter XIV, a breeder reactor programme will ensure that fissile material is freely available.

According to *Undercurrents*, the critical mass for a sphere of plutonium is 16.2 kg (35 lb), but this is reduced to 8 kg if the sphere is surrounded by a neutron-reflecting shield. Since breeder reactors contain something like 3 tons of plutonium, there should be no problem. Over two hundred pounds of uranium were found to have 'gone missing' from an American processing plant in 1965—some say the Mafia arranged it, others that it ended up in Israel. According to Thomas O'Toole in the *Washington Post*, 'The AEC loses as much as one hundred pounds of uranium and sixty pounds of plutonium every year, enough to make more than ten atomic bombs.' Recently considerable quantities have been smuggled out of India, presumably for the benefit of Pakistan or China.

Radioactive substances provide another horrifying new weapon. Plutonium powder is the most poisonous substance known—even worse than botulinus toxin. If inhaled, death follows in a few hours. It could be dispersed by an ordinary explosive bomb, exploded above a city. Hundreds, possibly thousands, would die. In Austria terrorists have already poisoned a railway coach with radioactive iodine.

In any case, we can certainly expect to see many new weapons developed in the years ahead, all capable of misuse. Already it is possible for any bright schoolboy to construct a laser which will blind people a mile away. Detailed instructions have been given in popular scientific papers, and in America such lasers are increasingly provided as equipment for school laboratories. But this is child's play. The us Air Force has poured money into the development of a giant laser which could blast holes in metal miles away, bringing down an enemy bomber or destroying a guided missile.

It is a reasonable assumption that before the end of the century there will be easily portable 'pocket lasers' with which the possessor can scorch, blind, maim and kill at much greater ranges than are possible with a revolver. But before they become truly portable, vandals will have discovered how to perforate tyres, stop clocks, punch holes in petrol tanks and milk-churns, and start satisfying fires at a safe distance. Brunner forecasts that most buildings will need steel shutters, automatically triggered by the heat to drop over windows, while we shall have to wear spectacles which darken automatically, of the kind developed as protection against the flash from nuclear bombs.

Finally, perhaps we should add to the prospect of a small-scale terrorist or vandalistic wrecking pattern the possibility of highly-organised wrecking planned by a major power as a form of un-declared war or a preliminary to war. However, even if we avoid the perils of deliberate wrecking, our system is now so complex that it can come to a standstill of its own accord. This I call, for lack of a better word, a glue-up.

4 System Degradation

On 12 April 1945, when President Roosevelt died, so many people picked up the telephone to discuss the news with their friends that the entire us telephone network became choked for several hours and hardly any calls got through. In those days there were only 30 million subscribers. Today, with more than 100 million, the risks are greater. In the last few years the New York telephone system has frequently been choked; the advertising agency Benton and Bowles once took a whole-page advertisement in the *New York Times*, listing its staff and saying: 'You may think these people no longer work for us and that's why you couldn't reach them by phone. But they're still here. Come and see them.'

The position is analogous with traffic jams in the streets. Roads will only carry so much traffic; if the amount is exceeded, the whole system breaks down and *nobody* moves. Similarly, when power demands exceed supplies, the system fails and *everyone* is plunged in darkness, as in the eastern United States in 1965.

Roberto Vacca, an Italian electrical engineer, who has studied at Cambridge University and at Harvard and taught in Rome University, believes that the whole of our society will soon become jammed up in this way. 'My thesis is,' says Vacca, 'that the great technical and associated organisational systems will continue to grow haphazardly until they attain critical and unstable dimensions. At this point the crisis of a single system will not be enough to block the great metropolitan concentrations but a chance coincidence of congestion in several systems in the same area could initiate a catastrophic process which will paralyse the functioning of developed society, leading to the death of millions of people.'

Breakdowns of this kind are becoming ever more frequent. The Federal Power Commission investigated 179 cases of power-failure which occurred in the two years mid-1967 to mid-1969 and found that 80 were due to functional defects. Vacca points out that modern society depends on numerous 'great systems'—not only telephones and power, but postal services, trains, defence control networks and so on. When one breaks down, the strain on the others increases. If you can't reach someone by mail, you telephone. If the phone is constantly busy, you go in person by car. If the roads are jammed you take the train. So there is a real danger that one day all the systems will jam up at once.

Vacca thinks the scenario might develop like this. An air-traffic controller, exhausted after ten hours' continuous duty, because his relief has been unable to get to work, makes an error causing two planes to collide near O'Hare airport, Chicago. They bring down a main electric transmission line and this causes disturbances in the power network which black out a large area of the United States for several days. It is mid-winter; there is deep snow. Since neither traffic lights nor electric petrol pumps are working, motor traffic soon comes to a standstill. Many of those who abandon their cars and try to walk home perish in the snow. At home, the food in the refrigerator goes bad, the central heating (electrically pumped) fails; then the water supply. Petrol tankers cannot get through the jammed roads, and the telephone network packs up. People sit in the dark, cold, hungry and afraid. Fires start, but the fire-engines cannot get through. In the dark, cold hospitals people begin to die.

Those who are caught on the streets try to force their way into homes for shelter, but are driven off by the householders with guns. On the third day, people begin to loot the supermarkets for food. After two weeks of crisis, there are several million dead. Then, as things begin to recover, plague strikes. The impossibility of removing sewage (the electric pumps having stopped) and the mounting toll of dead, which hospitals and mortuaries cannot cope with, have given the rats their opportunity. And now the population really begins to fall. Tens of millions die. This, by analogy with black-out, Vacca terms 'the knock-out'.

I base this summary on the much fuller account in his absorbing book *Il Medioevo Prossimo Venturo* (*The Coming Middle Ages*). As Vacca points out, there is no body of theory which enables one to plan very large systems adequately. You cannot stop people suddenly deciding to use a service in numbers much greater than it was designed for. Much of the trouble with the US telephone service has been due to the new uses which have been developed: facsimile transmission, television, control systems and above all machine data transmission. According to Frederick R. Kappel, the President of A. T. & T. (American Telephone and Telegraph Co., the holding company for the Bell system), US computers already transmit more information by telephone than do human beings. Moreover, systems in dynamic balance are liable to 'overshoot' as well as 'undershoot'; as they get bigger these maladjustments get more costly, less tolerable and maybe uncontrollable.

Vacca's argument about the limitations of complex systems also applies to the growth of cities. Dr Kurt Leibbrand, a German transportation consultant, reckons that 20 million is probably the largest unit that can be held together. The calculation is based on the time taken to get to work. Assuming no traffic congestion, a theoretical maximum of 40m. is calculated, assuming a high population density (600 inhabitants/ha). But in view of street congestion, the limit may be less than half this. Today, the largest conglomerations are the New York–New Jersey metropolitan area and the Tokyo–Yokohama conurbation, each about 16 million and already experiencing severe difficulties. In particular, it is increasingly difficult to supply water and to remove wastes, especially those aerial wastes we call smog and air-pollution.

Vacca therefore foresees a New Middle Ages, in which travel will be limited to what one can do with the aid of a horse, and power to wind and water-mills. Scientific research, civil engineering and mass production will come to a halt. The breakdown, he thinks, will hit some countries sooner than others. America and Japan will collapse first. Britain, thanks to its slow national growth rate, will be spared for a while. Subsequently the third world will be affected. Society will break up into small groups and culture will be preserved in secular 'monasteries'. Recovery will be slow, but eventually a new renaissance will dawn, a new (and perhaps wiser) tradition will become established. The American commentator Professor Barrington Moore has had a similar thought: '. . . any substantial failure of the existing technical apparatus, including the failure to staff it adequately, could, if it happened suddenly, produce as many deaths as a major war, even a nuclear war, if the failure were complete and prolonged.'

Perhaps this scenario underrates the ingenuity and determination men can show in improvising and correcting failures. Much depends on the overall social situation and the effectiveness of the political leadership at the moment of disaster. The concurrence of social and technical breakdown is the real risk.

5 Self-Sufficiency and Survival

The trends I have outlined are extremely serious in their implications and the public and official response to them has so far been totally inadequate. There has been very little attempt to deal with causes and not much to limit effects.

It is society's new vulnerability which makes the alienation of a few of its members so crucial. How many ruthless, murderously inclined individuals can society stand? The answer is, clearly, very few: in Northern Ireland a few hundred gunmen succeeded in making government impossible and everyday life intolerable, for a population numbering some 1½ millions, and their techniques were primitive and unimaginative. Next time the pot boils up it could be much worse.

When a pot on the stove begins to boil over, you can either try to clamp down the lid or turn down the flame. The latter is quicker, more permanent and less messy. But our normal reaction to violence is to clamp down the lid. No doubt we shall see the imposition of severer sentences for political violence, and the creation of special squads of plain-clothes police and secret agents. As always in the past, spies, informers and *agents provocateurs* will flourish. Before the end of the century, everyone will carry cards of identity if not indeed indelible tattoos. Movements within countries will be monitored more closely. Mail will be opened and telephone calls tapped. Rooms, both public and private, will be bugged. Everyone will be frisked at entry to any sensitive area, while cars will be examined for concealed explosives whenever left unattended in such areas. As explosives get more powerful, brief-cases and parcels will become suspect. (Since I drafted this sentence, brief-case and car checks have been instituted at London museums and elsewhere.) Politically exposed people may be driven to having food-tasters and letter-openers, and to employing doubles, as in Italy 700 years ago; life could become very inconvenient even for those not directly at risk.

Moreover, these precautions will prove inadequate. Terrorists will be very ingenious in finding new modes of attack.

British police have already issued leaflets advising firms to appoint 'bomb marshals', to cover windows with wire mesh, to illuminate building exteriors, seal letter-boxes and paint drain-pipes with anti-climb paint, and so on.

The alternative course would be to diminish the appetite for violence. This is not simply a question of satisfying the political demands of the dissidents. (Sometimes the demands are impossible to satisfy, since they conflict with the demands of other groups.) As we have seen, political movements attract persons who are naturally prone to violence and see in them an opportunity to work off their aggression. Much avowedly political violence actually harms rather than helps the political end—as in Northern Ireland, where the indiscriminate slaughter of innocent parties has antagonised reasonable people on both sides.

Thus it will only be by attacking the social conditions which produce violent personalities—and perhaps by identifying such violence-prone individuals when young and giving them special treatment—that the problem can be met. 'Special treatment' might be anything from psychiatric help, through continuous surveillance, to preventive detention.

There will of course be a public demand for heavier sentences: no doubt the death penalty will be reintroduced. There will be a demand for flogging, but it is to be hoped that something more constructive, such as the obligation to do work of social value, will be substituted. Some small moves in this direction have already been made. I shall discuss such issues in a later chapter; here I am only trying to predict the probable future.

When people are scared, and still more when they have been injured or have lost loved ones, they often become ready to countenance severe measures: preventive detention, with or without public trial, will be used increasingly widely. It is better, in the view of most people, that a few people be held wrongfully than that many innocent people be maimed or killed. It would be assumed that most of those held were high-risk individuals even if they had not committed the actions actually attributed to them. Such measures imply an extensive system of internal espionage, the expansion of the secret branches of the police and army, and the near-advent of a police state.

Since, however, these measures will only be partially effective, and in any case will not reduce the risk of glue-ups, people may respond to the crumbling of the large-scale industrial system by turning to a different social structure based on smaller, more self-contained units. At the national level, governments will begin to recognise this by dismantling their national electricity grid and gas grid so that it is capable of functioning in smaller units. (This is comparatively easy for electricity, where regional grids are already tied together by a super-grid, less easy for gas.) But it is much harder to create economically self-sufficient regions, and government plans will hardly rise above providing reserve stocks of fuel, food and raw materials in each area. Similarly, they may set up regional administrative headquarters, but since they will not try out the actual administrative process, total chaos will ensue.

Much nearer the grass roots, people will try to make their own household independent by installing alternative fuel sources, such as butane, or, more radically, by using wind and solar energy. But these measures will only serve to bridge over temporary interruptions of supply. People will have to come together in larger units, as is already beginning to occur in Britain and elsewhere, and operate a balanced farming/industrial mini-economy. Governments, of course, will resist this, since exchanges within such an economy will generate neither income tax nor sales taxes, such as the Value Added Tax now in wide use in Europe. Penalties on the ownership of land, and the threat of eventual nationalisation of land, may make such attempts (which closely follow the pattern of the Roman *latifundia*) unworkable. In any case they can only cater for a minority of the population in overcrowded countries like Britain.

As the city-dwellers begin to find themselves deprived of food and fuel, they will leave the towns to scrounge what they can in the countryside, and will loot (and probably wreck) the nascent communes. Only after the break-up of central government and the reduction of the population by starvation and disease will it be possible for a new feudal system to emerge. Leaders will assert themselves, by virtue of their political ability and ruthlessness, capable of forming communities from the disorganised rabble which has survived, and these will necessarily be largely self-contained at first. Then trading will re-start as each group develops specialities based on the knowledge and skill preserved by its particular members. So the cycle will repeat.

This scenario could, of course, be modified in various ways: for instance, a great power might choose this moment of weakness and confusion to launch an invasion or to attempt a takeover by political means. How things work out will depend on which country cracks first, on how many countries slide into chaos, and on how closely spaced these episodes are in space and time. I shall outline some further alternatives in later chapters.

The fact to which we currently fail to give due weight is that we live in an unprecedentedly fragile system, more vulnerable perhaps than that of any previous civilisation. It wouldn't take much to bring it down about our ears.

The complexity of technological society which makes it vulnerable to wrecking operations makes it even more vulnerable to the sudden withdrawal of labour. The strike has evolved from being a weapon deployed against a particular management and has become a threat to the whole society. Thus it is closely analogous to the blackmailing operations of the terrorists. The demands of the strikers have to be met unless one is prepared to accept the costs of people, who have no connection with the dispute, suffering or dying. In the case of strikes concerned with the health service this is true in a quite literal way. People who become gravely ill or die because no hospital bed is available as a consequence of a strike are indubitably the victims of that strike. But the same is true, if less directly, of the elderly woman who dies of cold during a power strike. The Hegelian change of quality with change of quantity has had its effect: the strike has become something else.

In short, it has become possible for organised labour to bring society to a standstill—and also to inflict lasting damage on its assets, as when a coal mine becomes unworkable because flooding has ensued from lack of maintenance. This has changed the entire political situation and the outlook for society's future to an extent which has not yet been fully appreciated. In a later chapter, I shall try to foresee what it may mean. But first let us look more closely at antisocial behaviour, for the type of violence we have just considered is but the tip of an iceberg, and to deal with it we must understand its social origins in frustration and lack of purpose. That only a small proportion of violent individuals turn their resentments into political channels is a state of affairs which may not last.

V

TIDES OF RESENTMENT

*The crisis of violence is really the crisis
of man.—M. F. Gilula and G. Daniels*

1 Safety Last

There are still people who deny that the world has become more
violent* than it was twenty-five years ago. So let us look at the facts.
A recent US survey showed that one person in three living in urban
areas had been the victim of an assault or robbery in the past year.
Forty per cent of people felt unsafe walking within a mile of their
home. Police now ride the New York subway and cab-drivers are
separated from their fares by a bullet-proof partition. Britain has
not moved as far, as yet, but even in London muggings on the
Underground and in the streets are beginning to be commonplace.
while burglary figures are rocketing up. Nor is it only the better-off
who are affected: blacks are the chief victims of black robberies in
the US and anyone who happens to enter a bank or post office at the
moment it is about to be raided is liable to be held hostage or perhaps
to get a bullet in the neck. All this in addition to the fact that letter-
bombs arrive by post, cars blow up in the street and anyone who
takes a plane has a gnawing doubt whether it may prove to be the
odd one which is hijacked or blown up in mid-air.

Small wonder that people now keep their doors on a chain and
peer through a spy-hole to see who has just rung the bell. In the
village where I live no one thought of locking their front doors when
I first came there a few years ago. Now they do. It is a sign of the
times when books are published† instructing women how to defend

---

* It has become fashionable to use the word 'violence' for legal and social constraints
and injustice generally. I shall use it only in the familiar sense of physical attack on people
or property.

† *Survival in the City* by Anthony Greenbank, Wolfe, 1974.

themselves against physical attack: there is now even a science dubbed 'victimology'. ('BITE the ends of fingers, toes, noses; CHEW ears, cheeks and other sensitive spots; TUCK head in and charge like a mad bull. . . .')

The new violence bears especially hardly on old people who are often selected for mugging precisely because they cannot resist or run away. Many have become virtual prisoners in their own homes, afraid to venture out for fear of assault. And it is not only the old who are afraid. Even in a once-peaceful city like Bath, people are becoming reluctant to wait at bus-stops at night. In larger centres, bus services now stop running at 9.00 p.m. or earlier because the crews refuse to work the service, having so often been assaulted, reviled or hustled.

Possibly the most significant and worrying aspect of the problem is the way in which violent behaviour is beginning to be displayed by people not ordinarily thought of as criminals. During the fuel shortage of 1973, striking American truck-drivers armed themselves and shot at fellow truck-drivers, who were not on strike, killing two and wounding others. On a single day, no fewer than 53 violent incidents involving drivers were reported. In Britain, too, industrial disputes show signs of becoming more violent. Police cowered when a gang of 300 'flying pickets' descended on a building site where men were not on strike shouting 'Kill the bastards!' When asked in court afterwards: 'Would you have been prepared to intervene?' a police sergeant replied: 'No, sir, I would not. Frankly, we should have stood no chance at all.' Witnesses described the invaders as 'a mad horde, a bunch of Apache Indians, a frenzied mob'. On another such occasion, the pickets marched to the site office chanting 'Kill, kill, kill,' and shouting: 'Capitalist bastards! This is not a strike, it is a revolution!'

In normal times such passions are kept under some measure of control. Once a group is formed, however, each member feels licensed to let himself go—even approved for behaving thus. Thus when a near-revolutionary situation develops, things can deteriorate quite rapidly. Even in normally law-abiding Japan, infuriated passengers set fire to stationary trains during a railway go-slow in Tokyo.

Games like football also seem to provide the sense of a special occasion licensing violence: the wave of assaults and wrecking carried out by supporters of a British football team, Tottenham Hotspur, in Rotterdam as I drafted this chapter is, up to now, an extreme example, though at many football matches there is a degree of violence unknown in the past. When the Glasgow club Celtic visited Madrid recently, the authorities took no chances: the stadium was ringed with water-cannon, while police, armed with tear-gas grenades and rifles firing rubber bullets, were everywhere. The plane carrying supporters was brought into a special airfield, and the fans were escorted to the stadium under a heavy police guard. Even the struthious must see in this something extraordinary.

Such episodes are sometimes just orgies, but often express hatred of other social groups, and not only in England. Italian football crowds also reveal such hatred: when the Verona team lost and was relegated to a lower division in 1974, some of the team's supporters collected outside the amphitheatre where a new production of *Aïda* was opening and, as soon as the music started, began to shout, sing football songs and raise a racket so effectively that the audience could not hear a note, and kept this up until the performance ended. This cannot be called 'class hatred' in the ordinary sense, since there are opera-lovers in every class—especially in Italy. It is the hatred of the tough for the tender, of the barbarian for the civilised.

What we see in such episodes is not simply a growth of impulsive violence but a growth of ruthlessness and more than a tinge of sadism. I can more or less understand a revolutionary shooting an opponent, but when I read that four members of the Ulster Defence Association, all good Protestants, seized a Mr McCartan in a Belfast hotel, dragged him squealing to a 'romper room' where he was beaten and stabbed before being strung upside down from the roof by a rope, my mind begins to boggle. 'Mr McCreery told Mr Doherty to hit him with a pick-handle, and he did so several times. Mr McCreery stabbed his hands.' Subsequently he was shot.

I do not see how to avoid the conclusion that a moral and social crisis is fast approaching. Society cannot stand more than a certain amount of asocial behaviour. And as we shall see in the next section, there is no reason to suppose that the trend is due to reverse itself. We must therefore prepare ourself for its extension. There will be bigger gangs, better armed and better prepared. *The Times* recently reported that 'A judge at the Central Criminal Court was told yesterday that six Yemenis were among two hundred members of a professional crime syndicate based in Cairo and Italy which travelled the world committing thefts. The six are alleged to have stolen £20,000 in cash in six weeks in London and the Home Counties. . . . Sergeant Jones said that five or six others involved had returned to the Middle East. After their arrest the six defendants "told lies for three days. They told different stories and gave various addresses which we were unable to check."' Theft and vandalism will increase. No work of art or public sculpture will be safe. Any public figure will risk vindictive damage to his home and personal attack, with the probability of attack on his family too.

In their attempts to cope with this, the police will become more violent, and will exert a more extensive surveillance, stopping people and cars for spot checks and descending on houses without warning in the middle of the night. At the same time the police themselves will become more corrupt, for it will be harder to find conscientious recruits. But it will be unwise to offer any criticism since one day you may need their help, and it is easy for busy police to turn a blind eye on the excuse that they have other problems. And, as we can already see in France, they will become more violent and arrogant.

Private guards and security forces will become commoner. Houses will become fortresses. Citizens will form groups of vigilantes, and the police will unofficially encourage them to arm themselves, insisting only that, if they shoot, they shoot to kill.

2 The Future of Violence

Despite the general impression that violence is increasing there are some struthious individuals who have attempted to show that violence is no worse than it was, and nothing to worry about. It is extremely difficult to form an impression of crime-rates a century or more ago. In large cities, where social structure was weak, crime seems to have been fairly common, but the diaries of people living in small towns or the country hardly mention crime, apart from petty thieving, drunkenness, etc. Even in cities, major crimes were rare enough for a sensation to be caused when one occurred. A book on the subject like Chevalier's *Labouring Classes and Dangerous Classes in Paris during the First Half of the Nineteenth Century* has to appeal repeatedly to literary descriptions, such as those of Sue and Balzac, contains no firm estimates of crime rates and does not even mention such crimes as kidnapping or bomb-explosion. Drunken brawls and the crimes of poverty such as infanticide and prostitution are what it is mostly about.

We must therefore take a look at the figures. The point, of course, is not so much whether there were ever periods in the past which were more violent than today: there certainly were. The point is, rather, were there ever periods which were less violent, in which case our own age is revealed as more violent than it need be.

The figures, though far from satisfactory statistically, show decisively that in our own lifetimes—say, over the past forty or fifty years—the situation has deteriorated dramatically. American figures are not very useful for establishing this point, for a number of reasons we need not go into. The British figures, which concern a relatively small and uniformly administered area, are more instructive—all the more since Britain is a much less violent country than the US. These figures show that crimes of violence against the person have risen steadily from 6,249 in 1950 to 52,432 in 1972. (These figures refer to 'crimes known to the police' and not to convictions.)

The eminent criminologist F. H. McClintock of the Cambridge University Institute of Criminology has made a detailed analysis of some major types of crime for the years 1969, 1970 and 1971, from which I have extracted the figures which concern crimes of violence. It can be seen at once that, with the interesting exception of rape,* such crimes increased by more than twenty per cent over the three years.

	1969	1970	1971	% increase
Murder†/attempted murder	448	470	543	+21
Wounding/act endangering life	2,708	2,956	3,287	+21
Rape	869	884	784	−10
Robbery/assault with intent	6,041	6,273	7,465	+24

†victims aged one year or over

One of the arguments used by struthes is that the rise in recorded crime is due to more efficient police action and more careful recording. Even if this were true of minor crimes, it is unlikely to be true of the serious crimes referred to above. And again, they argue that the bulk of crime goes unreported and hence the apparent increase is due to the police, thanks to modern equipment, intercepting a larger proportion of cases. That is also unlikely to be true of these major crimes.

Struthes also draw attention to the fact that it was possible to be waylaid by footpads (mugged) in London parks in the eighteenth century: ignoring the fact that violence was extremely rare in areas outside the centre of big cities, before the nineteenth century, whereas today it is common in the suburbs and even happens in the heart of the country. The Gallup Poll which, as I have mentioned, reported that one person in every three of those living in central city areas of the US had been mugged or robbed or had suffered property loss during the previous twelve months also revealed that, even in the suburbs, the rate was one in five and was rising twice as fast as in the cities. It also disclosed that one person in six did not feel safe and secure in his or her own home at night. What an indictment!

FBI crime figures have been challenged as artificially inflated so as to justify an FBI demand for bigger funds. For what they are worth, they show violent crime zooming from 160 to 393 cases per 100,000 in the sixties. There is certainly no doubt about the fact

* It is believed that at least half the victims of rape in Britain never report the fact to the police for fear of disagreeable publicity.

that last year nearly one million Americans were physically attacked. And, as San Francisco police chief Lieutenant William Koenig, commented, 'the big change over ten years ago continues to be in viciousness.' In 1973 Detroit, the nation's 'murder capital', had the record number of 750 murders, nearly 15 per cent up on the previous year and about four times as many as England, Scotland and Wales together. (I here take murder and manslaughter together.)

President Johnson, after the assassination of Martin Luther King and Robert Kennedy, appointed a commission to enquire into the causes and prevention of violence. In due course the commission advised that unless massive action were taken, 'central business districts . . . will require substantial police protection; high-rise and residential apartments will need protection by private guards and security devices, thus turning them into fortified cells for the middle classes. Without a change in the law, ownership of guns will be almost universal. All private and commercial vehicles will be equipped with unbreakable glass, light armour and other security features. Armed guards will ride shotgun on all forms of public transport.'

Is this also the path which Europe will follow? In Britain, security organisations are booming; they already own more guard dogs than the police, to say nothing of aircraft and armoured cars. The number of employees is said to exceed 30,000.

The future will no doubt see more and more surveillance by closed-circuit television. Already common in large stores and the entrance lobbies of large buildings, it will spread to railway and subway stations, public washrooms, underground car parks and eventually many streets. Houses and offices will become difficult to enter without passes or magnetic admission-cards, and there will be means of trapping anyone who commits an offence once inside. Places like telephone exchanges, grid control stations and air-traffic control centres will have to be fortified, with multiple checks on those who enter and leave.

Oscar Newman has argued in his book *Defensible Space* that many housing developments are at present planned so as to favour the criminal, both because they provide dark corners and many avenues of escape, and also because they create a no-man's-land in which an intruder cannot readily be identified as such. When houses are surrounded by gardens or marked-off areas, anyone who crosses the limits is clearly up to no good. Moreover, when houses look inward onto an enclosed space, a sense of neighbourliness develops which militates against crime, whereas the social isolation of each unit in a big apartment block causes people to bolt their doors and turn the television up louder, rather than to investigate, when they hear unfamiliar noises outside. Newman has shown, in practical architectural form, that housing estates can be designed so as to minimise crime and no doubt we shall see increasing use of this approach. Indeed, some American embassies are already designed so as to make political attack difficult, with fire zones and obstacles to slow up attacking crowds, such as sloping barriers and steps rising to the main entrance.

All this will go further. Those countries which do not have gun-control laws will introduce them, sooner rather than later, and these laws will of course be evaded, especially by the violently-disposed. This will load the scales still further against the peaceable. The attempt to control violence by repression will certainly fail.

If we seriously want to reduce the level of violence, instead of simply struggling to live with it, we need to look a little below the surface. The first thing we find is that violence starts very young. The problem of violence is, at least in part, a youth problem.

3 Blackboard Jungles

Take the case of George Riddell, 15, sentenced to be detained during Her Majesty's pleasure, for stabbing to death a boy, quite unknown to him, whom he found standing at an Edinburgh bus-stop. In evidence, Riddell described how he and a friend had armed themselves with knives and had gone out to look for trouble. The intention, he told the court, had been 'to stab somebody'. He 'approved of' boys getting stabbed. He alleged that his friend had said some days before the murder: 'I fancy getting blotto [drunk] at the weekend and going stabbing.' He alleged that his friend had committed the murder, but in court, Riddell admitted murdering Nicol by stabbing him repeatedly. And so Stephen Nicol, 19, described as 'a quiet lad who suffered from asthma' died.

One month after this the 15-year-old son of a British MP, walking home with his 17-year-old sister, was attacked by a gang of fifteen youths, stabbed and savagely beaten. Two weeks later, a boy of 11 was alleged to have tried to kill a baby by suffocating it. And soon after, a child of nine was charged with murder.

In the US three high-school boys, aged 15 and 16, were charged with manufacturing 'infernal machines' and were said to have sent anonymous threats to blow up the police station and high school. The local school committee received anonymous threats of 'death by bombing'. This was in the New England mill-town of Haverhill, 40 miles north of Boston. Near-by schools have also been closed because of bomb threats.

The situation in US metropolitan schools is well known. Typical is Public School 304 (that's a name to build loyalty round!) three miles from the centre of Manhattan, which has been turned into a fortress after the beating-up of a secretary in an upstairs corridor during the lunch-break. All exits, except one, have been sealed off, the outside handles of all the doors to the street have been sawn off, there are wire meshes on the windows, an armed policeman patrols the corridors, the teachers hold their lessons behind closed doors and it is now impossible to get into the school without a security check. As one teacher complained 'We are always on edge, looking over our shoulders'. Is this the pattern of the future?

In the first nine months of 1972, there were no fewer than 4,724 *school* crimes including four murders, 28 rapes, 496 robberies, and 3,200 burglaries in New York's five boroughs. At one school the alarm system was stolen as it was being carried from the supplier's truck into the school. Under pressure from teachers, for the first time the city has allocated $6m. to pay for some 1,200 specially trained security guards.

Europe follows the US with a time-lag of about a generation. In Britain, school violence, which used to be confined to a minority, has taken a horrifying upward leap. Thus attacks on teachers, of which only ten were reported in 1971, rocketed to 600 in 1974. It is not only aggression towards teachers but violence between pupils which is becoming worse—even lethal. In 1971 a pupil was stabbed to death in the playground of Wandsworth School. The playground fight, which used to involve only fists, is now conducted with boots, knives and chains. An increasing number of children carry weapons, including revolvers, knives, chains, razors and knuckledusters. More ingenious weapons include an iron-filled tennis ball and an exercise book spiked with drawing-pins. Thieving is also commonplace and cloakrooms remain unused for this reason.

Violence now also involves girls. Violent crimes by girls rose 179 per cent between 1969 and 1974. Britain's Union of Women Teachers declared in 1972 that head teachers were concealing the amount of classroom violence for fear of being accused of inability to keep order. Mrs Norrie Shelton, a vice-president of the union, declares: 'It is growing and it is time everyone knew the facts. We want more discussion and we want support in dealing with it.' The participation of girls in violence 'has crept up over the past three years and it is extremely worrying'.

Warnings of this kind evoked a soothing response: 'stories of school violence are much exaggerated.' This ostrich-like attitude was rendered untenable when an extensive survey by the Institute of Research Techniques reported: 'Tolerance for minor violence is fairly widespread and there is a hard core of at least ten per cent who seem attracted to or even enthusiastic about the use of violence generally.'

The study covered 1,565 boys aged 12 to 17, picked at random: in a six months' period every boy was 'a bit violent' 68 times and 'fairly violent' 36 times. The first of these terms meaning deliberately smashing a school window, for example; the second, breaking down a young tree in a park. Thus every boy committed 104 such acts in 90 days, more than one a day. Each boy was 'very violent' twice— like hitting someone in the face with a broken bottle; but 'extremely violent' acts, such as stabbing or setting a building on fire, occurred only 0.01 times a boy. But this means that there were 15 or 16 such events in the course of six months in a population of 1,565 boys. Eight of the boys admitted cutting somebody with a razor, 33 had beaten up somebody. Thirteen of the boys had committed 'fairly violent' acts between 100 and 500 times. The director of the Institute said: 'I made the mistake of taking some of them home late at night and I feared for the safety of my car. We dealt with so many kids who were illiterate it was frightening.'

The key statistic is perhaps the fact that twelve per cent of the boys committed acts which were 'quite' or 'very' or 'extremely' violent at least ten times in six months. Subsequently the secretary of the National Association of Schoolteachers commented: 'I am shocked at the high proportion of extreme violence indicated by the report . . . if 12 per cent of any age group is viciously violent, then God help us!' But the Inner London Education Authority said: 'Don't all kids commit some kind of act of violence at some time?' To which the simple answer is: when 'violence' means arson or a bottle in the face, no.

Reports from Europe show violence increasing and spreading down the age scale in Germany, affecting even six and seven-year olds. In France and Italy, according to a *Times* survey, violence is mainly politically based: teenage fascists fight teenage anarchists with petrol bombs and thunderflashes. The mindless violence of British and American schools is rare. And in Belgium and Holland, violence is uncommon. Belgian educators attribute this to the stable family background of most pupils.

I am coming in a moment to the explanation of all this violence, but let us first look at the growth of vandalism, since this provides us with important clues.

4 The Vandals

A group of eight young men, aged from 17 to 20, armed themselves with spray-paint, Redex guns stolen from petrol stations (these guns inject upper-cylinder lubricant) and other weapons and drove through the towns and suburbs of east London spraying passers-by and groups of girls with these substances, merely to ruin their clothes. The graphite in upper-cylinder lubricant causes a stain which is virtually impossible to remove. Experiment had also shown them that lemon-juice is particularly effective in staining mohair suits, so they also took that along. Altogether their destructive course covered 100 miles. Subsequently they pleaded guilty on 47 charges, including 'causing actual bodily harm'. Four people ended up in hospital.

I choose this episode to introduce a discussion of vandalism because, though by no means the most destructive, it brings out what has been called the 'wanton' element in such behaviour. It was not a social protest: the people affected were not the upper classes, not even the bourgeois classes. Young girls and boys of just the same class as the vandals had their summer clothes ruined and their afternoon spoiled. Nor was it done on the impulse of the moment. These points are worth making since some sociologues—the term sociologist seems hardly appropriate for such special pleading—have tried to excuse vandalism on these grounds. Vandalism is the wanton destruction of objects of beauty, use or value and thus differs in essence from crime, which brings the perpetrator some material advantage.

Typical examples of malicious destruction noted in a recent *Sunday Times* article were: 'pouring acid on motor cars, pulling all the flowers from floral clocks in municipal parks, strangling swans in ornamental lakes, slashing the tyres of all the cars in a car park, stripping the insulation from round water mains, dumping manhole covers in a sewage farm, throwing life-belts in the sea, placing sleepers on railway lines, throwing stones at drivers of passing trains, urinating in public telephone boxes, pouring dye into swimming baths, placing bicycle chains on overhead cables to cause short circuits.'

Newly completed apartment blocks seem to have a special attraction for vandals: before the occupants can move in, doors are smashed, lavatories blocked, paint is flung about and windows are broken. This is now a recognised risk in the building industry and applies more often to public housing for poorer people than to dwellings intended for the rich. Occupied buildings are, increasingly, being invaded and wrecked around the heads of the occupants.

Vandalism speedily extends to the point of threatening property on a serious scale. Here is an example quoted in Colin Ward's book *Vandalism:* 'Sabotage or vandalism may have caused a massive leak of explosive naphtha which threatened thousands of people in Liverpool yesterday. Leakage of the liquid explosive caused the river Mersey to be closed to shipping, and a whole area of the city to be sealed off.'

Finally, vandalism begins to threaten human life itself. Recently in Britain, the driver of a train near Durham was killed by a heavy boulder dropped on his cab from a bridge. Other serious incidents include placing obstacles on dark sections of high-speed roads and putting oil-drums, sections of rail, or other solid objects on railway tracks. Hooliganism of this kind 'now constitutes one of the most serious threats to rail safety in Britain,' observes Colonel J. R. H. Robertson, Chief Inspecting Officer of Railways. In 1972 17.3 per cent of *all* train accidents were caused by malicious acts, a trebling of the rate in nine years. Altogether 147 trains ran into obstacles in 1972 (against 50 in 1963). Eight trains were derailed; others were set on fire as a result. 'The increase in hooliganism is a national problem,' commented Robertson.

The underlying factor in vandalism is the working-off of resentments: it is just one more example of the psychological process known as displacement, in which anger is directed not to the person arousing it but on to some object or person unlikely to hit back. The man reproved by his employer snaps at his secretary, the exasperated husband kicks the cat. Violence is the product of the way we organise our society, as I shall argue in more detail in a moment. But to recognise, and even sympathise with, the frustration of individuals is not quite the same as approving or defending their actions. The fact that some sociologues are beginning to do just this is a social development of alarming significance in itself.

Thus Stan Cohen of Essex University says firmly: 'Vandalism is just right.' He approvingly quotes the remark of the Russian revolutionary Bakunin: 'The urge to destroy is also a creative urge,' a remark which makes nonsense of language. The urge to destroy is a substitute for, and a perversion of, the urge to create.

For Colin Ward, from whose book *Vandalism* I have already quoted, vandalism is 'an indication not of social malaise but of moral health'. And he quotes the American writer Guy Debord with approval as saying: 'I fully support any act of vandalism, etc., without qualification and without providing excuses for the people who do it.' An anonymous writer in *Skelf* declares: 'Spray-paint gang-slogans ruining shop-fronts, especially new ones; wrecked, ripped buses; the enormous volume of pilfering that goes on in shops and works. . . . These are the only things that give me hope.'

Some of these sociologues have sought to excuse vandalism as an expression of high spirits, the lower-class equivalent of a university rag—but the examples I have cited clearly go far beyond a rag. Many upper-class activities, they say, would count as vandalism if done by the lower class. Cohen also refers to the case of some residents who resisted the tarring of their previously stone-paved road as an example of vandalism. Comment is superfluous.

When some unidentified individual collected all the Little Tern eggs in a nature sanctuary in Scotland and smashed them, it was not done spontaneously and it was not 'fun'. Vandalism exhibits a vindictiveness quite foreign to high spirits. But it is true that vandalism can cater to young men's need for action, as Ward argues. 'Even as I write these lines, the night sky to the north is aglow with the reflection of fierce fires blazing down in Ashdown forest, fires that are deliberately started by highly mobile young hooligans. Each evening this week the fires have raged, reducing the variety of plant

FOREST FIRES DELIBERATE

Thirty-eight of 46 fires which have destroyed a tenth of the 6,400 acre Ashdown Forest, Sussex, in the past three weeks were started deliberately, Lieutenant-Commander John Angell, forest superintendent, told the conservators.

The Times 24 April 1974

and animal life and producing a surface slime that increases the run-off of surface water. Last night there were ten outbreaks at the same time . . .', a writer laments. This exercise, explains Ward, 'provides scope for the very qualities of enterprise, courage, and the spirit of adventure that warrant general approval'. True— but society's failure to provide more constructive outlets is a disaster, and such destructive alternatives are a matter for deep concern not for approval. Destruction is not an equivalent of construction but an antitype to it.

Given this attitude of approval, it is perhaps not surprising that methods of vandalism are now actually being taught to young children. The *Children's Rights Magazine* offers a 'Children's Angry Brigade Communiqué' which urges: 'All sabotage is effective in hierarchical systems like schools—unscrew locks, smash Tannoys, paint blackboards red, grind all the chalk to dust—you're angry— you know what to do.' This is known to sociologues as 'creative delinquency'.

Hence it is virtually certain that the next twenty years will see such behaviour reach unprecedented levels of destruction and disruption. National Parks will be ruined, public statuary and sculpture will have to be withdrawn, public facilities like lavatories and telephones will no longer be provided.

Both Al Toffler, in his *Future Shock*, and the fiction writer John

Brunner, in novels like *The Jagged Orbit*, foresee the institutionalisation of vandalism as a recognised leisure activity. Just as 'phone phreaks' enjoy beating the system by finding out how to make long-distance calls without payment, so other tightly organised groups, says Toffler, may tamper with computer programs, intercept and alter broadcasts, reroute mail, tinker with the stock-market, or corrupt the random samples on which opinion polls depend. They may even, he suggests, 'commit complexly plotted robberies and assassinations . . .' as a thrill-laden leisure activity. The novelist John Brunner, however, sees this trend moving into even more viciously destructive areas, ranging from provoking racial outbreaks to forcibly injecting mind-blowing drugs into total strangers and observing the results (you hit the jackpot if you cause permanent insanity). How can we account for such trends?

5 The Bad and the Bored

A girl of 16 was returning home, in the city of Bath, about 6 p.m. after collecting for a charity near the Abbey. She noticed six youths coming towards her, spread across the street, and she felt some apprehension. As she made to pass through the line, they kicked her so that she fell to the ground, then all joined in kicking her violently, after which they passed on laughing. Not a word was said. The incident took ninety seconds and was witnessed by an elderly lady who was afraid to intervene. There were two policemen within a hundred yards or so.

Afterwards, interviewed in hospital, the girl said: 'I quite understand. You see, they were bored.'

'I have a single overwhelming conviction—that the problem underneath is boredom. . . . People no longer seem to know why they are alive,' asserts the playwright Arthur Miller, pointing out that many current novels and plays deal with this theme. 'People seem to live in a state of psychological stasis, punctuated by a string of near-experiences.' This theme appears in the reports of social workers too numerous to count. James Patrick, a teacher in an approved school became a member of a Glasgow teen-age gang for a while, as he describes in his absorbing book *A Glasgow Gang Observed*. He makes it very clear that the object of the week-end battle with another gang was to import some excitement into a dull life, most of which was spent standing on street corners. The feeling when you were going into battle was described by one boy: 'Yir heart's racin', ye feel sick; it's better'n sex.' His friends agreed. Actually it was not the fight so much as the preparations and the moments before it which were attractive: the planning and organisation gave life a purpose. As an American worker, W. B. Miller, noted of American teen-age gangs: 'A major objective of gang members was to put themselves in the posture of fighting without actually having to fight.'

Patrick says: 'Bored they certainly were at school, discontented at work, but they were not openly rebellious.' Paul Goodman emphasised the feeling (among the very underprivileged Puerto Rican boys with whom he worked in New York) that they could never escape from their groove, never hope to earn a good income by honest work. While a small proportion of gangs are motivated by 'a desire to strike at society' for its rejection of them as failures, the average gang is concerned more with a 'cult of manly toughness'. Boredom is another name for lack of purpose. In addition, the adolescent needs to prove his manhood.

In an unsophisticated society, the adolescent graduates as a 'young brave' and proves his manhood by killing or scalping some member of an enemy tribe. To drain off this aggression, many such peoples substituted dangerous and painful initiation ceremonies, all of which enabled a young man to prove his courage—and in some cases his ability to support a wife. The same desire for self-validation is seen at work in the violence at British football matches. One reporter describes the 'bandaged and bloodied youngsters proudly sporting their injuries on the streets' after the match, observing: 'For the hooligan element the match is not the thing—it is the trappings that are important: an arena, an audience and an opposition.' It is not 'letting off steam' but self-validation which provides the motive.

Pat Elton Mayo studied delinquent groups in Marseille and on a British housing estate, finding remarkably similar patterns in each; but she makes a different point: 'The sentiment of "not belonging" to the parents' society was the one constant attitude found in all the offenders interviewed, whatever their age, intelligence, job or educational standard. They felt rejected by society and justified in forming what amounts to a resistance movement. In other circumstances, members of a resistance movement can be regarded as heroes, and this is fundamentally what they want to be.'

Adventurous pursuits that are lawful, like mountaineering, sailing or hunting, have been traditionally the prerogative of the upper and middle classes. Modern society gives the underprivileged boy little opportunity for manly prowess.

In Marseille, an unusual police chief established a club for such boys, enabling them to sail, camp and undertake other constructive activities. 'One of the joys of the club are the sporting outings, underwater fishing, mountaineering and sailing, all of which involve real physical adventure,' reports Dr Mayo. 'Intellectual adventure is also provided and they are astonished how exciting it can be. They are mainly intelligent boys; and the effort of writing and producing plays, for instance, has surprised them by the sense of achievement.'

And she adds these significant words: 'When one has worked over a period of time in two communities such as the Marseille Housing Estate and Queen's Park, one has an overwhelming sensation of human wastage. The fact that these people are no longer starving does not mean that their human and social needs are met.' That should be engraved in gold on the desks of all those politicians who confine their attention to matters of economics, and could profitably be noted by union leaders too.

In the current jargon, these boys were alienated from society. They did not feel themselves to be part of the system. This is the condition sociologists refer to as anomia. For those who are not part of society there is no need to observe society's norms. At the same time, the exclusion is resented and seen as insulting. Such alienation is naturally commonest among young people who are facing for the first time the need to find a place in society. Many will eventually do so and will 'settle down'. But modern society (unlike 'primitive' societies) offers no clear-cut way of graduating to manhood, and some will never find a way.

To put it another way, the adolescent's problem is one of self-respect, and it is the problem of many criminal adults too. Hans Toch examined 69 men guilty of actions of violence and considered that over a quarter were defending their self-image and a further ten were defending their reputation. He comments that 'once a person has discovered that the ego can be buttressed at the expense of others, the discovery seems to be recurrently reapplied'.

While the majority of alienated youth are the unwilling victims of a pathological social situation, it is important to recognise that a small proportion suffer from a personal pathology and tend to be the leaders and 'hard cases' in asocial behaviour. It is the man who feels vulnerable to manipulation, and the man who sees others as tools, who are most likely to resort to violence.

6 Pathological Cases

In his absorbing book *The Frying Pan*, Tony Parker reports a statement made by a prisoner, with a long history of violent behaviour, in Britain's progressive prison at Grendon Underwood. Here the prisoners are given extensive psychiatric help and support, and Parker tape-recorded long interviews with prisoners and staff. The

prisoner in question was an Irish boy who had been born a bastard;
not long after his birth his mother, a waitress, also abandoned him
to the care of relatives.

'I wasn't wanted right from the start—that's plain enough for
sure, and I think it makes you grow up on the defensive and hating
other people because you know you are not a fully-fledged member
of their society. So you turn your back on it. You think "Oh, sod
the lot of them . . .!" ' and he added, 'I hate everybody, that's the
fact of it; and most of all I hate myself. Hatred, violence, I'm full
of it. I think if I had a chance I'd destroy the whole world.' It would
be hard to find a clearer expression of the link between early
rejection and political nihilism. As Dr Kellmer Pringle, director of
the National Children's Bureau, says: 'Anger, hate and lack of concern for others are common reactions to being unloved and rejected.'

Another factor emerges in the remark of a 19-year-old boy (not
a criminal) who wrote: 'I feel so frustrated at times I feel like
destroying everything in sight . . . if I read about a big job, i.e.,
burglary, being done or a murder, I want to do the same, so that
people will know I'm equal to anyone . . . I can't stand being taken
a figure of no account.' Similarly, one of the Arab terrorists, whose
motives were ostensibly political, said after his arrest that he had
taken part 'in order to *be* someone'. As these quotations show, the
desire to achieve identity in a mass society is a central factor and
I shall have more to say about it before the end of the book.

A third factor in such personalities is an emotional blunting, an
incapacity to feel, which, if severe enough, is classifiable as schizo-
phrenia. It has often been observed that schizophrenic murderers
show no emotion even when they are condemned to death. Certainly
none at the fate of their victim. As one prisoner told Tony Parker,
if you meet me after I've been released, and you're driving a car,
don't stop. If you do, I'll drag you out and drive the car away. And
when Parker smiled, he said, 'Don't laugh. I mean it.' Such people,
having been emotionally wounded in early life, have responded by
saying, in effect, 'If I cease to feel, I can't be hurt any more.' At
the same time, they want to strike back at a harsh world, generalising
their private experience to include the whole society. (Conversely,
the child treated with secure affection may later overrate the goodness of other people.) Because of this emotional deadness, such
people need the strong stimuli of danger and violence (also drugs)
in order to dispel their boredom and feel anything at all.

Bert (not his real name) was a prisoner with a reputation for extreme
ferocity, who had served a 5-year and then a 9-year sentence, and
was serving an 8-year sentence at the time Parker saw him. He had
lost all his remission due to escape attempts. Creating trouble was

what kept his spirits alive: 'I used to enjoy it—it made me feel terrific, it was wonderful to be locked up in solitary on bread and water. They weren't beating me, that was what life was about— smashing yourself up against authority, fighting the whole lousy system. Same as when you were outside; you made your own rules, you didn't give a fuck for the whole of the rotten, lousy, poxy society at all.' It is obvious that deterrent punishment (his next sentence will be 10 to 14 years) has not the slightest effect on a person in this frame of mind.

'The ability to terrorize people,' he said, 'was terrific . . . smashing blokes down with pick-axe handles.' He laughed when he heard that one man nearly died, another was off work for three months, while a third had sixteen stitches. 'I'd describe myself as 100 per cent anarchist. I don't believe in rules, laws, regulations or anything. I think people should be allowed to do exactly what they want.' Not surprisingly, one learns that he was against authority at school. At the same time, much as in the *Clockwork Orange*, he liked listening to the music of Bach, Beethoven and Vivaldi, while his favourite painters were van Gogh, Matisse and (significantly) Munch. Here, in an extreme form, we see the anarchic attitude of many politically-oriented individuals today, such as those we discussed in Chapter III, and I have reported Bert's remarks for the light they throw on less extreme cases.

The extraordinary extremes to which such personality-damage can go are shown by the written statement of a man who, before his execution, wrote: 'In my lifetime I have murdered 21 human beings, I have committed thousands of burglaries, robberies, larcenies, arsons and, last but not least, I have committed sodomy on more than one thousand male human beings. For all these I am not in the least bit sorry. I have no conscience, so that does not worry me . . . I hate the whole human race, including myself.'

It is sometimes maintained that violence is inborn, so that no social changes could eliminate it. As I have argued elsewhere (e.g. in *Conditions of Happiness*, 1949) this view is based on a misunder-standing. Men have, not an aggressive urge, but an inbuilt drive to modify their environment or overcome opposition to attempts to fulfil their needs. When a man fells a tree to make a house for him-self, we call it constructive; when he fells a human being who opposes him, we call it destructive. We cannot eliminate this drive, nor do we want to. What we have to minimise is the fixing of this drive in hate-filled, destructive forms by emotional frustration in infancy, in the manner demonstrated by the cases just related. In Chapter XVIII I shall discuss in some detail what we ought to be doing. Here I only want to establish the point that personality disturbance, almost to the point of pathology, underlies all our problems, and this is not sufficiently recognised.

In short, there is a spectrum which runs from relatively normal boys in frustrating social circumstances to psychotics with personalities deeply wounded by lack of affection and support in infancy.

CONSUMER REACTION

In Hollywood, goaded by the sight of glittering new Oldsmobiles in an auto agency, unemployed painter Clifford F—— wheeled his dilapidated 1951 Chevrolet through the showroom window, smashed against a new Holiday sedan, explained: 'I was mad at the world.'

Time 13 August 1956

A sense of security is imbibed in a mother's arms, listening to her affectionate sounds and having one's needs gratified by her, consistently. In the absence of that basic security, the adult disguises his sense of vulnerability by aggressiveness. In the gangs observed by Patrick, the leader was usually one of these psychotics; the gang members themselves recognised this and called their leader's outburst of fury 'throwing a maddie' or 'running a psychie'. They acquired names like 'the Mad Mexican' or 'the Big Sick'. Says Patrick, 'These boys displayed no guilt feelings; they were social inadequates, their interpersonal relationships were never anything but shallow; there was a calculated and sadistic cruelty about some of their actions. . . .' Big Dave Malloy spoke of lacerating the carcasses of animals as a childhood pastime. Core members smashed the window of a tailor's shop and ceremonially beheaded the dummies. Though no advocate of crude penalties, Patrick is forced to the conclusion that 'For the immediate protection of society, the core members of the gang need to be arrested and imprisoned.'

While run-of-the-mill delinquency has a social cause, this kind of pathology is rooted in the break-up of the family. The boy who gets home from school and finds no mother and no food; the boy who never shares activities with a father he can respect; these are the boys who become monsters almost beyond hope of rehabilitation. The family is the microcosm of society: a permissive family means a permissive society; a disordered family means a disordered society; a hate-filled family means a hate-filled society; a disintegrating family means a disintegrating society.

The problem is not so much the growth of violence as the growth of resentment, desperation and destructiveness, amounting to pathology. This forces on us the question: how much of this can society stand? How much longer can we afford to let things drift?

None of the social factors which make for resentful personalities and for emotional blunting is growing appreciably weaker. Slums remain. Challenging activities for teen-agers are insufficient. Youthful unemployment is high and likely to get much worse. Families are increasingly disrupted as more women go out to work and more fathers fail to meet their responsibilities. It follows that violence, ruthlessness and resentment will increase between now and the end of the century. (The teen-age thugs of 1994 have already been born and are learning the lessons of asociality as you read this.)

This pathology is part of the price we pay for rapid change, the break-up of the family, high mobility, the loss of cultural uniformity and group structure—to name only the main factors. Since we show few signs of wishing to change our course in these respects, and since our value systems are incompatible with a return to a more cohesive social pattern, it is safe to predict that social pathology will grow worse.

This is society's most urgent problem, more pressing than the economic and political disputes on which our leaders spend almost all their time. The facts are available. Unless a major onslaught, with top priority and lavish funding, is launched in Britain and America particularly, we have no hope of surviving. For uncontrolled violence leads to a breakdown of the mechanism of daily life.

We have got our priorities wrong. We have become insensitive to violence. We look only at the deaths; if we read that a few people were discharged from hospital a few days after the explosion or the bank-robbery we feel that that is not much to be concerned about. But a woman with a broken jaw, a man with a damaged kidney, a child with a burn, *suffers*. And a man who loses a hand, a woman who is blinded, is incapacitated for *life*. No amount of material wealth can make up for such losses, and if violence is the price of high technology it may be getting too high a price. Certainly, the reduction of violence should be our top social priority, second only to health in its general aspects, perhaps even ahead of education.

For violence is not just an isolated *ad hoc* problem. It is a product of the loss of social cohesion which, like some psychic Black Death, has afflicted our society. Just as in Rome, decline was marked by uncontrollable crime, violence and hatred, so in our own day. How much violence can we stand?

Violence, of course, attracts attention and each new manifestation is reported to the horrified delight of readers who perhaps find in such stories some outlet for their own suppressed violent impulses. Less obvious, less fascinating, but just as important are the non-violent forms of asociality, to which I shall now turn.

VI

SOURCES OF COHESION

The breach of custom is the breach of all.—Cymbeline

1 Blind-Man's-Buff

On a cold February evening in 1966 Mr Harry Minton stood in the buffet on Waterloo Station, London, drinking a cup of tea while waiting for his train home. Suddenly there was a strange sensation in his left eye. . . . 'It felt as though someone were sticking a piece of Sellotape over the pupil,' so he described it later. The faces round him grow hazy. Maybe it is a smut? He blinks several times. His eye begins to water. Gradually people, bookstall, lights, luggage dissolve and vanish and merge, 'to leave me looking into a dark, sluggish, yellow, muddy river'. He has suddenly gone blind. It is due, as he later learns, to a rare virus disease.

Sightless, he reaches out and grasps the sleeve of someone standing near him. 'Please help me! Would you fetch a policeman for me?' The owner of the sleeve is puzzled. 'I don't fink I understand. You've lorst your sight?' But he promises to help: ' 'Ang on a minute. I'll see what I can do.' He goes, but he does not return. Eventually Harry Minton asks another person, with the same result. And then another. In all he asks eight people. The eighth, a young man, is different. Guiding Minton to a seat, he duly fetches a policeman and arranges for an ambulance. He brushes Minton's thanks aside: 'Good heavens, that's nothing. Anyone would have done the same.'

This episode epitomises vividly the central defect of our society: in the dry language of sociology, it is loss of sociality.

I am confident that such an incident could not possibly have occurred in the village where I live, and it is worth analysing why. First, people retain a sense that they are dealing with individual human beings. A transaction in the village shop or post-office is not, as so often in a town, a mechanical process such as one might have with an automatic vending machine, but a personal contact with someone whose name is familiar, whose family circumstances you know: where they live, whether they have children and so on. There is time for gossip or an exchange of civilities. Secondly, in a cohesive local group, there are social pressures. Any member of the community who was known to have done something as heartless as abandoning a blind stranger would suffer a loss of reputation and would have something to live down.

To be sure, there are disadvantages in living in a small community precisely because one is, so to say, supervised. That is why people often prefer the city where they are 'free to do as they like'. But the price of that freedom is precisely loss of social cohesion, and all it means.

Mr Minton's story, to be sure, is less horrifying than the still-remembered episode in which a girl named Kitty Genovese was stalked and murdered in New York, while more than 20 people looked on from their windows, without so much as telephoning the police. (Soon after, with much less public comment, a similar episode occurred in Liverpool.) Perhaps, seen through a window in the cold illumination of street-lamps, Kitty Genovese appeared little different from the familiar images of violence on the television screen. Maybe watching television fosters a sense of remoteness and impersonality.

But precisely because Minton's case was so ordinary, so devoid of horrified fascination and because it implied no danger of 'becoming involved'—of having to give evidence in court and so on—it seems to me to be peculiarly telling, which is why I have placed it at the start of this chapter.

In the story of Mr Minton—and that of Kitty Genovese—there is, in addition to the loss of community, a second causal factor: loss of conscience.

One almost has to apologise for using such an unfashionable term as conscience, but it is scientifically, as well as morally, respectable. Psychologists have explained to us how conscience (or super-ego) is formed by the introjection of parental models, and especially of a father-figure—a process which starts very early in life, perhaps as early as $1-1\frac{1}{2}$ years old. For introjection to occur successfully, the father must be at least somewhat affectionate, even though he may be severe: a wholly brutal father, or a wholly unloving one, is usually rejected psychologically and the child will tend to defy rather than to imitate him. Now, as I have shown elsewhere, modern society tends to cut children off from their fathers, who often return from work after a two-year-old has gone to bed, or are absent for weeks at a time, as in the case of seamen, travelling salesmen and busy executives. In addition, fathers who are inadequate—especially if the mother rubs this in—alcoholic, criminal, inconsistent or otherwise poor models impair the son's conscience formation. The American sociologist C. Wright Mills lamented the absence of what he called Representative Men; in other words, noble individuals whose lives serve as models for others. (Hence, he thought, the current interest in the biographies of historical figures.) '. . . the creation of such Representative Men should be a major aspiration of our collective political life,' he opined. Their job would be 'to make articulate genuine crises of moral choice'. Disastrous is the general absence of any understanding of the social contract—the fact that a citizen has more duties than rights: that limitations of selfish impulse is the price one must pay for social support. This basic truth should be imparted by parents and reinforced at school.

Failure to accept paternal models explains the general rise in permissiveness and also the fact that it is coupled to a rejection of authority, which is, unconsciously, a search for a strong authority: the challenge is issued in the hope that it will be accepted, as some university chancellors have failed to realise. But permissiveness is not confined to sexual permissiveness. It also permits tax evasion and social security frauds; it permits television repairmen to charge for repairs which were not necessary and museum directors to buy works of art which they know must have been illegally acquired.

In Australia, after the recent floods in Brisbane, looting was general, as it was in some US riots. The days when, if one found a lost purse, one took it to the police, are gone.

To lack of conscience we can also assign much social apathy—our failure to help the old, the crippled and the insane as we should; bad workmanship and poor service, and much else. The functioning of society depends on the maintenance of conscience. Today, however, conscientiousness is no longer admired as an ideal: it has been called 'the policeman inside the head' with the implication that, like real policemen, it is an oppressor to be defied. Conscience, to be sure, can become obsessive and inhibiting, as it did among the Puritans; but today the pendulum has swung to the other extreme. The restoration of conscience to a reasonable mean position is urgent. But it will not be achieved by argument or lamentation—only by social changes which restore the family as an effective psychological and social unit.

The whole thing was put with great clarity by an unnamed citizen of Blackburn in an interview tape-recorded by Jeremy Seabrook in 1969: 'When we were at school, even if your mother was working, there was always the neighbours to come in and help, but now you find that the family's breaking down,' he said. 'I still think that a lot of our troubles stem from moral standards having declined. All the permissiveness that we've got. The number of adults in court for stealing, it would have been practically unknown in an age where everybody kept an eye on what the neighbours were doing. . . . There was terrific poverty but people did help each other out . . . they had to pull together then, they did help one another humanly. But people have grown very much away from one another. This is why you have social workers coming in and trying to make people understand each other.'

Society depends on cooperation, voluntarily given. Even the most aggressive and competitive of pre-literate societies display a wide area of conventionalised and accepted behaviour. It is not merely a question of mutual help: it is also a question of being willing to observe the same conventions, and of not damaging the common stock, not muddying the pool from which others will have to drink.

We seldom stop to think how profoundly our society depends and has been developed on the basis that people will not harm the common stock. Railways were able to replace wooden seats with upholstered ones when, and only when, the vast majority of travellers could be relied upon to treat the coverings with reasonable care. They could provide electric light and washing facilities on the same assumption. It does not readily occur to us that plate-glass shop windows are only possible as long as people refrain from breaking them. Similarly the telephone system only functions as long as people are willing to replace the receiver on the hook. Sometimes a 'technological fix' can be found to outwit the anti-social individual— as in the case of elevator doors which close automatically after a while, but often this is not possible.

In the same way, restaurants can only provide fine tablecloths and tableware when the customers can be relied upon to treat them as they treat their own. Motorway restaurants in Britain now provide the cheapest trays, paper cups and stainless Formica because anything better is stolen. Mirrors have to be glued, not screwed, to washroom walls and lavatory seats welded into position. Even weighty juke-boxes are sometimes stolen while the restaurant is in full use.

Of course all societies contain a proportion of anti-social members, and the law and the police force are intended to limit their activities. The situation changes qualitatively once a sizeable proportion of the public begins to behave anti-socially, and speedily becomes uncontrollable. Mass pilfering is socially a quite different phenomenon from the planned robberies and burglaries of the professional criminal. Decay of conscience among a wide section of the public, and especially when urgent need is not present, is a serious development, threatening to undermine the social process at its foundations. The person who will pilfer is, one may assume, the person who will loot when an emergency occurs. And figures show that the person who is dishonest in material things is likely also to be dishonest in emotional relationships.

It is therefore worth enquiring in more detail how far such trends are extending.

2 Fiddlers We

While everyone knows that modern society is marked by asocial behaviour, it is hard to quantify it. The motorist who leaves his car blocking the exit of another, the customer who omits to point out that he has received too much change, the passer-by who averts his gaze when he sees a child being bullied, are all too common, but such events go unrecorded. And sometimes there may be excuses for such asocial behaviour: lack of time is often one. There is however one fairly clear-cut type of behaviour, which is widespread and growing, to which figures can be put and for which there are no valid excuses: shoplifting. Let us examine it, therefore, not because it is in any way as important as some of the behaviour noted in later chapters, but because it is a straw which shows how the wind is blowing. Some shoplifters, it is true, are driven by a compulsion and psychiatrists tell us that they are taking goods as a substitute for love. Emotionally deprived children not infrequently steal from their mothers—and, typically, they steal jam, sweets and eatables. In the misty mind of the infant the mother as provider of nourishment and the mother as provider of warmth, care and love are inextricably confused. Some shoplifters are people who have never outgrown this pattern.

But shoplifting in recent times has extended so greatly that this can no longer be regarded as the main cause. According to an American study, one shopper in every fifteen in big department stores in New York, Boston and Philadelphia is a shoplifter, although fewer than one per cent of them are caught. This figure is based on a study of 1,647 shoppers in four stores in the three cities. Shoppers were selected at random and secretly followed to see what they would do. Of 109 people seen stealing, only one was arrested by a store detective.

England saw a wave of shoplifting offences by foreigners visiting the country in 1973. Many of these were well-off, the wives of diplomats and other officials, for instance, and what they took greatly exceeded their personal needs.

A Home Office working party found that shoplifting is seldom reported to the police except when the offender is caught in the act, and hardly ever when the offender is an employee. Police policy varies, but the trend is shown by the fact that, while known shop-lifting offences increased 75 per cent between 1966 and 1971, prosecutions increased by only 54 per cent and formal cautions by 169 per cent.

Children, of course, are seldom prosecuted and some of them trade on this fact. Some stores in the Thames Valley towns, during the Christmas shopping spree in 1973, estimated that three-quarters of their losses from shoplifting were caused by under-fifteens and some by children as young as five and six, stealing toys and cheap jewellery as Christmas gifts. Attempts to explain shoplifting as a reaction to social injustice can scarcely account for 'nicking' by schoolchildren or wives of diplomats.

Europe does not lag far behind Britain and America, according to a report by Lisa Schmidt for the magazine *Europa*. 'Shoplifting today is much more than the little old lady taking a meat-pie to feed her starving husband. It is a big business for thieves and for security men,' she says. In Paris, the detective at the Bazaar de l'Hôtel de Ville said that shoplifting had risen ten per cent in the last year, many of the culprits being tourists, and some schoolgirls who 'descend like locusts'. A Brussels store detective said: 'In other years kids would take one mini-tape-recorder. Now they are helping them-selves to six or seven.' Copenhagen also reports rising losses. 'Shop-lifting is increasing dramatically throughout Europe,' sums up Lisa Schmidt.

A curious feature of this trend is that many, presumably not them-selves shoplifters, are quite tolerant of the offence. Thus a Belgian judge, in Liège, after letting off eighteen shoplifters, commented: 'Theft from large stores using the self-service system is unavoidable and is usually taken into account on the loss side of the store's turn-over. Shoplifting does not presuppose a premeditated attitude towards thieving. Neither does it merit a prison sentence or a fine.' However, it is not the store, but its honest customers who suffer. And the woman with the colour television set rented at £7.50 a week, who stole meat because she could not afford to buy it, could presumably have limited herself to a black-and-white set as other people manage to do.

While shoplifting gets attention, and is recorded in a special category so that figures can be produced, there are numerous other forms of pilfering, ranging from siphoning petrol out of cars, tampering with telephone boxes and gas meters, to carrying parts out of the factory in which you work. British food distributors, for instance, lose £1m. worth of wooden pallets annually. A British

Ford executive told me, twenty years ago, that they reckoned to lose the equivalent of a car a day in stolen parts, but flattered themselves none had managed to steal a completed vehicle. At British Motor Corporation, one much admired achievement was that of a man who walked out carrying a complete cylinder-block with a geranium planted in each cylinder. He was going, he said, to a flower show, and the security guard congratulated him on his fine geraniums without noticing what they were planted in.

Fiddling is always endemic in armed services, of course. The presence of masses of material owned by no one in particular is an obvious temptation. In a recent study of theft by hotel employees, one waiter told the investigator, Gerry Mars: 'Fiddles are part of wages. The whole issue runs on fiddles, it couldn't work otherwise.' The British Security Industry Association has estimated that thefts from shops and offices cost £12m. yearly. Department stores even have a special euphemism for it; they call it 'inventory shrinkage'.

Decay of conscience explains most criminal acts where sex and violence do not enter. Unfortunately the figures of non-violent crime are too vague to be of much help. A large proportion of such crime goes unreported, so that a higher figure may be due to greater police effort rather than more crime; legal definitions change, so that comparisons of past with present or of one country with another, are unreliable. One American study suggests that actual rates of minor crime are five times reported rates. The position becomes a little clearer if we confine ourselves to those serious crimes known as indictable crimes, which are less likely to be glossed over, and if we allow for the growth of population when comparing past and present. American figures are unhelpful owing to differences between states; I therefore take British ones. Here are the rates of indictable crime for England and Wales at the start of each decade since 1930, expressed as offences per 100,000 of the population:

1930	369
1940	729
1950	1048
1960	1625
1970	3176

It is obvious that indictable crime has increased so dramatically that explanations in terms of greater police activity, etc. are untenable.*

There is one form of crime where the figures are pretty reliable: arson. Nearly every fire involves an insurance claim and insurance

---

* This argument, which appears regularly in the Press, works both ways. If the police are more active, they catch more criminals so the rate goes up. But if they are less active, criminals commit more crimes, so the rate goes up. Actually, there are no grounds for supposing there is any long-term trend in the effectiveness of the police.

assessors closely study the causes of such fires in order to eliminate the claims of those who have started the fire deliberately in order to claim, and with the object of reducing fire risks in the future. Their findings are unambiguous. Arson is occurring in the US at a rate ten times as high as in 1950 and is spreading from the centre of cities to the suburbs.

The cost of arson exceeds the cost of all other kinds of violence combined. Thus in 1971 there were 72,000 fires due to arson, causing damage put at \$233m. The number of incendiary fires has tripled since 1960, risen by a factor of 13 since 1960 (a tenfold increase when population growth is allowed for). Only one per cent of arson cases result in a conviction.

From Britain comes a similar story; though arson is less clearly distinguished. Total fire damage reached an all-time high in 1973, and malice was assigned as the major cause in respect of fires costing more than £10,000. Particularly striking was the fact that many more schools are being set on fire: the cost of school fires in 1973 was over £60m.—five times as high as in 1970. Such figures show only the immediate costs, and do not allow for lost production, the cost of the fire service itself, etc.

But it is not simply the quantitative increase which is significant so much as the qualitative change. Perhaps a couple of recent incidents may convey what I mean. On the Paris–Istanbul express, according to two passengers named Francesco and Maria Bernardi, two teenage girls were dragged into a compartment packed with men where they remained screaming continuously for half an hour, to emerge half-naked and crying. When the Bernardis sought to rescue them, they were threatened with long knives. They also saw a ten-year-old girl sexually molested, but when they reported all this to the police at Trieste, they were told 'these things happen'.

The idea that mass rape could occur on an international express never entered people's minds before now. Widespread robberies on Italian trains are reported by the rail correspondent of *Corriere della Sera*, Signor Mario Righetti: bands of robbers, mostly Yugoslavs, Turks, Greeks and Latin-Americans, squirt anaesthetic gas through cracks in the compartment door, afterwards entering with duplicate keys and robbing the insensible passengers. It sounds like an episode in a cheap *feuilleton*, but among those robbed in this way was M. Jean Marabini, a correspondent of *Le Monde*. Plain-clothes police now ride the trains.

As these incidents demonstrate, police cannot be everywhere. The real limitation to crime is a sense of what is possible and permissible. Today the feeling that 'you can get away with anything' has become general. Thanks to technology, you usually can. Gangs of South

American pickpockets now work the airports, arriving on a morning plane, and departing with their gains for another capital on an afternoon flight, before any effective steps can be taken. Only a totally new approach to crime prevention could put a stop to this sort of thing.

What is unquestionably the case is that criminals are becoming more daring and more imaginative, in the sense that they are turning to forms of theft less obvious than taking money and jewellery. 'In the old days,' says Howard Nixon, Deputy Keeper of Printed Books at the British Museum, 'we assumed people would not steal books. Now we have to assume that they bloody well will. In entering the British Museum nowadays they search you to make sure you haven't got a bomb and as you leave they search you to see you haven't got a book.'

Librarians used to assume that exceptionally rare books were immune from theft on the grounds that they could not be sold, as the buyer would realise that they must have been stolen. Today there are buyers and dealers who are less conscientious, while thieves have realised that they can often claim a ransom against a threat to destroy the book. (The same is true of pictures, of course, and of some other works of art.) An attempt was even made to steal the Gutenberg Bible from Harvard Library: fortunately it is so heavy that the rope by which the thief was descending broke under the weight. Book thefts have risen so much in the past couple of years in Britain that a working party was set up in 1972 to consider what could be done about it.

In all this we see of course the failure of conscience. (In many shoplifting cases, a mother and her daughter are involved—which shows the kind of parental model offered.) But while such cases are at least recognised as offences carried out on a 'let's see if we can get away with it' basis, there is now a more alarming development: the actual advocacy of antisocial behaviour as morally right.

3 The Anti-culture

Though we hear a great deal about the need for 'new values' what we can see happening in society is merely the emergence of an 'anti-culture' by the simple reversal of existing values. And the desire to destroy the old often seems stronger than the desire to build something new. The motivation is suspect: it seems based on hatred rather than love—hatred of the old is more crucial than love of the new.

Clothing is always a good clue to attitudes: the culture-rejector goes to every extreme to avoid the formality of his parents, and seeks to indicate his scorn (and to annoy) by wearing old uniforms, bizarre combinations of old and new, etc. He takes pleasure in breaching taboos, such as those on nudity or the use of obscenities, and gets an added pleasure from smoking pot because he knows it teases. Masochistically, he even rejects good food, clean clothes, comfortable surroundings and the organisation of his time, as being bourgeois.

The trend becomes even wilder when it goes on to rejecting honesty. 'Stealing books from libraries can't be ruled out,' says a magazine produced by the Antistudent Pamphlet Collective. 'There's nothing you can steal from college that wasn't made by the people and stolen from them in the first place,' declares *Antistudent* firmly if obscurely. 'By hook or crook,' one should get hold of such college equipment as 'photocopiers, printing presses, duplicators, projectors, video, cameras, tape-recorders, typewriters, postage franking machines, mechanical, electrical, electronic and chemical laboratories [*sic*].' But when you steal traceable equipment, it warns shrewdly, 'it's a good idea to arrange an exchange with people in another town'.

By the same token 'in order to make sure your energies are not sapped in their game [i.e., by trying to learn something] it's necessary to organise some good, honest cheating'. So you should create essay pools from previous years' work, sign each other in for lectures and smuggle in prepared answers to examinations where you know the questions beforehand. Better still, refuse to take examinations at all. This is all right 'because every exam is a cheat against decent learning'.

A curious magazine, decorated with cartoons, is produced for schoolchildren, under the name *Y-front*. The contributions, carefully mis-spelled, are ostensibly by children too, and appeal for 'schulekids' to unite under the banner of the Schools Action Union or the National Union of School Students. 'Having come to the conclusion that our education process is just one long, mechanical, exam-festered slog, we arrive at the big problem: 'HOW DO WE CHANGE THE SYSTEM?' Thirty-six suggestions to this end are offered, ranging from hiding the chalk (children knew this one in my own youth, long before the SAU was thought of) to 'use chemicals from your chemistry lesson for unofficial purposes'. (In my schooldays, making people's urine go green was a popular pastime, and one young scientist nearly blew up the science master with trinitrophenol, the recipe for which he had found in his chemistry book.) Particularly charming is No. 18. 'Breed mice and let hundreds loose on open day, school concert, beginning of term, or whenever.'

Less charming is the appeal: 'Reform or Revolution? A head-on attack. Hitting them where it hurts. Fucking up the system which fucks you up. Indiscriminate and violent attacks on their property . . .

We outnumber them by millions . . . Fight on—and we'll win.'
(You have nothing to lose but your O-levels.) Also mentioned is
'. . . stealing from their employers, ripping-off supermarkets, fucking
up production, creating cultural chaos . . . we cannot lose—we're
all in this together—this conspiracy.' An official disclaimer that
'there is no intention to incite anybody to commit, or to conspire to
commit illegal acts, or legal acts by illegal means', precedes the
Guerrilla Pupils Manual from which these passages are taken.

Besides being revolutionary, the anti-culture rejects the whole idea
of a parliamentary system based on representation because they see
it as hierarchical. They also reject Marxist solutions, as too authoritarian, in favour of anarchy. A polemic by Murray Bookchin,
Listen Marxist! disavows being a manual of revolution. 'It was written
to destroy all manuals by validating the need for revolutionary
struggle to find its own spontaneous-organic forms, by validating the
capacity of all people, when unmolested by the domination of
leaders and doctrines, to find truly visionary ways of relating to each
other. . . .' Visionary is probably the *mot juste*.*

This inspissated rejection of authority leads them to reject the
authority not merely of teachers but of the whole culture, which they
dismiss *in toto* as an imposition. Thus to attend a university is not
seen as a privilege but as an indoctrination to be resisted and a
system to be fought and destroyed. This extremism is clearly
pathological. Violence is not only recommended but is actually made
into a virtue.

In an inside account of the culture, Michael Lerner of Yale
University puts the hippies at the core of the counter-culture and
comments on its 'widespread acceptance of violence as a tactic',
observing that some of the young who are 'into violence' have a
clear predilection for physical assault that characterised storm-
troopers. Commenting on the view that the violent act of rebellion
is 'somehow sacred' he suggests that it is not an aberration but
related to recovery of the capacity to love. This 'transvaluation of
values' (splendidly empty phrase) is seen in the fact that Charles
Manson, who ordered the murder of Sharon Tate and her friends,
is not utterly condemned but 'has become a hero and symbol of
revolt'. By a similar hypostasis, it is a worthy thing to be a criminal.
'And being under sentence now for three years in the federal prison,

---

* It makes a visionary attempt to establish a good relation with the reader by opening
with the words: 'All the old crap of the thirties is coming back again: the shit about the
"class line" the "role of the working class", the "trained cadres", the "vanguard party"...
Progressive Labor (Movement) is not the only example; it is merely the worst. One smells
the same shit in the . . . National Office of the sds, in the various Marxist and Socialist
clubs on campuses, not to speak of the "Militant Labor Forum", the Independent
Socialist Clubs, and the Youth against War and Fascism.'

the one thing I can say is that I find no more honourable position in modern America than that of criminal,' wrote an anarchist named David Harris. A well-known record by The Band was titled: 'I am a Thief and I dig it'. Lerner comments: 'This acceptance of the role of criminal is connected to the pervasive "no" with which the counter-culture confronts the dominant culture.' One aspect of this pervasive 'no' is the rejection of modern technology.

Major features of this rejection are the rejection of discipline for spontaneity, of saving for spending, of thought for emotion. Unfortunately, society cannot function without some degree of discipline, some thought for the future, some measure of rationality. Even the confirmed hippy would hardly want the surgeon removing his appendix to be casual about counting his clamps, or the mechanic who serviced his car to forget about screwing on the oil-drainage cap. From aircraft pilots and navigators down to television repairmen and those who sterilise milk bottles, unremitting attention to duty is desirable. Naturally, a degree of self-discipline which produced serious constraint of the personality (as happened too often in the last century) is not to be desired. A happy medium between spontaneity and restraint, as also between saving and spending, has to be found. Many values have this bipolar character; a compromise must be found. But to the hippy compromise is a dirty word. The philosophical position of the hippies is too extreme to be tenable.

Above all, they confuse the ideal with the real. In an ideal world, people could be totally free, totally without thought for the morrow. They could in fact give reign to their impulses without need for super-ego control. In the real world impulse is often disastrous, and the restraint of the super-ego, though often unbalanced or mistaken, is indispensable.

The belief in absolutes like liberty, spontaneity, equality, and so on, is an example of non-rational prejudice. The permutation of these fixed attitudes I term 'mythic thinking'.

At the personal level, it is evident that this is an aspect of the shift from patrism to matrism—from the authoritarian values derived from a family headed by a father to the permissive and spontaneous values derived from a family where the mother is boss. The change in family structure and the absence of the father during the crucial years of childhood, which I have already discussed, suffice to account for the trend in psychological turns, and show us how to reverse it if we wish to do so.*

In addition to its matrist configuration the youthful personality tends towards what I have called soft-ego: there is a sense of unity

* For an explanation of the terms matrism and patrism see Appendix.

with others and with nature, and a rejection of the cerebral in favour of the intuitive. Hence 'understanding' is thought of as non-verbal, non-intellectual. It follows that verbalised, conceptualised understanding is rejected as misconceived. Drugs, on the other hand, by seeming to open one up to new experience, are seen as a truer kind of education. Taken together, matrist rejection of authority and soft-ego universalism combine to support a dreamy conception of people coming harmoniously together, without organisation, and in some inspired manner achieving their ends without conflict. This too is unrealistic. To say so does not of course mean that authoritarianism and isolation from others are any better. In an imperfect world, we have to make the best compromise we can between the two.

All this being so, the holder of such beliefs or attitudes finds the practical world intolerable and wishes to annihilate it. His idealism convinces him that once the man-made structures are destroyed the true pattern of nature will be revealed without further effort. It is in this spirit that he tries to strip functional objects of their function and to 'understand' them as things-in-themselves (*Ding-an-sich*). This is the basis of Pop art. Music and, still more, dance, are preferred to the labours of sculpture, orchestral composition or literary endeavour.

These preferences culminate in a rejection of dualism: mind and body are one; man and nature are one; man and woman are one. As Charles Frankel, Professor of Philosophy and Public Affairs at Columbia University, New York, has phrased it, in *Science*: 'The underlying assumption in much radical thought today is that the universe is, in the last analysis, totally and perfectly integrated with human needs. Difficulties arise only from our imperfect understanding; with better insight, all forms of separateness and division—between individuals and also between the subjective and objective worlds—will disappear.'

He has analysed this tendency under the label of 'irrationalism' and considers that the irrationalists subscribe to five propositions:

1   The universe is divided into appearance and reality.
2   People mistake appearance for reality because of cultural and practical presuppositions.
3   In human beings there is a war between the cerebral and the emotional.
4   We know we have gone wrong when we feel separate from other human beings or alienated from Nature or divided within ourselves.
5   Hence all human problems are reducible to a loss of harmony.

I do not go as far as Frankel in dismissing this position as merely irrational, and hence something to be stamped out. I regard it as a good idea pushed to an absurd extreme. The hard-ego position, in which man is conceived as wholly separate from society and the environment and out of harmony with it, is as wrong as the contrary assertion. The pendulum has simply swung too far.

In the same way, even reason becomes suspect and irrationality is praised as somehow better than rationality. The anti-student seeks to build a counter-culture in which dishonesty, irrationality, pre-judice, intolerance, incivility, violence and destruction appear as prime values, while honesty, reason, impartiality, tolerance, manners, care, effort and creation are denigrated and made anti-values. Such a complete reversal is unprecedented in the history of Western culture.

We should take it more seriously. The efforts of the radicals are reinforced by the skills of modern technology, which enable them to spread their doctrines. But the extreme views of the radicals are not, one must stress, to be seen as a minor pathology. They merely express in strong terms what many relatively conventional people feel more mildly.

4 Moral Crisis of the West

Solzhenitsyn put the situation in acc rate if unfashionable terms when he described the West as going through a 'grave moral crisis'. The extremes of the anti-culture only dramatise the tendency of society as a whole. The notion of a social contract, as Rousseau intended the term to be used, has been lost. The idea of a personal duty to society has been lost sight of; the emphasis is now on one's 'rights'—on what society owes you. But there can never be rights without duties.

Altruism, once admired, is now at a discount. Two American sociologists, J. M. Darley and B. Latane, in a study of altruism, illustrate the point with the story of a poor man who found a sack of money which had fallen from a Brinks truck. He returned the money to Brinks who were much startled, as they had not yet dis-covered the loss. 'Although publicised as a hero, he received scores of threatening and vilifying calls and letters castigating him for being a fool and exhorting him to look out for himself in the future.'

The stress on self-help, on getting on in the world, which is marked in America, naturally weakens altruism, as Berkowitz has shown by actual experimental studies. He makes the further point that philosophies of 'self-actualisation', such as are now fashionable, based on the writings of Abraham Maslow, will tend to strengthen the self-concern. Indeed, writers such as Ayn Rand have condemned altruism as one of the major sins of our age and have urged people to concern themselves deliberately with their own goals and feelings, regardless of others. Miss Rand has even founded an institute to propagate this doctrine.

As sociologist M. J. Lerner comments, 'We want to believe that we live in a world where people get what they deserve—or, rather, deserve what they get.' Obviously, this kind of individualism is just as disruptive of cohesion as the woolly communalism of the hippies and certainly makes the latter more understandable.

Finally, it is important to note that the constant challenging of authority denotes, at the unconscious level, a search for authority. (As one eighteen-year-old labourer told Clancy Sigal: 'I like the Communist Party. It's powerful, like . . . I admire Russia. . . . When they say they'll do a thing, they do it. Not like us.') The current defiance of authority provides fertile soil for a renaissance of totalitarianism. Professor Marie Jahoda noted that the obscene drawings of teaching staff circulated at Sussex University resembled those she had seen before the Nazi takeover. Thus there is even better reason to take this situation seriously.

I confess that my imagination boggles at the notion of current trends going much further. It is true that during the Black Death there was a vogue for fornication on the altars of churches, but this probably represented an outburst of Satanism by people who rejected the whole idea of a deity so cruel and capricious as to inflict such a plague upon mankind. Satanism is becoming a minor vogue in our own time, and from desecrating graveyards to desecrating churches is a comparatively small step.

Since all the causal factors are themselves growing stronger and are beginning to infect more and more communities as yet untouched, it seems quite certain that asociality itself must increase. In the Western world we see areas like the North of Scotland and Alaska, where a local group structure has somehow survived, being 'opened up' to meet the demands of a technological society, regardless of the protests of those who see their culture and security vanishing. As a Scottish fisherman said to me in a boat off Skye: 'It may mean we'll get the electricity a bittock sooner, and the tourists will bring in money, but it's the end of our way of life and there's not a man here that does not regret it.' In the underdeveloped world, of course, the problem is identical but in a somewhat earlier stage. Thus far the world has managed to absorb the stresses somehow. When the bulk of its population has become a mass society, instead of a culture, it may not be able to do so.

What could go further is the disregard for property. In the South of France, and no doubt elsewhere, hippies break into empty houses for a night's sleep, take what food and drink they can find and such attractive portable objects as tape-recorders, but do not burgle the property in a professional sense. In some communes clothes and even toothbrushes may be shared—not to mention beds. Cars are already treated as fair game. Perhaps this attitude will be made official, and no one will have the right to decline to share what he has—just as in the Middle Ages and up to the mid-seventeenth century, you could not refuse to render up the excrement from your house for manure.

Be this as it may, we have certainly done much to discourage altruism. By encouraging the idea that the state is responsible we have undermined private charity and, more important, local group charity. By breaking up local groups, we have weakened the controls and affective links on which an effective altruism can be based. In so doing we have weakened cohesion.

It is a striking fact that in Japan where group affiliation is the central cultural feature, crime rates are astonishingly low. For instance, where New York has 1,131 burglaries per 100,000 population, Tokyo has only 4.3. And whereas New York has 18.6 murders per 100,000 annually, there are only 2.37 in Tokyo.*

In short, cohesion is weak in modern society and is growing weaker. If it decays much further, the standard of living will begin to be affected, while those who contribute to society more than they receive will become increasingly restive at supporting asocials who claim assistance and are loud in complaints if it does not reach the standard they think is their due, but who are unwilling to contribute when not happy to obstruct and destroy.

The forcible restoration of cohesion by totalitarian means is what history warns us to expect. The only alternative is to alter the entire pattern of technological society.

But our minds resist the really gloomy prospects. We know that other civilisations have declined, but somehow our own case is different. It is like the car accidents that only other people have. Perhaps the best way, therefore, to see our own situation in a better perspective is to start by looking at the decline of another civilisation. At the same time, this will enable us to look at the social process as a whole, instead of simply projecting individual trends. The obvious instance to take is the civilisation which was born in Greece and reached its summit of power and wealth in Italy: the Roman Empire.

---

* Actually these figures, issued by the Japanese Ministry of Justice, underrate US crime. According to US sources, New York had 1,820 burglaries per 100,000 in 1971; ten other cities had over 2,000, while murder rates run as high as 38 per 100,000 in some cities.

PART III

Flashback

VII

THE ROMAN PARALLEL

Systems have passed away before you. Do but travel in the land and see the consequences for those who did deny the messengers.—Koran

1 Rome in Decline

Just before the end of the fourth century AD, Roman senators were complaining that it was no longer safe to walk in the broad valley of the river Po. The situation, however, was worse than they realised. In AD 395 the Roman Empire split in half. Within a few years the barbarians overran Africa and the Balkans; they had already occupied France. In AD 407 the Romans abandoned Britain. In AD 409 the Visigoth Alaric invaded Italy itself; in 410 he sacked Rome, the Imperial City, the hub of the empire. True, the Roman empire in the west struggled on until 476 when the last western emperor was deposed, mainly because the invaders were reluctant to finish the empire off; but for all practical purposes the great wave of Graeco–Roman civilisation was already spent at the time when the Roman senators were bewailing the growth of public violence.

The parallels between the decline of the Graeco–Roman civilisation and the decline of the European–American civilisation are so remarkable and so detailed that it is worth our examining them carefully to see what lessons we can learn.

At its peak, say about AD 100, Roman civilisation was extraordinarily prosperous and assured. It was the belief of the historian Edward Gibbon that the people of Europe were never happier than under the 'five good Emperors'. Agriculture was flourishing: Roman corn, oil, wines and pottery were being exported all over Europe, against imports of textiles from the Danube, paper (papyrus) from Egypt, leather from the Near East, woollen goods, steel and esparto from Spain, and much else. People moved freely over a vast communications network, provided with inns and rest-houses and efficiently policed against brigands and pirates. India was only 16 weeks away. Of the magnificent architecture, the great aqueducts and public baths, the collections of statuary and pictures, and of Roman luxury it is unnecessary to write. As Gibbon put it, 'In their dress, their table, their houses and their furniture, the favourites of fortune united every refinement of conveniency, of elegance and of splendour, whatever could soothe their pride, or gratify their sensuality'. Carpets from Babylonia, amber from the Baltic, furs from the forests of Syria. Every year a fleet of 120 vessels sailed to Ceylon and Malabar to bring back silver, aromatics, and precious stones. Pearls from Ormuz and Cape Cormorin, diamonds from Bengal, were exchanged for amber, brass, tin, lead, coral, chrysolite, storax, glass, dresses and, of course, silver and gold.

The currency was stable, being based on gold. The Roman *aureus* was acceptable everywhere; specimens have been found as far afield as Scandinavia, China and Ceylon. Credit was easy to obtain: banks lent freely at 6 per cent or so. The postal system reckoned to carry letters 40 miles a day.

The population of Rome has been debated; according to Carciofino it was 1.2 million, much of it crammed into vast apartment blocks. The population of the Empire as a whole may have been 50 to 60 million at the beginning of the Christian era, some five million of whom were Roman citizens.

But all this prosperity was based on being first in the field and on being a growth economy; when growth ceased it began to crumble. The growth was, of course, physical growth—military expansion. Few technological advances were being made; output per head was hardly rising. It was the plunder of conquered territories which was raising living standards. So when the Empire became too unwieldy to hold together the rot started. Moreover the colonies were learning to compete and do it better. The production of oil and wine (oil meant light as well as food) shifted to Provence, the growing of grain to North Africa, the manufacture of pottery to Aquitaine. Tile-making and glass-blowing grew up on the Danube. Jewellery came from the Orient. We hear complaints that the market was being flooded with French safety-pins. Gradually the trade balance became adverse. Before long an energy crisis developed. In the Roman Empire energy was derived from the muscles of slaves. Books were produced by reading slowly aloud from the manuscript while a hundred slaves, seated in rows, copied down the spoken words. Slaves made the pottery; slaves rowed the ships. The scale of slave-power is not always realised. The slave-market in Delos disposed of tens of thousands in a single day. One freedman, as we know from his will, left over 4,000 slaves. A large house might employ 200. While Rome was expanding, the supply of slaves was adequate.

More serious, however, was the food crisis. The soil was worked by an inefficient method: shallow ploughing, which had to be done several times to be effective. Fertility was gradually lost, and was not put back. There was little natural manure (as cows and sheep were few) and the use of clover to supply nitrogen was not known. Deforestation cut back the water supply and caused erosion. Farm taxes, however, were not paid on profits but as a specified amount of actual farm produce. So, as yields fell, there was less and less for the farmer, until finally there was none. Everywhere small farmers began to abandon farms and move to the cities or, when they could, became serfs to the large land-owners who still had unexhausted land. Others joined the army or went into holy orders. Gradually, self-supporting 'communes' emerged, often on the sites of towns.

In the cities, therefore, a landless proletariat grew up with little purpose in life. Free food and entertainment, with wine at subsidised prices, were provided to keep them from tearing the place apart. Frustrated as they were, their taste was for violence. Others, of course, turned to crime. Robbery and brigandage became serious problems and travel became risky. A network of new police stations was set up, and new police crime-squads were recruited.

As a further result, and aided by the terrible plague in the 160s, a population problem developed: the problem of declining population. Cities became deserted, roads and public buildings began to fall into decay, as municipalities could not afford to maintain them. The population declined by some 20 million. Immigration was therefore encouraged; soldiers of foreign parentage were settled on the land. Much of north Italy was settled by Yugoslavs (more accurately, Dacians) and northerners who felt no special loyalty to Rome or Roman traditions.

In their attempt to meet these problems, and to provide money for the army and the social services, the emperors built up a vast and increasingly corrupt bureaucracy. Under Augustus the state had encouraged private enterprise. Now the state gradually became the biggest industrialist, taking over shipbuilding, arms manufacture, the supply of food, the mining industry, iron and steel, and the building industry. A military-industrial complex emerged. At the same time, membership of unions was made compulsory in many trades, and eventually hereditary. (Indeed, in some cases a man could only marry within his own union, a development yet to come in our own day.) Workers in the mints were put under military discipline. Those working in mines and arms factories were branded.

By the fourth century 'there was complete control over the individual throughout the empire'.

Professor F. W. Walbank considers that the pattern was not so much that of socialism as of the Corporative State, later to be revived by Mussolini. It was totalitarianism.

To this triple crisis of energy, food and population was added a continuing financial crisis. While Rome was expanding the army had paid for itself, in effect, by the plunder it seized. Now it became a burden. The new bureaucracy had to be paid for, while the drying-up of plunder necessitated heavier and more extensive taxation. It used to be said that the governor of a province had to make three fortunes, one for himself, one for the tax collectors and one with which to bribe the judges when he was tried for extortion. Those who were unable to pay the taxes were made bankrupt or imprisoned and their property expropriated. Naturally, this increased unemployment.

But even these measures failed to balance the budget and so the rulers resorted to another method, equally fashionable today; they debased the currency, by mixing base metal with the silver and by clipping the coins. The silver *denarius* ceased to circulate outside the empire, as it once had done, and even within the empire banks sometimes refused it. (It contained a bare 5 per cent of silver.) The golden *aureus*, too, once universally acceptable, lost its shine, and Constantine introduced a new coin, the *solidus*. At this time the *denarius* was reckoned at 1389 to the *solidus*. By AD 338 the rate had become 150,000 to 1 and eventually it went to 275,000 to 1, when the coins were called in as worthless. Since the rich paid mainly in gold, while the poor used only silver and copper, this inflation against gold made the rich richer, the poor poorer.

By the beginning of the fourth century, the rulers were attempting to introduce wage and price controls in an attempt to limit inflation. And, as always happens in times of inflation, there was hoarding and speculation; people turned to real property. Vast estates were acquired by men who had no interest in working them. Pliny said, exaggerating slightly, that six men owned half North Africa.

That brings the story to a point which seems to resemble the stage we are in today. What happened next?

2 Between Dictatorship and Anarchy

By the end of the second century we find a military government of the left, which consciously set out to woo the masses—the peasants and the soldiery. The social role played by the soldiery in Rome parallels, in important respects, the role played by the trade unions

today; that is, the army had the final power. Hence it could defy
the law, demand special privileges, impose its views on the Senate,
and even ensure that the Senate was packed with retired army
officers. Naturally, emperors wooed the support of the army. Its
pay was raised repeatedly, and soldiers were given bonuses and other
privileges.

The socialist programme which had been initiated under Septimus
Severus (who amassed a large personal fortune, incidentally) was
carried even further by his successor Caracalla (a man who had
murdered his brother in order to secure his position). He appealed
even more frankly to the masses while showing his scorn for the
intellectual and propertied classes whom he systematically sought to
impoverish by imposing crushing taxes and doubling death duties.
As a further measure of egalitarianism he abolished the privileged
status of Roman citizenship, by declaring virtually everyone to be a
citizen. Furthermore, the distinction between soldier and peasant,
once important, was obliterated by simultaneously militarising the
peasantry and giving land to soldiers. This applied not only in Italy
but in Africa and Germany as well. (Perhaps we can see in this the
prospect, in our own time, of a society in which everyone must
belong to a trade union, whether they like it or not.)

Landowners retreated to their country estates, fortified them, and
lived with their slaves and tenants on as self-sufficient a basis as
possible. The feudal system was being born.

These moves were intended to provide a secure basis for a military
despotism, but in fact the system drifted ever further into anarchy.
The troops became ever more insubordinate, treacherous and
impossible to please. Emperor after emperor was put into power:
often they only lasted for a few months before being murdered. There
were some thirty emperors and claimants in less than fifty years.
(When Decius was chosen he wanted to decline so risky an honour
but his soldiers said that, if he refused, they would kill him anyway.)
Sometimes there were several emperors at once, as different sections
of the army put up rival candidates.

Rome was not unused to reigns of terror, but these reached new
intensity. A secret police force was established under the euphemistic
name of 'business agents', whose task was to detect everything from
tax evasion and desertion from the army to refusal to serve on
municipal councils. (This had become so onerous a duty that no one
any longer wanted the responsibility.) The overnight disappearance
of respectable citizens and their eventual emergence from gaol,
mutilated or beaten up (or their failure to emerge) became common.
Torture, which had long been ruled out as uncivilised, was reintroduced, i.e. the torture of free men: slaves, captives and those

convicted of certain crimes such as treason had always been considered
to be outside the system.

As the situation deteriorated, political pamphlets circulated;
strikes and revolts became common. They were crushed ruthlessly.
The bureaucracy was gradually filled with soldiers, and became ever
more corrupt, extorting money and goods from the middle classes.
As Aristides said in appealing to a new ruler to mend matters: 'The
provinces lay trembling in their bondage. Spies went hither and
thither in the cities listening to men's talk. No man could speak or
think freely. All that was just and reasonable in liberty was suppressed and each man shuddered at his own shadow.'

The aristocracy was killed off *en masse*, not only in Rome but in
Africa and elsewhere. Because robbery was becoming so general,
corps of vigilantes were formed to supplement the police and special
robbery squads were formed. City and country were at loggerheads
and country people sometimes attacked and destroyed towns. Meat
shortages developed. Rich men were hustled out of their chariots
and made to run behind while the slaves drove. Peasants began to
defy landlords and slaves their masters.

People became desperate. 'What people in that century were
longing for,' writes M. P. Charlesworth, 'was escape, though they
hardly knew escape from what.' They looked for a Saviour or
Liberator. Some looked for a happier life beyond the grave and
turned to religion. New-fangled faiths—Persian Mithraism, Zoro-
astrianism, Gnosticism, Christianity—began to supplement the
older Graeco-Roman beliefs. Oriental and mystical religions
flourished. So did astrology, futurology and fortune-telling. Emperors
sought to cash in on this demand by declaring themselves divine.

But religious intolerance is even more bitter than political intolerance: the Christians urged the state to persecute its rivals. A
farmer who looked at the sun would be executed for Mithraism.
Everyone hated everyone: the tax collectors, the police, and the
army above all. Writers like Cyprian speak of the complete exhaustion of man and nature. 'A movement which was started by envy
and hatred,' says the great economic historian M. Rostovtseff, 'and
carried on by murder and destruction, ended in such depression of
spirit that any stable conditions seemed to the people preferable to
unending anarchy. They therefore willingly accepted the stabilisa-
tion brought about by Diocletian, regardless of the fact that it
meant no improvement in the condition of the mass of the population
of the Roman Empire.' Diocletian's solution was to create an even
stronger central bureaucracy, supervised by an even more effective
secret police force, to close a few tax loopholes, and to double the
size of the army.

Rostovtseff makes it clear that the central cause of this débâcle was the 'revolutionary movement of the masses of the population which aimed at a general levelling', a levelling of standards as well as of classes. During the period of commercial prosperity, a wealthy bourgeois class had gradually ousted the old aristocracy; below it was a thriving petty bourgeoisie of shopkeepers and traders. What the new lower-class rulers did was to turn the soldiers, peasants and disorganised masses against the middle class.

As Professor Toynbee has shown, during the expansive phase of a society, the lower classes tend to model themselves on the upper class or dominant elite, whose probity and competence inspire their respect. The declining phase is marked by a reversal of this mimesis. The elite, having lost its creative elan, now seeks to cling to its privileges as best it can, and begins to ape the manners of the lower class and to court its favours. The era of the 'common man' dawns.

This was certainly the case in Rome, even the emperor himself not standing aloof. Caracalla, a 'monster whose life disgraced human nature', is known to have affected the dress and manners of a common soldier when with his troops, and to have encouraged their familiarity, though normally his manner was haughty in the extreme. Commodus not only publicly exhibited his skill at killing wild animals, specially imported for the purpose, but embarrassed everyone by entering the arena as a gladiator. Since it would not have done to defeat the emperor, many a patriotic gladiator had to accept a death-blow to prove his loyalty.

A new mentality developed hostile to the intellectual achievements of the upper classes: religious conviction was also hostile to the achievements of art and literature, except insofar as they served its needs. In such an age there was little room for the artist–craftsman. It is certainly the case that artistic standards declined sadly during the third century. One has only to compare the quality of the bas-reliefs on the column of Marcus Aurelius with those on the arch of Constantine to see the difference. The change can also be seen in literature. It was a literature of protest, produced mainly by provincial authors. The type of reading most in demand was non-fiction —encyclopedias, how-to-do-it books, and fact-books generally. The days of creative writing and intellectual innovation were gone. In technology too, as in economics and social administration, new ideas were conspicuous by their absence.

Rostovtseff concludes: 'But the ultimate problem remains like a ghost, ever present and unlaid: Is it possible to extend a higher civilisation to the lower classes without debasing its standard and diluting its quality to the vanishing point? Is not every civilisation bound to decay as soon as it begins to penetrate the masses?'

All authorities agree that it was not, as is sometimes supposed, the attacks of the Vandals, Goths, Visigoths and Huns which caused the fall of the Roman Empire. In point of fact they moved into a power vacuum. Indeed, the Vandals admired Rome and the Vandal Stilicho, who was master of the troops, drove the Visigoths out of Greece and frustrated their efforts to invade Italy. As Professor S. Dill has pointed out: 'The Empire was not an object of hatred to the barbarians. Indeed they were often eager to be taken into its service, and many of their chiefs, like Alaric or Ataulphus (Atawulf) had no higher ambition than to be appointed to high military command. On the other hand there was a corresponding readiness on the Roman side to employ barbarian forces in war.' The Visigoth Alaric's occupation of Rome only lasted three days and was marked by little looting. He was a Christian and specifically ordered his men to spare the temples. He took only the supplies needed for his starving army, and this after several attempts to obtain them by negotiation had failed. To be sure, the systematic sacking of Rome by the Vandal Gaiseric, later on, was so destructive as to give rise to the word 'vandalism' as a label for wanton destruction ever after.

To sum up: the evidence of history gives us some solid reasons for suspecting that our own crisis may be more than just a physical crisis of supplies outrunning resources. It strongly suggests that a process of social evolution—not to say deterioration—is occurring which may prove hard to arrest and which our current policies are actually fostering. Of course there are many differences. The Romans were almost wholly lacking in the technical inventiveness which is so striking a feature of our own culture. The population was falling rather than rising. They lacked any understanding of economic processes like inflation. But the main social features of our own time were there: the transformation of a structured, traditional society into a mass society with no traditions. The destruction by crushing taxation of an upper and then a middle class which had evolved certain standards of behaviour in favour of a mass concerned with immediate satisfactions. The turning to violence to relieve the frustrations of such an existence, and the eventual turning to religion in despair of earthly comfort. Even—whether we like it or not—the replacement of a vigorous capitalism by state ownership and a voracious bureaucracy; all are there.

Thus there is, on the face of it, a good *a priori* case for thinking that we, too, may be faced with more than short-term problems. We may, in fact, be on the way out. Many civilisations have declined before, and it may help us to see our own case in perspective if we pause here to consider how far civilisations have a lifespan.

3 Life Cycles of Civilisation

Long before Rome's flowering the Greek philosopher Plato claimed
that societies went through a recognisable political cycle. In the
first stage there was a dictatorship or monarchy (meaning, the rule
of one person.) This was replaced by oligarchy (the rule of a few).
This in turn gave way to democracy, where power was in the hands
of many. Democracy gradually deteriorated into anarchy. Since
anarchy is intolerable, people soon welcome a dictator who restores
order and the cycle starts over again.

In the modern world we have seen monarchy replaced by oligarchy and its transformation into democracy. We are now entering
the phase of anarchy and can therefore reasonably expect that, when
it becomes intolerable, we shall prefer dictatorship. Italy and
Germany have already demonstrated how this can occur. The time
is fast approaching when a second attempt may be made.

These processes were vividly demonstrated in a community
established, towards the end of World War II, for children evacuated
from Edinburgh to avoid the bombing and regarded as too unruly
to be placed under foster-parents in billets. Some fifty boys, aged
9 to 12, were assembled in a house known as Barns, under the
guidance of a Quaker youth-leader named David Wills. As the boys
were unamenable to discipline, Wills ordained that there would
be no rules, apart from the most basic things like swimming in the
river without supervision or running away. There were school
classes but no compulsion to attend them. After a period of anarchy,
the boys got together and appointed a dictator. This proving
unsatisfactory, they formed a Citizens' Association and experimented
with cabinet government. They instituted a system of taxation. As
they became socialised, the boys began to attend classes which
interested them and rapidly caught up with the work. Unhappily,
this promising experiment was discontinued by the education
authority, which insisted on the boys being compelled to attend
class whether they liked it or not.

In recent times, historians have made attempts, based on much
fuller data than was available to Plato, to chart the life-story of
civilisations. We shall find it easier to interpret our own problems
if we cast a brief glance at them. Fifty years ago the German philosopher Otto Spengler caused a sensation with his *The Decline of the
West*, a work of immense learning, deep obscurity, and bedevilled
by a belief in Nietzschean theories of the 'great man'. Spengler
follows Plato in seeing feudalism giving way to aristocracy, and this
being challenged by the people, but he makes additional points.

Parallel to the victory of the people over the aristocracy is the victory of the city over the country, of money over policy, and of intellect over tradition. Finally, however, force beats money: a growing despotism, which he calls Caesarism, is exerted over an increasingly formless mass, until eventually primitive conditions replace civilised life once more. Of England, France and the US he remarks 'race suicide set in long ago'.

More recently, Professor Arnold Toynbee, in twelve mighty volumes, has tilled the same field. He analyses the life-cycle of civilisations in terms of 'challenge and response'. Every civilisation, he suggests, is faced with a series of challenges. At first it responds vigorously and successfully, and climbs higher and higher. Eventually its responses become ill-judged or inadequate and it begins to decline. The pattern is not mandatory, he concedes. Sometimes there may be no serious challenge for a long period and a culture may persist despite its hardening arteries for hundreds of years, as happened in China after the Han dynasty. Sometimes a nascent civilisation will meet an insuperable challenge and never get going. Nevertheless, the paradigm of success followed by decreasing effectiveness can be seen to have a certain general validity.

Toynbee attributes the downturn to a loss of competence on the part of the 'dominant elite', by which term he means the leadership in all its forms from the administrators to the generators of new ideas. At first they gain their position by merit. After a while they are merely trying to hang on to a position for which they are no longer fitted. In the first phase, people follow them willingly. In the second, people turn from them and the elite spends its time wooing their support.

Whether or not such patterns have a universal historical validity or not—and Toynbee claims to find the story repeated in all the world's great civilisations—the fact that such processes happen at all provides us with a warning. Toynbee himself does not hesitate to say that 'it may be that Death the Leveller will lay his icy hand on our civilisation also'. But this is not inevitable and Toynbee hopes that the West will find salvation by a religious revival, or, in his phrase, 'caught up in the arms of an ancestral church'. Nevertheless, he gloomily notes the appearance in our own time of the various signs of sterility, *hubris* (or arrogance), overspecialisation of technique and abandonment of traditional style. He quotes the historian Dr Edwyn Bevan: 'I do not think the danger before us is anarchy but despotism, the loss of spiritual freedom, the totalitarian state, perhaps a universal world totalitarian state . . . there might be local and temporary anarchy, a passing phase. . . . Then the world might enter upon a period of spiritual petrifaction, a terrible order which for the higher activities of the human spirit would be death.'

4 Could we Repeat the Roman Debacle?

The parallels between the Roman story and our own day are probably already obvious to the reader, but it may be worth cataloguing them nevertheless.

1   The break up of small-scale farming leading to urbanisation and the formation of a 'mass society' with massive immigration as a further factor causing cultural disintegration.
2   The break-up of the empire and the development of an adverse trade balance.
3   The issue of doles and benefits to the urban masses and their growing preoccupation with conflict and violence.
4   The passing of power to the prime functional group, the army. (In our day, to the trade unions.) The irresponsible use of this power.
5   The break-up of the aristocracy under middle-class expansion, followed by the destruction of the middle class in the interests of the lower classes.
6   A continuously escalating inflation, and ever heavier taxation to support the constant increase of army pay and of social services.
7   Decline of public safety as armed bands, drawn from the middle classes as well as the masses, seek to make a living outside society.
8   In place of lower classes modelling themselves on higher ones, the process is reversed and popular manners, dress, etc., are imitated.
9   Further concessions to the masses, all of whom are declared equal.
10   Growth of superstition, belief in astrology, etc., and turning towards prospects of bliss in another world, this one proving a disappointment.
11   A reign of terror, in which spying, denunciation, torture and violence are employed. A wealth-tax is followed by confiscation of property outright.
12   Steady mounting of external threats: food supplies become unreliable because of irrigation failures, soil erosion and the desire of the third world to retain food for itself.
13   A decline from artistic and technical greatness.
14   Corruption and intrigue reach unprecedented levels.

These similarities form a strong *a priori* case for supposing that our own society, more particularly in Great Britain and Italy where several of these trends are furthest advanced, is in the declining phase of some ill-understood long-term social process. If so, we are headed for a period of extreme political violence—perhaps marked by assassination—of inflation and crushing taxes, of public violence and insecurity, culminating in a reign of terror, and of intellectual and artistic decline. And since the modern world is so closely interlocked, it is a solid presumption that other nations, beginning no doubt with Italy, will follow in Britain's wake.

Moreover, technological societies have additional problems unknown to Rome, and have to maintain themselves in a world economy and polity.

However Professor Toynbee tells us, on the basis of his study of some thirty civilisations, that challenges are often met by a new spurt of vigour. It is only when response fails to match challenge that a culture goes into the long slide towards anonymity. Can Western civilisation rise to the multiple challenges now confronting it? Certainly not by struthiousness. So I shall try to identify the challenges and suggest some appropriate responses. For at present we are certainly not responding appropriately or adequately.

DOES WAR HAVE A FUTURE?

Entering into the realm of prediction, however, I suggest that breakdown within a national society, leading to violent civil strife that draws in outside powers, constitutes the greatest danger of international war that the world faces in the foreseeable future.

In the course of history, there have been like developments on a smaller scale . . . The moral and political bankruptcy of Athens put an end to her democracy, bringing her under an authoritarian receivership to which, ugly as it was, there was no workable alternative.

Again, the evolution of democracy in the Roman republic rose to an apparent optimum, after which it became identified with an increasing disorder and irresponsibility in the conduct of affairs until, having become unworkable, it was replaced by Caesarism. I take a long view, not referring to the headlines of the day, when I ask whether our liberal societies in the West, some of which seem to be increasingly ungovernable by the procedures of liberal democracy, are not approaching the like termination of a like development. Tocqueville predicted an increasing egalitarianism that, as an aristocrat, he found distasteful; and I myself fear the prospect of an authoritarianism that I hope I shall not live to see if it comes.

In sum, I foresee widespread and continual disorder, with its accompaniment of inhumanity and its tendency toward barbarism. I foresee barbarism.

Louis J. Halle, *Intellectual Digest* (1974) 4(5): 71

The suggestion that Western society is on the way out will strike many people as incredible. Our society is something we have always known, and our parents and grandparents before us. We take it for granted and fail to see that it is fragile. (Though as Paul Valéry said, 'A civilisation is as fragile as a life.') We are not accustomed to take the long perspective of a thousand years. And yet civilisations do fail. Of the twenty-six civilisations* which the earth has seen, sixteen have collapsed and nine of the rest are dying, according to Toynbee's celebrated analysis. As long ago as the 1930s he concluded that our own civilisation seemed to be in the early stages of breakdown.

It seems worth, therefore, taking a few moments to give the idea more precision. What does such an assertion mean? Clearly it does not mean that countries cease to exist. Though the Greek culture succumbed two thousand years ago, there is still a country called Greece, with people living there. Though the Roman Empire collapsed, Italy continued and, a thousand years later, in the Renaissance, was again a powerful influence. (On the other hand, older civilisations like Babylonia and Assyria have vanished from sight.) By 'breakdown' Toynbee means, first, a failure at the practical level; second, a loss of confidence and creativity. As Rome declined, the postal service became erratic, buildings and roads fell into disrepair, the monetary system failed to function, justice became corrupt, and so on. At the mental or spiritual level, Rome failed to find effective ideas for coping with the situation and ceased to produce new ideas, technical innovations or serious works of art. The same appears to be true of other civilisations which failed. Is this what is in store for us?

If the Roman experience is anything to go by, we might have five hundred years of a new Dark Age, in which everyone goes in terror of naked power, in which art and literature vanish, history is replaced by myth, and original thought is persecuted. In the case of Rome, a new society arose substantially upon the ruins of the old, first in Provence and then, after the religious persecutions of the Albigenses, in Italy. Today of course, the situation is different in very many respects. Things move more quickly and there are many other centres of nascent civilisation which may flower before the Americo-European culture can arise from its own ashes. States which are dictatorships now may have become democratic in two or three hundred years' time. On the other hand, the world is far more closely inter-connected, and the decline of the West may create overwhelming difficulties for the rest of the world. On the most optimistic view possible, I suppose it would take two or three generations to absorb the shock and create a new pattern. Short of massive intervention from some external source, I suppose one can hardly hope for anything much before 2025.

It is also true that, although the Roman Empire in the west broke

* In a later revision of his *Study of History* Toynbee raised the number to thirty-two.

up, its offshoot in the east, centred on Constantinople, endured for another thousand years, and for a while reconquered not only North Africa but the Italian homeland from the Ostrogoths and part of Spain from the Visigoths. So, in our own day, after the British monarchy has removed to Australia, it may be that some continuity will be preserved even when Europe is a wasteland.

The lessons we can learn from the story of Rome can be reduced, I think, to three. Governments cannot govern when they (*a*) are technically incompetent, (*b*) cannot maintain order, and (*c*) are at the mercy of a sub-group of the population. Roman leaders were at the mercy of the army, were ignorant of how to limit inflation while maintaining employment, and certainly could not maintain public order.

Today, similarly, governments in many countries seem to lack the whole-hearted support of their electorates: it is not only that they do not have majorities—they are not terribly popular even with those who vote for them, who seem to have followed Hilaire Belloc's advice to 'hold tight on to Nurse for fear of finding something worse'. And they are certainly unable to control inflation or maintain order.

Warned in such dire terms, let us pause to consider the conditions in which tyranny can emerge. A brief dip into social theory will make it easier to understand what is going on in our own society today. Why *do* societies decline?

VIII

FROM CHAOS TO TYRANNY

I think, then, that the species of oppression by which democratic nations are menaced is unlike anything that ever before existed in the world . . . I seek in vain for an expression that will accurately convey the whole of the idea I have formed of it; the old words despotism and tyranny are inappropriate: the thing itself is new.
—Alexis de Tocqueville

1 The Theory of Mass Society

Much of what seems obscure in our own day becomes clear when we examine what has been called 'the most influential theory since Marxism': namely, the concept of the mass society. Unlike Marxism, unfortunately, it has been greatly neglected. The dominant social process of our time is the formation of mass societies—and mass societies, as we shall see, are prone to become dictatorships.

Mass societies stand in contrast to organic societies, and we had best start by describing the latter. The most noticeable feature of organic societies is that they are made up of numerous overlapping groups, at various levels between the family and the state itself. Thus most pre-industrial societies of any size consist of tribes divided into clans or septs. In addition they are often split into moieties, linked by intermarriage. There may also be age-groups with defined obligations and rituals, and often sex-groups equally well defined. If we turn to the somewhat more elaborate structure of the Middle Ages in Europe, we find not only trade-guilds, religious orders, corporations and other groups, but we note that authority is distributed among them. In some matters, the abbot decides, in others the shire-reeve, in others the lord of the manor, in others the parish. The British social historian, G. M. Trevelyan, says: 'The unit of

119

medieval society was neither the nation nor the individual but something between the two—the corporation.' A man's status was determined by the corporation he belonged to. This diffusion of power is often called pluralism, and de Tocqueville noted its existence in America in his day.

This diffusion of power, obviously, limits the freedom of any individual to act in a dictatorial manner and is resistant to attempts at overall dictatorship.

These various groups owe their internal cohesion to loyalties— that is, emotional links built up with time on the basis of shared experience. The strength of such loyalties is demonstrated by the 'reunions' of former members of a regiment, sports club, school, boat crew, or whatever, long after the functional purpose which brought them together has vanished. They are reinforced by symbolic means, such as uniforms, flags, special language or terminology, and rituals. Army commanders whose job it is to weld a mass of men into a cohesive unit know a good deal about how to create *esprit de corps* and use deliberately just such methods as society at large uses more spontaneously.

In contrast, a mass society lacks these 'intermediate structures' and these emotional links and shared behaviour patterns. Pick ten thousand people off the street and dump them in, say, a football stadium and you have a mass. Give them time and they will begin to evolve a social structure. Leaders will emerge, groups will form, recognised behaviour patterns will be set up. What we have seen in the fall of Rome and again in our own day is the reverse of this process. An agricultural or a hunting society is composed of such groupings; but when, as a result of industrialisation, people stream into cities, masses are created. People belong to no defined groups, share no symbols or rituals, have no structures of authority.

Western societies have clearly gone a considerable part of the way towards becoming mass societies, originally because of the shift of people from country to towns, but subsequently for other reasons, such as increasing mobility and the tendency to centralise power. But before considering the mechanism of this change, let us look at its effects.

First, members of masses tend to feel insecure and unwanted. It was the French sociologist Durkheim who, after studying thousands of cases of suicide, suddenly realised that the common element in most of them was not so much a personal pathology as the social pathology of living in an atomised society. While some react with despair and turn aggression against themselves, others attack society itself or turn their back on it. 'If you don't want me, I don't need you,' is their attitude. And because they are thus alienated, they feel free to ignore social norms and rules—hence, free to attain their

ends by anti-social means. This state of affairs is termed 'anomia'.
Anomia was the underlying factor in the violence and antisocial
behaviour we looked at earlier.

While members of a mass society thus have more freedom of
action than members of groups, this freedom contains the seeds of
self-destruction. The member of a group is under pressures to conform; he cannot seriously offend other members of his group since
he may later need their help; if he incurs their enmity they can
make life unpleasant for him, even expel him from it. This is why
crime rates are always far higher in towns, where group structure
is lost, than in the country. They are highest of all where population
turnover is rapid, e.g. in ports and the centres of large cities.
The same trend is found in rates of mental disturbance.

In Europe and America, urbanisation and 'massification' occurred
most rapidly in the nineteenth century, and crime rates rose rapidly.
Now the third world is repeating the process.

And just as cohesion is created not only by structures but also by
a shared culture, so also alienation can be seen as lack of a cultural
identity. The Scotsman distinguishes himself from, say, the York-
shireman by his porridge, his bagpipes, his kilt and his accent, and
by awareness of his clan history, and so acquires a measure of
identity. The member of a mass society lacks any comparable claim
to cultural identity.

In a pluralist society, there is one serious danger, however, that
some one group, well-knit within itself but poorly linked to the rest
of society, will secede or attempt to dominate the rest of society in
its own interests. Thus the Welsh or the Basques, sharing a common
culture and emotionally linked by intermarriage and by intermediate
groupings, wish to secede. It has been noted that communities which
are cohesive within themselves, such as mining communities, but
somewhat separated from the rest of society, tend to form factions.
Commonly, they complain that they are underprivileged and infer
from this that they are looked down upon by the rest of society.
Today, trade unions show signs of becoming factions as here defined.
Durkheim saw the danger very clearly. Secondary groups, he said,
'must not be able to get a mastery over their members and mould
them at will'. There must be some overall authority which must
remind such groups that they are part of a whole and must remain
within the framework. It is the absence of other groupings to divide
the loyalties of their members which has made the trade unions
disproportionately powerful, as I shall describe in detail in the next
chapter. It is the cohesive structure of the mining community which
gives mining unions their unusual strength.

This picture of society as structured, as consisting of a network of overlapping and interlocking groups, stands in sharp contrast to the better-advertised picture of society as split into two factions, governors and governed, or, in its Marxist variant, owners of capital and hired workers. The Marxist view is achieved by making economics the decisive criterion—an understandable bias in the conditions of the nineteenth century. But other criteria, such as political power, for instance, are at least as important: those with political power are not necessarily owners of capital, while the latter are more often governed than governing. Today, in any case, the Marxist view is obsolete since many workers own capital, and many capital-owners work. The persistence of this extremely inadequate analysis is a tribute to the power of myth.

But while the Marxist distinction becomes steadily more remote from the facts, the Machiavellian distinction between governors and governed becomes steadily more relevant, as power is increasingly centralised. Part of the problem of social disintegration concerns the widening gap between governors and governed and we shall have to examine it later. What is the relevance of all this to us today?

2 The Appeal of Totalitarianism

As William Kornhauser demonstrated in his important book *The Politics of Mass Society*, mass societies are particularly open to penetration by totalitarian ideologies, whether of the right or of the left, and to rabble-rousing of Poujadist or McCarthyist type. Having no other loyalties, alienated individuals are relatively easily recruited by political movements which provide them with a purpose and supply the group membership with the sense of purpose and status which they so sorely lack. Surveys in countries like Italy and Germany show that it was precisely the alienated individuals, such as ex-army officers, dispossessed farmers, unsuccessful intellectuals, the unemployed and those with a low opinion of themselves, who were attracted to these movements. When all hope of success is blocked, the danger is at a maximum.

Today leaders can speak directly to such masses as never before. 'There has never been a time which offered the technical opportunities of today to transform the whole people into masses and keep them in this state,' observed Emil Lederer as long ago as 1940; that can be stated with even more assurance today.

In an organic society, the existence of intermediate structures means that there is some kind of class or status structure, and this itself acts to make tyranny difficult. '. . . the body of nobles and the wealthy are in themselves natural associations which check the abuses of power,' as de Tocqueville puts it. The student of totalitarianism,

Franz Neumann, pointed out that a flattening of the social pyramid precedes dictatorship. It follows that the contemporary yearning for equality implies a growing risk of dictatorship, for a completely egalitarian society is necessarily a mass society.

From Plato to Burke and down to today, political thinkers have stressed the dangers of equality. Thus de Tocqueville wrote: 'I believe that it is easier to establish an absolute and despotic government among a people in which the conditions of society are equal than among any other; and I think that if such a government were once established among such a people, it not only would oppress men, but would eventually strip each of them of several of the highest qualities of humanity.' Plato's point was a different one; namely, that in a democracy effective and wise government would become impossible because of pressure from the uneducated but arrogant masses. 'At Athens the mischief began,' he complained, 'when the uneducated began to think their own opinion about music and the drama as good as that of the educated, and the same delusion soon spread to political matters; the Athens of today is not really a democracy, but a "theatocracy" of ignorant sensation-lovers.'

In a totalitarian society, all power is concentrated at the centre, and no opposition is brooked. Centrally-made decisions are carried out by means of a vast bureaucracy. Hence the gradual transfer of authority from local authorities and bodies to more central ones, such as is now occurring, prepares the ground for dictatorship. When decisions are made locally, the person concerned knows more of the situation and is likely to be a member of groups to which those who are subject to his decision also belong. He must watch his step because he has to live with the consequences. Not so the central bureaucrat, whose lack of feeling for local nuances is legendary. Max Weber, the father of modern sociology, believed that the growth of bureaucracy, not the class struggle, was the key factor in the modern world.

3 Causes of Decohesion

Today many forces are at work which tend to break up intermediate structures and promote the 'massification' of society. Immigration of aliens and, for that matter, the movement of people in terms of change of residence for occupational or other reasons, is a major factor. Some of the opposition to immigrants comes from an ill-defined awareness of this fact. The steady growth of bureaucracy contributes, as does the formation of ever larger industrial corporations, themselves taking decisions remote from the lives of the people affected. Especially important, perhaps, are social and economic changes, particularly unemployment and bankruptcy which leave people without status or purpose. It was in the appalling distress caused by runaway inflation that Hitler came to power. But in the twenties his appeal was to small traders squeezed out by big business, army officers squeezed out by the reduction in size of the army, young people who had never found a job or a role, and others of this sort.

But as I have said, alienation occurs not only at the level of groups but also at cultural and symbolic levels. An individual is alienated if he is taught nothing of his country's history and achievements, if his food and clothing are standardised and characterless, and if there are no rituals in which he can take part and thus realise his community with others. Our society has replaced functional occasions involving the whole social group—such as bringing in the harvest or launching a boat—with mass attendance at a football match, as a spectator. It is not the same thing.

Basically, the irresistible forces which are destroying cohesion are two. First the movement of peoples, which leads to the formation of social groups with no unity of cultural background. The United States has faced this problem in extreme form, and the fact that it has far higher rates of crime and social pathology than Europe is certainly due to the cultural chaos resulting. The second, which is in part a reaction against the first but mostly a result of mass production, is the emergence of a universal culture at the material and even the non-material level. The same food, clothes, conventions—and even the same books, music and ideas—are found throughout the developed world. As Toynbee points out, the emergence of a 'universal state' is the invariable precursor of collapse.

But in addition to these irresistible trends, governments are busily undermining the cohesion of their own societies by moving groups of people about, ironing out local differences in the name of standardisation or 'uniformity of practice', centralising decisions formerly taken locally, disrupting ancient loyalties by changing names and boundaries, and so on. Administrators see people as so many ciphers, as units whose behaviour is to be regulated, and regard as 'efficient' those arrangements which save the administrator time and trouble. All administrators should be compelled to take a course in social anthropology. As the sociologist Patricia Elton Mayo has put it: 'Nearly all modern governments have become so enamoured of centralist bureaucracy that they have forgotten the cellular origins of social organisations.'

Also to blame is the educational system, which fails to illuminate to pupils the nature of their culture. More will emerge on these points as we go along.

Putting the anthropological and sociological viewpoints together, we can conclude by looking at cohesion as a problem of communication and confidence as between the governors and the governed. We have chosen to destroy the blind acceptance of the system which characterised pre-industrial societies by universal education; more, we go out of our way to teach young people to be critical, to challenge ideas and look for new ways of doing things, to adapt (rather than to conform to traditional ways of doing things), and then we are amazed when they put this advice into practice by criticising society and the administration. If we want to maintain a few shreds of cohesion we had better pipe down on this and start teaching them a measure of conformity again. (Obviously, this does not mean that I am recommending *total* conformity.)

Criticism has its merits; so has cohesion. The idea that you can have a full measure of both is simply not on. As always, we have to compromise between two goods.

It has been said that cohesion endures as long as people accept its moral basis—which I take to mean, as long as they feel that the system is meeting their long-term aims as well as is possible in all the circumstances. Administrations that wish to maintain cohesion must therefore not only tackle the perceived defects of society vigorously, but must also demonstrate that they are making as much progress as is feasible. This they singularly fail to do. This is true even in such basic areas as housing. It is impossible to convince someone who has been on the waiting list for ten years that the country really couldn't have built him a house instead of putting energy into supersonic aeroplanes, the space race or some other non-essential. Finally, governments ought to demonstrate to the public where they are making mutually incompatible demands, such as the demand for freedom and the demand for equality. They need to initiate a public debate on such inconsistencies which will, with luck, lead to the emergence of a consensus.

No doubt some readers will object that it is impossible to restore the ancient group structure of society, that this is an attempt to turn back the clock, a kind of social Ludditism. If that is true, then the outlook is black. Because the only way in which cohesion can be achieved in an inorganic society is by totalitarianism.

Given all this, what does the immediate future hold for the industrialised West? To what will the decline of cohesion and the growth of faction actually lead? The answer depends mainly on three things: (1) how far the unions are prepared to go, (2) how far the economic situation deteriorates in consequence, and (3) how effectively governments respond. In the next section I offer some speculative scenarios. I consider particularly Britain, Italy and the US which seem to be the countries most advanced in social decay, but similar events could easily flare up in France and elsewhere.

PART IV

Danger Zones

IX

UNGOVERNABILITY

*Revolution broke out in city after city, and—in places
where the revolution occurred late—the knowledge of
what had happened previously caused still new
extravagances of revolutionary zeal, expressed by an
elaboration in the methods of seizing power and by
unheard-of atrocities in seeking revenge . . . Love of
power, operating through greed and personal ambition,
was the cause of all evils. To this must be added the
violent fanaticism that came into play once the struggle
had broken out. Leaders of parties in the cities had
programmes which appeared admirable—on the one
side political equality for the masses, on the other
safe and sound government of the aristocracy—but in
professing to serve the public interest they were seeking
to win the prizes for themselves. Here they were
deterred neither by the claims of justice nor by the
interests of the state; their one standard was the
pleasure of their own party at that particular
moment . . .—Thucydides:* The Peloponnesian War

1 Unions in Control

In 1920 British dockers refused to continue loading a merchant
vessel known as the *Jolly George* which was preparing to carry
arms and equipment to the British armies in Russia, which, with
the Americans and the French, were attempting to defeat the
revolutionary government. Whether or not their gesture decisively
influenced the outcome, it was certainly historic in being the first

time in Britain this century that industrial action had been directed
to an unambiguously political end.

Since then things have moved a long way, notably in Italy and
Britain. Unions now defy with impunity laws of which they dis-
approve, claim to intervene in government policy and even undertake to force governments to resign. In Britain, matters came to a
head in 1973 when several unions refused to obey the provisions of
the Industrial Relations Act, refused to attend the courts appointed
to deal with such cases, and refused to pay the ensuing fines. This
battle culminated in a strike which was openly admitted to be
political: its leaders publicly undertook to force the elected government to resign. A union of some 250,000 members (many of whom
were opposed to the strike) thus overruled a government returned
by millions of voters. Soon afterwards, in Northern Ireland, a twelve-
day general strike brought about what five years of bombing,
murder and violence had failed to do, the collapse of the government's policies in that area.

To an increasing extent, the most basic decisions affecting the
future of Western economies are now taken in private discussions
between the leaders of industry, the leaders of the unions and the
government—the consumer is unrepresented and the proceedings
are secret. Inevitably solutions are reached which, if satisfying to
employer and employee, are not necessarily satisfying on wider
social grounds. It is a negation of the democratic process which aims
to restrict the exercise of power to elected leaders.

In Britain ultimate power has now passed out of the hands of
government into those of organised labour and the government only
acts by permission of the major unions. While Britain is showing the
way, a similar situation seems to be developing in Italy and could
easily do so in France.

In Italy, in June 1974, trade unions claimed the right to dictate
the country's economic policy, threatening massive strike action if
the government rejected their plans. The unions demanded a say in
public investment policy and in the siting of new factories and
industries, as well as guarantees against the erosion of wages by
inflation. The unions demonstrated their power by calling a general
transport strike in early June: trains, buses and aircraft all came to a
halt. The unions argued against the government's £1,200m. plan to
re-equip Italian railways and demanded higher staffing levels
instead. As the state had just agreed to a reduction in the working
week by 4 hours and had recruited 20,000 extra railway workers, it
was reluctant to engage still more manpower—especially as a recent
enquiry had shown that some 20 per cent of Central Italian railway-
men were using their free time to take up second jobs.

In short, unions have undergone a sea-change which merits careful examination. They have acquired power to affect the whole community without responsibility to the whole community. In some countries, the unions have not as yet realised the strength of their position or have hesitated to exploit it. As a British union leader recently noted, even in Britain they have failed to equip themselves for these new responsibilities and have no long-term policies or machinery for reaching agreement among themselves. Moreover, since it is much easier to criticise than to govern, they will themselves become the objects of criticism when they take an unpopular line and will find it hard to act in a statesmanlike manner.

But while the union *leadership* finds itself in an unexpectedly powerful position, it is also the case that at the *local* level the union member's power has increased, and often it is used in a petulant, short-sighted or partisan manner. The fact is, the whole nature of industrial action has changed—both as to aims and as to methods—more than we yet fully realise.

Labour is, to an increasing extent, demanding that factories, shipyards, etc., which have become uneconomic be kept going to secure the jobs of those who work in them. It is as if grooms and ostlers demanded to be employed despite the advent of the car. The result can only be to weaken the country's position in world trade. Socialist minister Mr Anthony Wedgwood Benn currently puts the cost of propping up jobs in ineffective companies at £6,000 million. No government can afford to finance inefficiency on this scale for long.

What gives unions the power to make demands of this kind is the vulnerability of a technical society to disruption. The strike weapon originated in manufacturing industry; a strike put pressure on an employer, but not on the public, who could go to other manufacturers and who were protected by the stock of goods held by wholesalers. The situation is obviously different when a strike cuts off, say, electricity, which cannot be stockpiled; different when it affects the whole nation; and still more damaging when it affects the administrative machinery—the banking system, the posts and telephones, the legal system, the police, or government itself. The health service is another example of an area where withdrawal of labour has quite different effects from those of the strike as classically conceived.

As Hegel pointed out, when things change their scale they change their nature. An acorn in a jam-jar is one thing; an oak tree in the living-room another.

Unions have acquired an almost sacrosanct status; any criticism of them tends to be judged biased or disgraceful. Actions which in employers would be held intolerable are freely accepted when performed by unions. The real achievements of the unions in improving the wages and conditions of their members in the past does not alter the fact that, in the very different situation of today, they can do great harm. When employers were strong, it was reasonable that labour should become strong. There was what Professor Galbraith calls a 'countervailing force'. Today the unions are stronger than any force opposed to them, and need taming just as employers once did. Moreover, in Britain, a series of measures now before Parliament will, if passed into law, make British unions the strongest in the world.

NURSE EARNS MORE AS A CLEANER

Mr Jock Watson, a mental hospital nurse who gave up his job after 16 years, is back in his old hospital as a ward cleaner, earning £5 a week more.

Mr Watson, aged 35, of Dunmowe Way, Fulbourn, Cambridge, last week resigned as a psychiatric nurse at the Ida Darwin Hospital, Cambridge, because he was earning only £26.98 a week to keep his wife and four young children.

The Times 20 March 1974

We are accustomed to think of the growth of union power as something which 'just happened'. It is useful to look at this phenomenon from a broader sociological viewpoint. As I described in the last chapter, an organic society is one held together by many overlapping groupings of intermediate size. This plural membership is what dilutes power and makes tyranny difficult to impose. What the unions have done is to expand into the vacuum left by the decay of 'intermediate structures'. Their power needs to be balanced out by the coexistence of other loyalties. It is not unions which are too strong but rather rival groupings which are too weak, or non-existent. Man as consumer, man as worker, man as political animal, man as student, man as social animal, requires to be represented by and served by different, overlapping and equally valid systems.

In the final analysis, the nub is this: power implies responsibility. But unions, although they can now impose their wishes on the whole country, are answerable only to their members—even this limitation is not a very effective one, owing to the apathy of some, the blind loyalty of others, and the block vote system which enables union delegates to wield disproportionate influence.

In political terms, the trade unions have ceased to be interest-groups and have become a *faction*—a group within the state working for power in the interests of a particular sub-group and outside the accepted political means of change. History warns us that countries rent by faction are in for trouble. (In Italy, however, unionised labour faces a rival faction, namely the Church.)

In short the situation closely resembles that which characterised the decline of the Roman Empire. In that case, the army developed into a functional group with its own loyalties, but quite unintegrated with the rest of society, which it exploited quite ruthlessly. As it possessed the crude power bestowed by weapons, none could oppose it, and emperors were reduced to flattery and to buying it off with pay and privileges. In our day, industrial force has superseded military force, otherwise the situation is identical. Just as Rome could not do without the army, we cannot do without industry and services. The monopoly of power is the death of democracy. There is no evidence that the trend can be reversed.

To judge from the Roman parallel, it seems possible that organised labour may (openly or unofficially) nominate prime ministers or presidents, or at least rule on the acceptability of the government's intended nominee. Indeed, as often happened in the Roman case, we may see rival unions nominating rival prime ministers—themselves generally trade unionists—and the emergence of fierce political rivalries between the leaderships of the several unions. Let us look, therefore, in more detail at how organised labour is changing its methods and its scope of activity.

2 New Style in Strikes

Almost unnoticed, 'industrial action' has gradually changed its nature and become something else. In origin, a strike is 'withdrawal of labour', i.e., the right not to make a contract if you don't like the terms offered. As such, not a word can be said against it.

Today, however, industrial action is by no means limited to the withdrawal of labour but takes highly aggressive forms. For instance, at the Ferodo Factory near Caen, French workers locked up three members of the management until they agreed to re-hire a workman who had been dismissed for striking a member of the staff. This was by no means the first case of its kind.

Again, at a factory owned by Ampex, the manufacturers of recording equipment, in Belgium, the strikers seized 10,000 tape-casettes and threatened to sell them at bargain prices if the company did not agree to pay them thirteen months' wages for every twelve months worked. Belgian militancy has gone much further than this. Workers at a bankrupt electrical-appliance factory near Liège threatened to blow up the entire Houblonnières district of the city unless the government provided enough money to get the factory going again. In Denmark, a factory which continued to work during a widespread strike was halted by three separate bomb threats.

Secondly, in place of a mere refusal to continue a contract we find

a deliberate attempt to impose losses on management by observing
the letter but not the spirit of the agreement, as in the go-slow. This
protects the workers' wages while cutting the management's profits
or compelling them to operate at a loss. As a rule the scrap rate and
the frequency of breakdown of equipment rise mysteriously during
such episodes. At the Accles and Pollock factory at Oldbury, where
steel tube is made, six hundred foremen found a novel form of
obstruction when they refused to take orders over the phone or
verbally. Instructions were only accepted in writing and were
answered in writing. A spokesman for the union, the Association of
Supervisory, Technical and Managerial Staffs, commented: 'It is a
remarkably effective tactic which could well be used elsewhere.'

Another means of imposing losses on management is the 'sit-in',
but recently unions have found it more effective to exploit the
technological complexity of modern industry by strikes limited to
key employees. When several thousand workers were in dispute with
Plessey, the electronics firm, instead of bringing out the workers on
strike *en masse*, the union brought out just 70 men from the despatch
warehouse in Nottingham. Thus Plessey could not meet delivery
dates and began to run short of cash. Similarly, unions have realised
that you can close an entire airport by calling out the firemen and
their officers. Some British unions now run 'colleges' to teach
members new strike methods.

However, there is a far more serious development: unions now use
their powers not just to influence the nature of the terms and conditions of work offered by management, but to put pressure on third
parties to impose censorship, and even to exert racial discrimination.
Recently in Britain, labour leaders threatened to call strikes unless
certain cartoons and editorials were withdrawn. Some unions are
trying to set up 'editorial advisory committees' which will influence
what editors print. This is objectionable in itself; the danger that
such committees will be dominated by extremists or sectional
interests is serious. A variant is the unionised boycott: in Yorkshire,
5,000 members of the National Association of Local Government
Officers were ordered by their union to refuse to buy the *Yorkshire
Post* and its sister evening newspaper for a week in revenge for the
paper's having printed the salaries of some of its members. Local
radio stations have also been boycotted. In Australia, unionists
refused to fuel the plane of singer Frank Sinatra because they
objected to his comments on the country!

Another ominous step was taken when British Airways shop
stewards demanded the immediate dismissal of Mr Henry Marking,
the airline's managing director, and called for a full investigation
into the suitability of the other members of the board. The airline

is in the red, as a result of fuel price increases and other difficulties, and board members had said that it would have to approach the government for a loan in order to pay wages in three months' time.

Strikes have become a sort of reflex action, and are often precipitated by a bloody-minded minority, the majority falling in from a sense of loyalty or from inertia. A new low point was reached when bus-crews in Leeds struck in protest at Sikh crews being allowed to wear turbans. This was an old issue—Sikhs are required to wear turbans for religious reasons—and a ballot had already been held at which the vote went in favour of permitting turbans to be worn. Simultaneously, crews in Blackpool struck to mark their annoyance with a local councillor who thought them overpaid.

Strikes have often been called to put pressure on third parties—I recall a strike more than twenty years ago by miners who complained that the public buses in which they travelled to work had no non-smoking section. But it was a far more sinister development when mental nurses refused to distribute medicines to patients at Glenside Mental Hospital, Bristol. Since mental patients are often maintained in a state of relative calm by minutely regulated doses, the omission of a single dose (as in the case of patients on L-dopa) could precipitate a crisis so severe as to imperil all chance of future recovery.

Strikes of radiographers, nurses and other health-service employees forced the London Hospital to cancel all open-heart operations and to cut down the use of the intensive-care unit. In July, the chairman of the West Midland Health Authority, the largest in Britain, warned the government that 'trade union action was raising the real possibility of death or permanent suffering to hospital patients. Immediate intervention at a political level was necessary. . . .' Blood transfusion services were also at risk because of a threat to an essential computer operation.

Lastly, strikes are now being called with the object of changing official policy. Some union leaders have sought to use strikes in this way for a long time, as I have related. But it is a new development when small groups of organised workers within unions attempt to impose their will on society without regard for the elected government. A startling example of this was the refusal of nursing staff at various British hospitals to minister to patients who were paying for private beds as distinct from those who were being treated free of charge under the National Health Service. The provision of this option was fully debated at the time the Act was passed and Parliament decided for various reasons, including the considerable sums accruing to the health service in payment, to permit it. On the strength of this, many people paid premiums to hospital insurance schemes in order to be able to afford privacy if they were ill. But when a few hundred nurses who held a different view sought to impose their views, the government began to back down, saying it had always intended to eliminate this privilege.

Finally, industrial action is beginning to imperil the administrative function which maintains society. This is in some ways the most serious development of all. Recently, a strike of local government staff forced the postponement of London borough elections: there was no one to count the votes. As I write, a prolonged strike at the government printing works is making it impossible to issue reports on debates, print pension books, or circulate the text of new Acts of Parliament.

A society in which all the normal functions are liable to be suspended is clearly not in good order. It is no longer a question of wage claims, of how the national income is to be shared out. It is a question of the disposition of power in society. In British law, industrial action is only legal when 'in furtherance of a trade dispute'. Moreover, when a contract has been made, there are legal penalties for breaching it. But unions constantly breach agreements voluntarily arrived at and, as we have seen, many strikes are not really in furtherance of a trade dispute. Yet attempts to regulate the power to strike by law have failed—indeed, have handicapped employers more than employees, since they have to keep their side of the bargain. Few employers have thought it worth taking a union to court—say, for trespass during a sit-in. And government attempts to enforce laws have been successfully defied. You cannot commit several thousand people to gaol at the same time, or even impose fines, without risk of provoking another strike. The situation has become unworkable.

Whereas in the fifties strikes were declining in number and scale, so that two American professors, Arthur Ross and Paul Hartmann, rashly prophesied the withering-away of strikes as a social phenomenon, today the trend is in reverse. Some writers foresee growing public objection to strikes and support for strong-arm tactics by the government but it is hard to see what governments can do: sending in the troops may suffice to move more coal, but soldiers cannot substitute for skilled workers, nurses or local government officers.*

---

* It is sometimes argued that the figures of days lost by strikes reveal that the industrial impact is insignificant. But today the all-out strike is a rarity. The sit-in, the go-slow, and the confining of strikes to key personnel minimise the number of days lost without minimising the industrial consequences. Moreover, a strike in one industry may seriously handicap others, especially a strike in power-supplies or transport. Days lost are no criterion of social loss.

Even more serious loss can arise from disputes where no industrial action is taken. Thus a new £12.5m. grain terminal at Liverpool docks has remained unused for two

The really discouraging thing about the situation is not so much that unions make these demands as that some leaders have created an atmosphere of hatred both within plants and offices and in industry at large. They have a vested interest in discontent, it is true. But it is the impression that they are animated less by concern for their members than by hatred of everyone else which is alarming. They do not really want to find a *modus vivendi*: the battle is the objective. Modern societies cannot be run on a basis of mutual hatred.

More sinister still is the use of industrial power for subversive ends.

3 Boring from Within

It is often asserted that most strikes are due to Communist influence. Is this true? The short answer is that most strikes are not, though some of them are provoked by fire-eating shop stewards who may or may not be Communists politically and who hope to emerge as leaders by strike organisation. A few, however, including some of the largest and most damaging, are indeed planned as disruptive manoeuvres, in which the question of pay is merely an excuse, and the real intention is political.

The exaggerated willingness of some anti-Communists to see reds under every bed has tended to obscure the real danger, which in Britain is growing steadily.

It is estimated that there are now as many as 175 Communists serving as full-time officials in the engineering branch of the Amalgamated Engineering Union alone, of whom about 40 are card-carrying members, the rest fellow-travellers. On the executive of the Transport and General Workers Union, 15 of 36 officials are understood to be pro-Communist, while on the National Union of Mineworkers about six of the 27 members of the National Executive are Communist and five are extreme left. (In 1971 only six seats were held by extremists.) How much help they get from the USSR is obscure, but Moscow radio let it be known in 1974 that a Soviet trade union had sent money to help workers in a British industrial dispute.

The extreme left does not feel bound by democratic or any other rules. It follows Lenin's advice to 'resort to all sorts of stratagems, artifices, illegal methods, to evasions and subterfuges, only so as to get into the trade unions, to remain in them and to carry on Communist work within them at all costs.'

---

years because dockers refuse to operate it. Its use would cut the cost of grain by £5 to £9 a ton, and the delay is reckoned to have cost Merseyside some £6m. so far—to say nothing of the fact that some firms which were planning to establish themselves in Liverpool have changed their plans. Others are now thinking of moving out.

In Britain, the structure of the trade union system lends itself to such manoeuvres. Trade unions control 88 per cent of the votes at the Labour Party Conference, which is the party's policy-making body. Further, the Conference and the unions have the right to fill 17 of the 24 positions on the Party's National Executive Committee. Finally, the unions provide some four-fifths of the Party's funds. Thus the Party is very much the creature of the unions. Communists attempt to dominate union branches and executives, an aim made easier by the system of balloting for posts. Only about 10 per cent of union members bother to vote. Indeed, the zealot Mr Hugh Scanlon was elected by the vote of a mere 7 per cent of the 1.1m. members of the Amalgamated Union of Engineering Workers. In addition, rigging of ballots by faked votes has been revealed in a number of cases, notably in the Electrical Trades Union.

Communists go to considerable lengths to discredit moderate rivals, by fair means or foul. Resolutions are prepared in advance: a favourite trick is to have a moderate resolution put by the platform, and a much stronger one by a confederate planted among the audience. The platform then gracefully gives way 'to popular demand' and adopts the fiercer motion. Another trick is to take a small hall and pack it with supporters, well in advance. When the moderate members arrive they cannot get in, and the 'public meeting' carries motions by a show of hands.

A main objective is to get Conference to 'commit itself to a large and specific pay claim. Once a definite figure has been adopted, it provides the extremists with a stick to beat the leadership. Any lack of zeal in pursuing the claim can bring a flood of critical resolutions from the branches, while any proposal to compromise at a lower figure can be characterised as a "sell out". This, broadly, was the technique adopted by the Communists and their allies at the National Union of Mineworkers conference in Inverness in June, 1973,' according to *Sources of Conflict in British Industry*, a report published by the Institute for the Study of Conflict. 'The master strategist was Michael McGahey, the union's vice-president, a member of the Communist Party National Executive, and of its "inner cabinet" the political committee. McGahey himself drew up the claim for £8–13 a week extra for the miners in the full knowledge that these figures were bound to exceed anything allowable under "Stage Three" [of the government's anti-inflation plan]. He then arranged for the claim to be proposed from the floor, although several other smaller claims were also on the conference agenda.' As he had hoped, delegates voted for the highest claim, and thus made the miners' strike that winter almost inevitable.

No bones are made about the general strategic objective: 'to overthrow the government' as the Secretary frankly said at the 33rd Party Congress. The strategy has two main planks: to discredit the government by presenting it with insoluble problems and so create the impression that the system is breaking down; and to provoke strong measures which can then be represented as oppressive. Thus unions demand pay increases which they know will be inflationary, so that they can be sure they will be rejected. When 30 per cent is asked for, and 7½ per cent is conceded, it can be described as niggardly. At the same time the unions oppose productivity agreements, since these would reduce the inflationary effects. They hope that a situation will be reached in which the whole public will begin to feel that traditional institutions are proving inadequate and so will be minded to accept some drastic new regime.

Thus, in Britain the danger of a deliberately precipitated breakdown of the social order should not be under-estimated. In Italy, and France, Communist elements are at least as powerful but seem inclined at present to hold their hands, on the grounds that the moment is not yet ripe for action. But if, as currently seems likely, Portugal becomes the first Communist state in western Europe, the probability of similar take-overs in France, Italy and Britain will become appreciably stronger.

4 Scenario for a Civil War

Powerful British union leaders have made it clear that, having ejected a Conservative government and secured an administration subservient to them, they mean to keep it that way. This raises a prospect which deserves thinking about. Let us suppose that, at the next election, a Conservative majority is returned, and that, as soon as an excuse can be found, massive strikes are called. Suppose, in short, that organised labour, on balance, simply refuses to accept the decision of the electorate. What will then happen?

Either the strike call fails, in which case democracy is preserved; or the Conservatives throw in the towel, and democracy is replaced by a one-party system, as in Russia; or the government decides to give battle, come what may. Appealing to the public by radio and television—while there is still a service—it announces that emergency powers are being invoked. All strike leaders and troublemakers will be arrested and placed on a remote Scottish island under guard. There will be a curfew, rationing of food and fuel, and the army will keep essential services going. At this point, the situation will polarise. Some will rally to the government: squads of vigilantes will be formed, as well as emergency work-teams. Others will claim that this is fascism, that the day of revolution has arrived, etc., and will go into opposition, smashing vital equipment wherever possible to frustrate the government's intentions. Bomb-happy revolutionaries will have a field day. In many areas, food supplies will fail to arrive. Power will be cut off. Starving people will begin to loot stores and then will surge out into the countryside to scavenge food at source. Sewage systems will fail and towns will become plague-risks. The army will close off each city and try to prevent all civilian movement, except as authorised. During all this the government will be in its underground war-stations and the regions will be largely self-governed: at least the regional underground centres will be doing what they can and discovering the gaps in their preparations.

Is this scenario past credence? Apparently many experienced people do not think so. Major-General R. F. K. Goldsmith, until 1968 an assistant controller in civil defence, considers that 'industrial militancy has come near the possible limit of non-response' and points out the lack of any national or regional chain of command in Britain's police forces, though police strength is now 100,000 (not counting the special constables recruited by the local police force). The police have no mass transport and depend on hiring vehicles. 'There is no regional organisation for co-ordinating police effort and the question is whether these traditional means are any longer adequate.'

A breakdown of physical services including the supply of fuel and food is seen by General W. Walker, formerly commander-in-chief of the Allied forces in Northern Europe, and by Colonel David Stirling, founder of the Special Air Service who has written a paper on how services could be maintained in face of a general strike. 'There are many people in Britain now who think some kind of crunch is coming,' he says. Early in 1973 a group called the Unison Committee for Action was formed by barristers, industrialists and others to form plans for maintaining the life of the country in the event of a collapse of law and order. While a military putsch is unlikely in the case of Britain, where the armed forces are professional rather than political, it could nevertheless happen that in conditions of real chaos and in the absence of strong leadership, the army might feel itself obliged to take control temporarily—and temporarily might prove a long time. Elsewhere, a military putsch is by no means out of the question.

Somewhere along this course the crucial factor will become plain. Either the army, air force and police will remain loyal to the government, or some part will refuse to act against the strikers and their supporters (I do not say 'against the workers', because a considerable number of workers will appreciate the government's position, while a proportion of 'non-workers' particularly the intellectual left, will leap into the fray against it).

If the forces remain loyal, the probability is that the revolt will gradually peter out. The perpetrators will try to keep the pot boiling, as they did in Northern Ireland, but some semblance of normality will return. If a part of the army defects, there could be a prolonged civil war. If the whole of the forces defect, the government would become impotent and its underground shelters would prove to be traps from which it could not emerge, except in handcuffs. There could be a Communist government.

However, these developments would be closely affected by two factors. First, whether the government kept its nerve and produced a leader who could inspire people with confidence and the belief that, when normality was restored, he would meet their just demands. And equally on whether the government's opponents produced a leader who could construct the administrative system necessary to sustain a prolonged struggle. Second, how far other countries proved ready to help or hinder. Capitalist countries might, or might not, divert supplies of food and fuel without any reliable prospect of ever being paid for them. Communist countries might infiltrate trained terrorists and drop supplies of arms and ammunition. (Here the loyalty of the air force would prove a crucial factor.) They might even provide military advisers and administrators, on the lines pioneered by the US in Indonesia. In the event of the tide of battle turning in favour of the rebels, these advisers might prove to be the advance-guard of a take-over, leading to the installation of a 'Provisional Government' of Communist pattern.

Hypnotised by the idea of Communist subversion, British army plans have been directed more towards the possibility of guerrilla warfare by armed, desperate groups than towards mass unrest and withdrawal of labour, and arrangements for meeting a situation of this sort have, it is widely rumoured, already been made. A leading army theoretician on such matters, Brigadier Frank Kitson, describes in his book *Low-Intensity Operations* how the army should prepare for such a situation. Training in countering subversion is already given at British Staff Colleges and the School of Infantry, he reveals, on a scale unimagined ten years ago, though the problem of 'the countering of small terrorist groups, especially in urban areas, gets less than its fair share of attention'.

Just before the miners' strike of 1973, 'there were ample signs that such preparations were being taken very seriously', reports Jonathan Rosenhead, co-author of a pamphlet *The New Technology of Repression*. 'Police forces were to be issued with riot kits. Moribund local government Home Defence and Emergency Planning Committees were drastically expanded. A firm manufacturing riot helmets was given special exemption from the three-day week. Military vehicles started shadowing left-wing demonstrations in London. And so on.'

The prolonged security operation at Heathrow airport, with tanks and regular army units, seems to have been more in the nature of an exercise than an attempt to prevent a terrorist attack. It was repeated a few months later, presumably to correct deficiencies exposed in the first rehearsal.

The Army has established a full-scale 'battle simulator' known as Close Quarter Battle (Urban). This is a mock-up of a network of streets, containing shops, houses and shoppers. 'As a patrol moves through the area, instructors using remote control consoles can simulate crowd noises, bomb-blasts and fire from pop-up snipers.' And the *International Defence Review* (Oct. 1973) reveals that the British Army has borrowed many of the electronic devices developed for use in Vietnam for detecting the presence of intruders, such as sensors which respond to body heat or vibration. Obviously plans for maintaining communications and broadcasting services have already been matured, and secret defence rooms, connected by microwave links, already exist in every region of Britain. Experience in Northern Ireland has enabled the Army to develop and try out new riot-control devices and unconventional technology, from new disabling gases to the 'sound curdler' and flashing lights which can drop a man in his tracks or induce an epileptiform fit. Minitanks for police use, fitted with such devices, have been built in America and can be ordered 'off the shelf'. A report on 'Riot Control' issued by the Royal United Services Institution in London, while this book was in proof, describes several of these new devices—including the firing of electric barbs into people's flesh and clothing ('public reaction to use unclear')—and suggests that the British police may have to be armed with these and other non-lethal weapons.

Kitson points out that riot-control measures can be used as a means of 'population punishment'. That is, they can make things 'reasonably uncomfortable for the population as a whole', which may encourage them to disown the militants.

'Actually when a friend from the UK Ministry of Defence told me there were contingency plans for keeping the population of the big cities from making a break-out when food supplies break down I couldn't believe it,' said an executive of a computer company at the Third European Management Seminar in 1973, 'but now I think they'll be eating human flesh in the streets in New York, London and Paris in 20 years or so.'

Kitson admiringly described how the French in Algeria established control of the civilian population 'by sending out teams into the towns and countryside whose job was to set up a complete chain of committees and cells supporting the government on similar lines to those established by the enemy. In this way they got right under the skin of the population, and by introducing identity cards, branding livestock with the identity card numbers of their owners (in Britain for "cows" read "cars") and by other similar methods they soon imposed a tight control over the people.' But he agrees it would be impossible to start on a programme of this sort in Britain until some violence had taken place, as it would be impossible to push through the necessary legislation 'until something had happened'. The US, however, maintains teams of this kind in advance of requirement, he notes enviously. The French and Italians maintain paramilitary police trained and equipped for riot control.

At a recent Defence Studies Seminar, held at the Royal United Services Institution, John Biggs Davison, MP, made the point explicit: 'If we lose in Belfast we may have to fight in Brixton or Birmingham.' 'Just as Spain in the 30s was a rehearsal for a wider European conflict, so perhaps what is happening in Northern Ireland is a rehearsal for urban guerrilla war more widely in Europe and particularly in Great Britain.' Davison is a Conservative of the extreme Right, but his words show the lines on which the Right expects to move.

I do not predict that these events will come to pass just as described. I do believe, however, that—especially if a Conservative government is elected in Britain, or an anti-Communist one in Italy —that there will be mounting trouble. Wage demands will be numerous, inflation will get worse, the unions will go even further in imposing political decisions which do not have legitimacy, and an increasingly chaotic situation will result.

For instance, if in Britain an attempt is made to start private clinics for those patients who wish to pay for privacy or extra care, these might be 'blacked'—radiographers refusing to take X-rays, pathologists to analyse samples of body fluids and so on. A step of this kind would be seen as tantamount to a declaration of class war. If one can judge from the promise of the leader of the union concerned to 'piss on' medical consultants, it would seem that those who do not wish to live in an atmosphere of deliberately-provoked hatred, recalling that provoked against the Jews in Nazi Germany, will have to leave the country. Up to now, the middle classes have been surprisingly apathetic about the erosion of their status. Eventually the worm may turn. The central question whether greater responsibility, greater self-denial and greater skill deserve greater rewards—and if so, how much greater—will have to be faced.

And, as happened in Rome, from time to time a strong ruler will make an attempt to restore a measure of order. Some of these attempts will be successful for a time. Eventually the national situations will become entrained by the world débâcle as a whole. Believing this, I nevertheless make an imaginative projection to show how fragile the structure of democracy has become. But it is more likely to crumble slowly than to come down in a run.

5 Endpiece

Whether or not a débâcle occurs, we must reckon on the strike weapon becoming ever more formidable. We must adapt ourselves to the idea that strikes will get more subtle and more damaging. Canal workers have realised that they could cause flooding. Sewage workers could cause plague. Late in 1974 an attempt was made to cut off the food supplies to the city of Glasgow, by coordinating strikes among a number of unions. Strikes aimed to wreck particular industries may be the next development; or we may see the simultaneous stoppage of all means of communication. British union leaders have been having talks with union leaders in other European countries so that Common Market strikes can be arranged. Eventually we shall have the inter-continental strike, the hemisphere strike and perhaps the world-wide strike.

At the same time the groups which are not at present unionised will be driven to protect themselves by unionising too. Already various grades of scientific workers, local government officers and managerial staff are becoming unionised, while professional associations begin to take on the function of unions. Britain had its first strike of state-employed scientists in 1974. In Italy, judges are organised into a National Association, which recently declared a two-day strike to demand not only higher wages but the reform of the judicial system. Protest meetings were held in court-rooms, to which journalists and members of parliament were invited. In Britain, consultant physicians threatened to withdraw their services from the National Health system, following the strike-imposed refusal of staff to service paying patients. Thus we here have a strike against a strike! These may become common.

We may also expect the ultimate folly of strikes against unions: clerical staff of the Amalgamated Engineering Union struck for more money recently, saying that the Union's president, Mr Hugh Scanlon, was 'terrible' as an employer.

Apart from strike-mania, I foresee the unions taking on an increasingly feudal character. Already they take responsibility, in many cases, for the general welfare of their members, providing savings-clubs, outings and other benefits; and they also intervene with organisations such as the health service and transport—even threatening individual doctors—when an individual member is dissatisfied. Thus they begin to resemble feudal barons, who offered protection against enemies in return for blind fealty. If society is becoming feudalised, it is for the same reason as before: because existing institutions are breaking up.

In the United States, where unions still confine themselves to negotiating rates and conditions, such an analysis may sound unrealistic; Americans should at least watch for this trend in Europe, for it may infect them. Little can be done to arrest these tendencies, short of a change in the structure of society itself—for they spring from the combination of mass technology and mass power. Only the decentralisation of power, and the integration of work responsibilities with other social responsibilities offers any real solution. Unions would be limited in size and matched to social organisations rather than to industries or crafts. But in the West such ideas are now unthinkable. In a more rational world, schoolchildren would be instructed not merely in the proper function of unions but in the nature of social cohesion, to say nothing of the significance of productivity. In a rational society, national strikes would be as unthinkable as lockouts and for the same reason.

However, it is at least equally likely that social collapse will start not with union intransigence as such but with a world financial disaster, leading to wide popular unrest affecting all classes equally.

X

FINANCIAL DISASTER

There is no subtler means of overturning the existing basis of society than to debauch the currency.—J. M. Keynes, Economic Consequences of the Peace

1 Inflationary Future

Inflation is rampant right round the world and getting worse. Western Europe's 10 per cent in one year is bad enough. As I write the us has a compounded rate of 16 per cent. Japan, the land of economic miracles, has recorded a general price rise of 23 per cent. Italy tops the European list at 25 per cent. Iceland is over 40 per cent. In the third world, price increases are crippling plans for development, notably in India, Pakistan and Vietnam, where price rises of around 65 per cent a year were recorded. In some South American countries, price rises have passed the one thousand per cent mark and are no longer accurately measurable. (These figures will certainly be obsolete by the time this book is in print.) This is not inflation as we knew it in the 50s and 60s. It's world-wide strato-inflation. Attempts to stop it could bring on a world-wide slump.

Inflations burn out into slumps, sooner or later, and massive world inflations burn out into massive world slumps. From those slumps fresh inflations arise. If this pattern continues, long before the end of the century the strains could cause Western society to collapse. It is the inflation *after* this one that we really have to worry about.

History shows unequivocally that uncontrolled inflation leads to political disaster. Some people can still remember the disastrous German inflation of 1923, when the mark halved in value every half-hour, and people collected their wages in a wheelbarrow—wages which were almost worthless before they got to the shops. On 20 November of that year, the mark, which had been 4.20 to the dollar in 1914, reached 4.2 trillion (10^{12}) to the dollar. Bankruptcies were widespread. Unemployment rose to unheard-of levels. Communism gained strength rapidly. Riots took place. People turned in

146

desperation to a leader who promised to restore order—and eventually did, which shows that inflation *can* be cured, despite the desperate cry of John Dunlop, head of America's Cost of Living Council: 'I don't believe it is clear that mankind today knows how to control inflation.'

An inflation on the 1923 scale is unlikely; no government, knowing what we know now, would print money as recklessly as the Germans then did. But double-figure inflation is quite serious enough. To make clear what is needed to prevent it, I shall have to plunge into economics, for the subject is bedevilled with misapprehensions. For unless it is to be cured by dictatorial methods, people must understand the mechanism and go along with the necessary measures. This is particularly true for Italy and Britain, where the collapse is most likely to start.

While there have been many inflations in the course of history, the present one is unique in being world-wide. Evidently it is not the consequence of misjudgment by any one government. And it seems to be gathering speed. In Italy, the take-off came in 1969. Before that year Italy had one of the lowest inflation rates in Europe; then a round of wage increases coupled with government spending caused prices to zoom at a rate of 20 per cent per year. At February 1974 the rise amounted to 12 per cent in 12 months. In America, the rot started under Lyndon Johnson, who raised too little in taxes to pay for the costly Vietnam war. In 1971, it is true, Nixon forced the inflation rate down to 3 per cent (from 5 per cent) by imposing a wage/price freeze. But when he lifted controls in January 1973, prices took off again, and by February 1974 the inflation rate was over 16 per cent (9.7 per cent over the previous 12 months). Nor is the virus confined to the capitalist world. Yugoslavia, where there is a market-system, is ballooning at 22 per cent per year. Even Switzerland, the heartland of financial virtue, has been infected to the tune of almost 11 per cent in one year.

In the uncoordinated inflations of the past, a country in trouble could borrow from one which was strong. The development of world-wide trade and world-wide finance has produced a far less stable system, liable to far greater swings.

What are the implications of massive inflation for the future? It is worth running over them in detail, since attempts have been made to deny their existence.* There are at least six consequences, collectively overwhelming.

---

* Thus a recent book addressed to the general reader (*Economics of the Real World*, Penguin Press, 1973) declares that the fuss about inflation is 'bogus'. Inflation doesn't really matter, says the author (a university lecturer), because if wages and prices both go up, the situation is unchanged. This is simply untrue.

1   When wages rise, they do so unequally, causing distress and injustice. Strong unions win increases which match the rising prices; weak unions do less well. People on fixed incomes, such as pensions and separation allowances are even harder hit. To take just one real-life example, Mrs X, awarded a maintenance allowance for her three children and herself in 1967, today has *one-third* less in spending power than she had. Old people scraping by on small pensions are being reduced below the poverty-line. Members of the armed forces find their pay does not go so far. Annuities buy less. At the same time all financially endowed bodies, such as charitable foundations and many educational charities and scholarships are hit. Scholarships and research grants become worthless. When people cannot make ends meet, they become desperate. We can therefore expect growing social unrest.

2   Saving for major expenditures, such as house purchase, is becoming ever harder: by the time you've saved the money you needed, the house costs more. What this really means is that people do without goods they might have bought, but when they come to spend the money it buys far less than what they denied themselves. They have, in plain words, been cheated, just as surely as if they had been overcharged originally. The same goes for life insurance and loans. The coin you are paid back in is worth much less than the coin you lent.

3   Because people have to spend more to maintain something like their usual living standard, they save less, and hence invest less. Consequently, money is becoming ever harder to borrow; interest rates have risen to prohibitive levels. So the man who wants a mortgage to buy a house is penalised, and industry is deterred from re-equipping or from launching new processes and projects. The money which firms have put aside in the past for re-equipment turns out to be inadequate. The economic growth of the country is slowed, which eventually penalises everyone. It is true that repayment of debt becomes easier, which helps some people, but tends to favour established firms at the expense of new ones, which is not altogether a good thing.

4   Thanks to the excess of buying power, shortages develop. This causes industrial delays, interest charges run on, delivery dates are missed. Once again industrial efficiency suffers, which affects everyone.

5   Industry is being increasingly hampered by the high cost of borrowing for modernisation or for launching new ventures and for bridging the gap between outgoings and payments. Money locked up in stocks of raw materials and finished goods costs it more. It responds by reducing its commitments, if it can. We must therefore expect

more bankruptcies, more firms going to the government for aid, and a drastic decline of business activity, leading in turn to unemployment, and eventually to deflation and a slump.

6   Finally, we must expect severe international stresses due to the disastrous effect on the trade balance. As money-incomes rise, foreign goods become relatively cheaper, while home goods become dear for foreign buyers. Imports begin to exceed exports, and eventually the exchange rates are adjusted to correct this. Of course if all trading partners equally are in the grip of inflation, the effects cancel out. In the present world-wide inflation, it is those countries with the highest rates of inflation that will run into balance-of-payments difficulties; those with low rates may be all right. Finally, inflation has a disastrous impact on the third world. Steel and fertilizer prices have doubled in little more than a year; that of wheat has tripled.

It is the young unmarried man who can best support inflation. It hits married couples with children to bring up harder, and old people hardest of all. It hits the middle class harder than the unions and workers, and harder than the rich who own real values. And, since it handicaps industry, it makes everyone poorer than they might have been in the long run.

The foregoing is true of common or garden inflation. A super-inflation, where prices are rising appreciably from week to week, paralyses confidence; no one wants to start any venture because the situation becomes uncertain. It even becomes risky to plan a foreign holiday, in case travel allowances of currency are curtailed, and much more risky to re-equip a factory or launch a new business. People begin to resort to desperate measures to protect themselves from ruin. This is why Denis Healey, Chancellor of the Exchequer in Britain's 1974 Labour government, warned: 'Unless we can somehow halt the accelerating inflationary trends in our economy, the political and social strains may be too violent for our democratic institutions to withstand.' Soon after, the Chairman of the us Federal Reserve Board, Dr Arthur Burns, issued an identical warning: 'If long continued, inflation at anything like the present rate would threaten the very foundation of our society.' The phrase is not false just because it happens to be a cliché.

The injustices wrought by inflation, he said, were causing a loss of confidence in the free-enterprise system. 'I do not believe I exaggerate in saying that the ultimate consequences of inflation could be a significant decline of economic and political freedom for the American people.'

Eventually, inflation tends to destroy itself. Since people cut down on luxuries before necessities and make expensive items last longer, firms making such items begin to price themselves out of the market. And if business confidence is weak, firms making industrial equipment are hit. Bankruptcies occur; employees are laid off; so buying power declines. More firms begin to lose money and lay off staff. A slump has been born.

This, then, is the prospect we face in the immediate future: galloping inflation leading to social breakdown. What then is the *cause* of inflation and what should we do about it?

2 Why Inflation?

Several factors enter into the rise of prices and not all are inflationary in the strict meaning of the word. If prices rise because real costs have gone up, that is normal. It so happens that world prices of many raw materials have risen (for reasons I shall discuss later) and this has forced up prices in manufacturing countries. Perhaps one-third of the current price-rise may be due to this, although the figure varies from country to country.

The other two-thirds is truly inflationary; that is, people have more money to spend than is sufficient to buy the foods available. Sellers therefore find themselves able to raise prices (which of course improves their profits) and this has the effect of mopping up the excess demand. If wages are now increased, to compensate for the price rises, the process repeats itself.

Despite agonised denials from the unions, it is self-evident that wage increases, unless matched by increases of productive efficiency, add to inflation and are at least a contributory cause, however justifiable they may be on social grounds. Limiting wages, limiting dividends, and for that matter cutting back pensions, would tend to put the brake on inflation. But there is more to inflation than that, and before we discuss cures, we must go more deeply into the matter. There are two other much-neglected factors. One is quite unusual. In the past, the economies of different countries have not been in step. When one country was having a boom, another was having a slump. These conditions tend to offset each other. The depressed country cut its purchases from the boom country, which weakened its inflation, and so on. Today, thanks to the growth of world trade, to the balancing activities of multinationals, the creation of the Common Market, and other factors, the countries of the world are pretty much in step, and their inflations reinforce one another. For instance, all countries were increasing their demand for raw materials simultaneously a few years back, which helped to force up raw-material prices. All simultaneously were calling for capital, making use of such international facilities as banking and shipping, and so on. This is something new we now have to live with. It calls for much closer international economic cooperation than we have yet got. (Note: a coordinated world slump will be even harder to live with than a world boom.)

But, while this explains the intensity and universality of the inflation, it does not explain its cause. Many explanations have been offered for inflation and it has even been said that no one knows the explanation of the current world-wide inflation. The situation is not as bad as that, and the key can be found in Keynes' *General Theory* written forty years ago. In the last analysis, the crucial factor is the balance between what people save and what they spend. If people decide to spend more and save less, there is a boom, prices rise, manufacturers expand to meet the demand; but capital is scarce, so interest rates rise. Conversely, if people decide to hoard their money, there is a slump but money is cheap.

Keynes was concerned to explain the trade cycle, and concentrated on what made big industrialists decide to draw on their reserves and build new factories, thus providing jobs, increasing buying power and starting off the boom. Basically, it is a question of confidence in the future. As soon as industrialists see profits being made, they feel more confident about starting new enterprises. But this was all in the days before governments knew enough to intervene. Nowadays the trade cycle is reduced to a series of stop–go jumps as governments try to regulate spending. And there are other factors at work. But the saving/spending ratio remains basic. Clearly today there is over-spending and under-saving, but we have to look elsewhere to explain the imbalance as a long-term process on a world-wide scale.

Now there *is* a long-term trend to which little attention has been given: the number of people who receive incomes without creating saleable goods or services. That is, the whole of the administrative machine from tax collectors to members of the government. The whole of public education, including student grants. The whole of the national health services. The whole of local government, including things like public libraries and social workers. The armed forces and police. The prison service and judiciary. The whole of scientific (but not all technological) research; also medical research.* Over the years, in practically every country, there has been a steady expansion of such services. Functions like town and country planning, which did not exist a generation ago, now employ relatively highly-paid staffs. Psychiatric services at public expense used not to exist.

* In Britain today, the central government, for the first time, is actually spending more than the private citizen, more than half of whose incomes it removes in taxes and social insurance—quite apart from what is taken by local authorities.

Scientific research is on a far larger scale than before. State pensions for retired people are steadily extended and increased. And, although armed forces are smaller in manpower, their equipment is more complex, and takes far more man-hours to make and maintain. This is true of almost every nation.

To pay for all this, money is taken away from incomes by taxes and death-duties. If people want town-planners, search-radars and student grants they must pay for them, doing without an equivalent amount of personal consumption. But the money thus abstracted does not necessarily cut personal consumption. A rich man, when taxes go up, may simply save less and maintain his previous standard of living. A firm may not cut dividends; it may prefer to postpone the day when it buys new machine tools. The man who receives a legacy may spend more of it, and save less. If so, inflation results. The government would have to abstract in taxes and duties more than it actually needs to pay the bills, to prevent inflation occurring. In actual fact, most governments abstract less, end up with budget deficits, and meet the gap by 'printing money'. (Since money, nowadays, consists of cheques rather than notes, they don't actually have to print it.)

In short, *the saving/spending ratio is out of balance* due to the way people react to the growth of public services. Every time a public service is initiated or enlarged, people ought to say to themselves: 'Now I must cut down my rate of expenditure to compensate for the fact that the state is spending my money for me.' But they don't. On the contrary, they expect their standard of living to rise.

Government subsidies to industry and agriculture (which in Britain have been running at over £3 billion a year) also have an inflationary effect for exactly similar reasons. Governments do not seem to understand this, and often claim that subsidising prices is a way of keeping prices down. It may keep down the particular kind of price which is subsidised—bread, for instance, or fertilizer—but by freeing the buyer's money to spend elsewhere, subsidies put all other prices up.

With all this in mind let us now turn back to the question of wages.

3 Grinding the Faces of the Rich

In negotiating wages and salaries, all sorts of arguments are used, such as 'what is a decent living wage' and 'widget makers have always earned more than gadget makers, so if the latter have been given a raise the former's wage must also be raised!' (This is known as preserving differentials.) Our ideas of what constitutes a decent living wage change, and always upwards. It is natural to wish for television sets, wall-to-wall carpeting and a Sunday joint. It is even natural to wish that other people should enjoy such pleasures (formerly luxuries) especially if it reduces one's sense of guilt.

But the central question is whether the country can manufacture enough goods to supply everyone with such items. If it can't, nothing is gained by distributing the buying power which would serve to buy them. The fact that some of the population enjoys great luxury (and receives large incomes) gives colour to the strongly-held belief that, if their incomes were severely cut down, and a proportionate increase made in the incomes of the mass of the population, this upgrading of living standards would be immediately possible. In point of fact this widely-held belief is false. Redistribution of incomes may be desirable on grounds of justice, and in a moment I shall consider this aspect, but from the viewpoint of eliminating inflation, it is counter-productive.

In actual fact the number of people with very large incomes is so small that such a redistribution would have a negligible effect. Thus in Britain it has been calculated that if *all* after-tax income in excess of £5,000 a year were confiscated and distributed uniformly, this would mean only 30p a week more for everyone*; and if all after-tax income over £2,000 a year were thus redistributed, it would mean a mere £1.56 a week more. An income of £2,000 per annum, corresponding to £40 a week, is less than many blue-collar workers already take home. In point of fact in Britain there were only 99,000 people earning more than £5,000 a year after tax in 1970–1 (the last year for which figures are available) and only 600 earning over £10,000 a year after tax. (Some authorities give the figure as £12,500.) Since that year inflation will have lifted many people into higher tax brackets but the principle remains unchanged. Moreover, social service payments narrow the gap still further.

The key fact, however unpleasant it may be, is that it is impossible for the *whole* population to have a living standard higher than the average, and the average is lower than most people think. In 1971 the average income per *household* in Britain was almost exactly £2,000 a year. Thus if buying power were distributed *absolutely equally* throughout the country, many British blue-collar workers would find their wages reduced. Surprise, surprise. Thus the root of inflation is an *unrealistic conception of the amount of wealth the country produces*, due partly to popular accounts of productivity, partly to emphasis by advertisers and the media on the life of the wealthy, making them appear more numerous than they are.

The deviousness of left-wing governments in the face of these facts

* According to *The Economist*, it would mean only 3½p for everyone.

is well illustrated by the promise of the British Labour government elected in 1973 to make concessions amounting to £2½ billion. Now, if all after-tax income over £2,000 a year were confiscated, it would only yield £1,629m. So, even at this confiscatory level, the gap could only have been closed by inflation. But the government had no intention of courting unpopularity by taxing anything like so heavily, least of all the incomes between £2,000 and £3,000 after tax, from which over £1 billion of the £1,629 million would come. So its plan clearly implies a decision to inflate sharply. In point of fact, an inflation at 17½ per cent per annum would be required to raise the required sum.

We can thus see that, in addition to wage increases, *deliberate government over-spending* makes a major contribution to inflation. An unbalanced annual budget is inflationary, and even a balanced one may be, if it is balanced by relying on inflation to bring that balance about.

However, it is often argued that income should be distributed more equally for reasons of equity, even if to do so would not justify big wage increases. But here there is a further difficulty: to do so upsets the saving/spending ratio. Since poor men save a much smaller part of their income than rich men, redistribution not only inflates the demand for goods but also causes savings to fall. As a result interest rates rise; money becomes dear. Hence industry is deterred from launching new projects, for unless they are unusually profitable, they will not be able to cover the high interest rates on the capital employed. In addition, the sums put to reserve by firms are now worth much less, so that firms cannot finance new projects without borrowing. Thus it is that we get the historically novel combination of industrial stagnation combined with inflation—the so-called 'stagflation', which is now turning, in Britain, into 'slumpflation'.

A mild inflation encourages business, since it buys raw material at one price level and sells finished products at a higher one. General prosperity makes the slight erosion of savings tolerable for most people. Stagflation pleases nobody.

None of this says that the very large incomes enjoyed by a minority are justified in equity, whether the minority be football stars or financiers. Still less acceptable are huge speculative profits and the profits of financial manipulation. It is very natural that low-paid employees are resentful when they read—as they recently did—that one man has made £5m. in a few months. The practical question, which no one has tried to answer is: what degree of inequality will
(a) provide the necessary incentives to hard work and risk-taking;
(b) provide the differentials which acknowledge differences in skill,

experience and responsibility; and (c) lead to the appropriate ratio of saving to spending?

At the moment, Britain seems to have pushed the process furthest, with very few incomes more than four times the national average wage after tax and very few less than half of it. (Contrast with this Russia's 40:1 ratio.) And it has brought about the change very fast. Not surprisingly, many of the most ambitious and creative people are leaving the country. It will be instructive to see what the long-term effect of this is, and whether other countries seek to follow her example.

If society goes too far towards equality it discourages those who accept poverty for many years in the hope of eventual success on a scale which will compensate them for what they have missed—a description which applies to many artists and writers as well as to inventors, doctors, mining companies and those who try to establish new kinds of products. Since their efforts increase the size of the cake for society as a whole, it may be in everyone's interest to dangle in front of them the prospect of an unusually large slice for themselves.

Today, we are increasingly engaged in an unproductive struggle to change the size of the different slices, when it would be more rational to seek to enlarge the cake. Just how far this dog-in-the-manger attitude can go was shown by a public opinion poll in which people were asked: Would you rather have £4 a week more for everybody, or £5 a week more for yourself but £6 a week more for everyone else? In Britain, the great majority opted for £4 a week and equality. That's known as cutting off your nose to spite your face.

How then can we arrest inflation?

4 Can Inflation be Cured?

There is a school of thought—and it is strong in the United States—which argues that prices and wages cannot rise if the money is not there; they conclude that the way to stop inflation is to turn off the money-tap. Mr Burns of the Federal Reserve Board is advocating this as I write. (Some people go so far as to say that increasing the supply of money is the *cause* of inflation. This may have been true when 'money' meant gold but today this is nonsense. Banks may be willing to provide credits, but nothing happens unless people are willing to take them up, as has often been demonstrated when governments sought to put an end to slumps by easing credit.) It is true that cutting down the money supply can turn a boom into a slump. But the method is too crude. Money-management just produces a series of hiccups.

The error of monetarists is to believe there is some quantity of money—not too much, not too little—which will produce economic stability: full employment with stable prices. Alas, they are wrong. Before you have pinched out inflation, you begin to depress industry, and start to increase unemployment. Thus, at the point of balance, you get 'stagflation'—a stagnant economy which is still inflating. Too little is being saved to finance industry, because the saving/spending ratio is wrong. The painful truth is that the capitalist system only works when incomes are unequally distributed. More equal distribution is only possible if wage-earners will save more and spend less.

This being so, money-management can only stop inflation by creating unemployment. But even this is harder than it was, because today an unemployed man receives up to two-thirds of his normal income in unemployment benefits (more, in some countries). Hence he does not cut back his consumption as sharply as was once the case. It follows that unemployment must rise further than before to produce an equivalent deflationary effect. Few governments are prepared to let unemployment rise far enough, and would probably be ejected from power if they tried it.

But the history of Germany suggests that, nowadays, people are no longer willing to starve quietly: they turn to any leader who looks as if he can restore order, whatever loss of liberty this may mean. Today, too, we can expect a much greater degree of public violence when food and fuel become short. If American truckers are prepared to shoot their co-workers, and car-owners to shoot garage proprietors who fail to supply petrol for their cars, they will certainly be still more aggressive when they are short of food, drink and heating.

The question is whether this public disorder will mount to the level of anarchy, how far it will be exploited for political ends, and whether or not charismatic leaders will emerge to impose a solution.

Finally, even if a strong government checked inflation in this way, a new boom would soon arise from the ashes of the old. The human costs of unemployment might be acceptable if it were a once-for-all solution, but it is not. It just checks the speed by periodically jamming on the brakes instead of relaxing the accelerator.

Nor are appeals to freeze prices and wages likely to be successful. Price freezes won't work if buying power continues to rise: a black market soon develops. More importantly, firms begin to go bankrupt, as they sell cheap while paying high wages. Wage freezes don't work, except for a few weeks, because unions exist to improve wages, and wage freezes put them out of business. In addition wage freezes perpetuate existing inequities, and prevent adjustment to changing conditions. Industries which are short of labour cannot attract more by offering more.

Clauses tying wages to the cost-of-living index are equally illogical, since they increase the buying power which it is the object of the price rise to reduce. But people are, naturally, exceptionally sensitive to rises in food prices, since everyone eats, and one cannot do much to postpone or restrict one's expenditure. So, when world food prices are rising, the demand for special treatment becomes too strong to resist. Subsidies and price controls at least give people the impression that the political leaders recognise the problem and are trying, even if they only make it worse in the long run.

Without doubt, in a rational world, a wages policy would be worked out, and continuously readjusted, so that, when taken *in toto*, buying power matched the goods available to be bought. In a rational world, unions would make it their job to thrash out between themselves how the various rates should be set within this global limitation. This would be difficult but not impossible, technically. The difficulties are human ones. Union leaders would object strongly to a system which removed their original *raison d'être* and would be at risk, since their members might repudiate them and elect more aggressive representatives, committed to win benefits for their own group, regardless of the effect on anybody else. In Britain, certainly, there is little public support for a wages policy. A recent survey revealed that only 31 per cent of Labour respondents approved the idea. More than half said it meant 'too much government interference'.

Thus, in Britain at least, any attempt to introduce an incomes policy would be rejected by union *members* even if union leaders agreed to it. Other countries are hardly likely to be more amenable, least of all the United States. Hence the outlook is black.

The logical counterpart of an incomes policy, or any other policy for that matter, would be to raise efficiency by the most obvious and inexpensive means: namely, elimination of featherbedding, restrictive practices, demarcation squabbles, poor timekeeping and all the other hallowed ways of restricting efficiency. The desire to protect entrenched positions is natural enough, and one can understand the concern which a man feels when his skill is no longer in demand. But unions have been reluctant to accept reasonable policies of restricting recruitment, of retraining and in some cases early retirement. The situation where an electric locomotive carries a fireman to stoke a non-existent fire is plainly grotesque. The increase in output would help to reduce the inflation.

At the same time, let us not forget that governments themselves are also responsible for inflation, whenever their budgetary policies disturb the saving/spending ratio. And unfortunately governments, particularly those of the left, are by no means as strongly opposed to inflation as they usually pretend. This is the real trouble.

Governments, even of the right, are lukewarm in resisting inflation since by raising people into higher tax-brackets the government increases tax-receipts and makes it easier to balance its budget. It may even be able to announce concessions, such as higher pensions or reduction in rates of income tax! Thus governments win cheap popularity while invisibly penalising all groups.

But worse than this, left-wing governments deliberately use inflation as a means of impoverishing those who possess wealth. The fact that thereby they erode the tiny savings of the ordinary man is unimportant to them provided they can feel that they are eroding inherited wealth. Actually, it is the middle class which is hardest hit, for the very rich own land, pictures and other objects which retain their value. It is the man with annuities or insurance for his old age who really suffers. Apart from questions of justice, inflation hits at those who save rather than those who are spendthrift. Thus it weakens those who are most likely to build for the future. Unfortunately governments do not welcome private virtue in this respect, preferring to determine the future themselves.

Finally, it might be added that Communists welcome inflation, which they hope may bring about general chaos in which they can come to power. Thus Communists join forces with socialists in an unholy alliance.

Inflation can be suppressed by letting unemployment rise. But it is already clear that we cannot have full employment, free bargaining for wages and stable prices simultaneously in a parliamentary democracy. To control prices the government must control wages, and if it tries that, it gets thrown out. And since no one, at least in Britain, is willing to give up the first three, it follows that unless democracy is suspended, inflation will continue.

To survive, one must either join a strong union or be self-employed, and die as soon as possible after your powers fail.

5 Rogue Gold

But it is in the balance between different countries that the crunch comes. One of the most awkward effects of inflation is that it causes imports (from any country which is inflating less) to look cheap and makes exports correspondingly dear. Consequently, an adverse trade balance tends to develop. The importing country therefore has to settle the difference with gold; few countries hold enough gold to do this for long. If the situation continues they are reduced to borrowing, as Britain is now doing. Finally, they exhaust the willingness of lenders, as Italy has already done.

If the country which finds itself with an adverse trade balance can manage to deflate, this will reduce its tendency to import. But (and this is a fact many financial writers overlook) if people particularly want the kind of goods which only other countries can supply, it may take a very severe deflation to discourage them sufficiently from buying; so severe, in fact, as to induce an internal slump. A country whose industrial methods are inefficient, whose products are badly designed, unreliable or out-of-date, will have difficulty exporting them, while its own population will prefer to buy the more attractive foreign goods to those made at home, even if they cost more. Politicians all too often attempt to boost exports by financial manipulations while ignoring these more fundamental factors.

A country caught in this trap has the possibility of introducing import quotas, but these tend to provoke retaliation by exporting countries and are forbidden by various trade agreements, particularly in Europe. It can also alter its exchange rate, but this too is unpopular, and makes its raw materials dearer into the bargain.

But if it fails to pay those countries which supply its raw materials, they will naturally refuse to continue supplying them, plunging the importing country into unemployment, bankruptcies and slump.

In short, there is a Catch 22, or Morton's Fork. If you reflate to restore demand and avert a slump, you see your balance of trade plunge and your exchange rate collapse. If you don't, you have inflation and the problems that it brings.

What makes this situation particularly perilous is the surprisingly small quantities of gold available for the conduct of world trade. Today many countries resemble companies with insufficient trading capital. Apart from financial experts, few people realise how small is the amount of gold available to finance world trade, in relation to the volume of trade. France, for example, has a bigger gold stock than many countries, yet its 1974 trade deficit exceeded its entire reserves. Countries can stand one bad year, or three or four poor ones, but a run of bad years bankrupts them.

Moreover, world trade expands faster than the supply of gold expands, so that national monies have to be equated to gold at ever higher levels. In other words, the price of gold constantly rises, which is nice for those countries which mine it, like Russia and South Africa.

In 1973 a spanner was thrown into this fragile system by the action of the oil-producing countries (OPEC) in raising prices spectacularly, thus putting the whole rest of the world into deficit. To keep the system functioning, it is essential that they return the gold, either by

investing or by buying goods. And it is important how they choose
between these alternatives, since it affects the spending/saving ratio.
If they buy recklessly, they could produce inflation in the countries
from whom they buy. If they save it all, they could produce a slump.
Not knowing which way the cat will jump, the finance ministers of
developed countries do not really know whether to inflate or deflate.
It is a game in which one player has picked up nearly all the chips.

In the nineteenth century Britain was in a rather similar position,
as supplier to the world. Britain accumulated gold but promptly
lent it back to the customer countries, which enabled them to continue buying. Eventually, most of the vast debts thus piled up were
defaulted—it should have been obvious that they would be, for
under-developed countries were in no position to flood Britain with
imports, thus effectively paying back in real terms what they had
received. No doubt Arab loans will also one day be defaulted. Later
I shall give reasons for supposing that other countries with much-
wanted commodities may try to repeat the Arab manoeuvre, which
could make world trade still more precarious.

Meanwhile, Western countries are faced with adverse trade
balances. Since their inhabitants spend more on oil (whether they
buy it directly, or because it affects the prices of what they buy) they
have less to spend on other things. If the Arabs do not step in and
buy goods on the same scale, the effect could be deflationary. If
they do so step in, but buy goods of a different kind—aircraft and
locomotives rather than dishwashers and television sets—countries
will be forced to expensive and painful structural changes.

Finally, it is obvious that for every country which achieves a
favourable trade balance, there must be a country with an un-
favourable one. Hence policies of 'export-led growth' such as those
currently popular are really cut-throat. The fact is, massive exports
put a country at risk, since it cannot ensure that demand continues.
In a fragmented world, it would make much better sense to minimise
both exports and imports.

6 A World Slump—and then What?

'Is the world heading for another 1929 crash?' asked the London
Financial Times in mid-1974, while *The Economist* bluntly announced
'The approaching depression'.

Economists tell us to watch for a rise in bankruptcies. Nationalised
industries, of course, cannot be allowed to go bankrupt and governments are reluctant to see the failure of important firms employing
large numbers of people, or those which embody national prestige.
When we see such firms asking for help, we know the lights have

turned to amber. When the state can no longer afford to bail them out, the lights are red. About a year after companies start going into deficit, history tells us, the Gross National Product begins to dip. A year after that, unemployment begins to soar. In March 1974 *The Economist* noted that deficits were rising, and by the end of that year the number of bankruptcies had reached the highest figure on record. Other firms have appealed to the government for help to avoid ruin. For many countries the outlook is bleak.

Of course, depressions come and go, but a major world depression on the scale of 1929 is something else again. Already stock values have declined by more than in 1929. Just ten years after that set-back a world war broke out. If history repeats itself exactly—which of course it doesn't—that would put World War III in the calendar for 1984. But though the date is unlikely to be exact, the risk is there.

As I have explained, the forthcoming slump will eventually generate a new boom, assuming war and Communism can both be avoided. If we avoid disaster the first time round, we may not be so lucky the second.

The countries most at risk are Italy and Britain. Superimposed on the world trend is the stop–go progress which governments generate in their attempts to regulate the balky economic machine: 'stop' when they try to limit inflation, 'go' when they try to limit unemployment. The cycle seems to grow steadily shorter. When will the breakdown come? Peter Jay, the Economics Editor of *The Times*, puts it about 1980. 'My own guess is that we may stagger round one more economic cycle, perhaps two, and that something should be allowed also for the tendency of logic always to take rather longer to work itself out in Britain than one expects. By 1980, give or take a couple of years, seems to me a cautious to middle view.' The problem, he adds, is not confined to Britain; countries with weak political institutions or poor economic performance will go first. Italy, which is weak both ways, may be the first. Countries which are strong both ways, like Switzerland and the United States, may never go at all.

The effects of a severe slump, with unemployment rising above the 10 per cent mark, would certainly be to strengthen leftward and Communist feeling. Probably demands for unemployment benefits and reliefs will be on such a scale that prices will continue to rise, in which case the middle class will also be progressively impoverished. Since they will prefer the restoration of 'order' by force if necessary, the stage will be set for a sharp right-left clash. This will happen in France, Germany, Austria and other countries, as well as in Britain. In Italy it is already happening.

Meanwhile, Communism is becoming increasingly respectable. France and Italy are strongly polarised; it would not take much unrest to swing them into the Communist camp. The Common Market would hardly survive such a change, and who can see what the further effect would be? The leftward forces are mounting, though more slowly, in Germany and Britain.

In this troubled situation, much will depend on the skill of governments and their ability to unify their own countries by displaying qualities of leadership.

But government, on the whole, is in a poor state.

XI

CHARMLESS ELITE

Well, fancy giving money to the Government!
Might as well have put it down the drain.
—A. P. Herbert

1 Lost Legitimacy

On some of the medieval town-halls of South Germany, for instance in Munich, there are vast clocks which show not only the time of day but the phases of the moon and other more or less relevant matters. At mid-day, crowds gather in the street below to watch them strike. For they do not appeal only to the ear. At the hour, doors open, beadles stagger out and bow, trumpeters blow, wood is sawn, old men drink, couples dance, the sun passes rapidly overhead and a good time is had by all. Out of sight, behind this flummery, vast, rusty cogwheels are grittily turning, warped wooden beams are sliding and jerking, leaden weights are descending, while rickety escapements whizz and whirr like demented bird-cages.

These clocks remind one of many democratic governments. Five hundred years old in design and technique, mostly irrelevant to modern needs, always seeming on the verge of breakdown from warping or the corruption of rust, the wonder is that they work at all.

In many countries, popular dissatisfaction with the system of government—as distinct from dissatisfaction with particular parties—seems to be coming to the boil. The desire of regional groups to break away and set up their own governments, and the rise of extremism are, in part, due to this. But confidence in the ability of governments to solve current problems has drained away among the most sober citizens, quite aside from extremists. It is a sign of the times when local government leaders begin to criticise the central government openly, not on party lines but in general terms. Thus the Chairman of the General Purposes Committee of the Greater London Council, Dr Stephen Hasler, has publicly declared that local

163

leaders 'are increasingly coming to resent the indifference of our national leaders to the alarming problems confronting our nation', and calls on politicians to abandon their 'intolerable and audacious commitment to out-of-date party games'.

Similarly in America. 'Everywhere there is disenchantment with the biggest and fastest-growing of these institutions, modern government, as well as cynicism regarding its ability to perform,' observed Peter Drucker in *The Age of Discontinuity*—writing long before the Watergate revelations.

As Professor Toynbee tells us, civilisations collapse when the elite loses its charm. Cynicism and doubt extend not only as regards competence but still more as regards aims. How far do we really endorse the decisions our elected representatives take on our behalf? The phrase which begins to appear in newspaper editorials is 'absence of social consent'. Where social consent is absent, there is a high probability that new leaders will appear with a programme which looks, at least at first sight, more in line with popular aims, and that a dramatic change of regime may occur. Perhaps we are living in the twilight of democracy.

2 Disenchanted Voters

In East London, during the election of spring 1974, a retired shop steward told a reporter: 'I'm fed up with politics. It's always the same. When people have been in power for a while they forget the people they represent,' and another old man commented: 'I can't see any government doing us any good at all.' Dick Taverne, going from house to house in Lincoln during his by-election, likewise reported: 'Disillusionment with both main parties emerged strongly —"You can't believe a word they say." '

Public opinion surveys show that, in several countries, voters think it does not matter which party is in power, and in Britain at least the proportion who think this way has been rising for a quarter of a century. In 1951 only 20 per cent of those questioned agreed with this proposition; in 1959, the proportion was 38 per cent; and in 1964, it had risen to 49 per cent. By 1966 it was over half. A similar survey in Germany yielded comparable figures.

Recent polls explore this rejection of government in more detail. Thus Dr Mark Abrams, director of the British Social Survey, asked a number of questions relating to people's satisfaction with life in general—such as health, housing, education, financial situation, friendship, family life—and found that the lowest level of satisfaction of all was registered in reply to the question: 'All things considered, how satisfied or dissatisfied are you with the level of democracy in

Britain today?' Dissatisfaction was greatest among the young and among those whose education had continued until age 18 or later. And when this question was analysed into six components, the commonest complaints were that voters had too little influence on the way the country was run, and that it was difficult for people like themselves to understand what is going on in politics.

The rapidity with which this erosion of confidence is occurring is shown by a survey conducted in April 1974, by the Opinion Research Centre, in which the same questions were asked as in April 1973. The number saying that they had a great deal of confidence in Parliament declined from 31 per cent to 27 per cent—in other words three-quarters of the public have no great confidence in their leadership! Surely that is an amazing figure and justifies asking how long a country can continue on such a slim basis of confidence. Confidence in local government, moreover, was even lower, and fell from 27 to 24 per cent, while confidence in the much-praised civil service declined from the unimpressive figure of 34 to the even less impressive figure of 29 per cent.

(Incidentally, it is worth noting that public confidence in trade-union leaders declined from 23 to a mere 11 per cent, which suggests that their entry into the political field may cause some backlash.)

Probably nothing has done more than television to disillusion voters, by showing them their representatives, warts and all. The words which sound so impressive spoken at a public meeting often emerge as insincere and pompous on the screen. 'Television is bringing them into our homes and now you can really see how awful they are, and how they are contradicting themselves and quarrelling,' an Ipswich housewife told *Times* reporter Penny Symon. 'Before you could only read what they said but now you see them in all their ridiculous reality, and it is clear that they do not care about the country, only themselves.' Symon comments: 'That was a typical view, repeated often in the streets of this city of 127,000 inhabitants.' And she sums up, 'The credibility gap has become a yawning abyss, and the constant cry is : "I'm fed up with the lot of them" . . . There is no doubt that the saturation television coverage, however much it would be denied by those whose faces are always appearing, has led to the utter despair of voters and has caused disenchantment and disillusionment.'

In the US matters are little different. A poll conducted by the University of Michigan Institute of Social Research in mid-1974 showed that the President and Administration were rated only 3.3 out of 8 and the Federal Government 3.86 out of 8, when people were asked how well various US institutions were serving the country. (No institution rated higher than 5.5—the score of the armed forces.)

According to Peter Drucker, 'The mood is ugly. The employed workingman is becoming very restive. He feels let down by politicians, intellectuals and labour leaders.' As reported by *Time*, Democratic Governor Jimmy Carter assessed voters this way: 'They are searching for some stability and for some faith in government, and they haven't seen it yet.' The Watergate affair, with its revelations of chicanery not only at the presidential level, but all down the line, has deepened cynicism.

And not only in America. 'Nixon's gave away the show,' was scrawled across one of the spoiled ballot papers at a Glasgow by-election in November 1973—an election in which a Scottish Nationalist romped home in a traditionally Socialist area. In the same week, news analyst Ronald Butt summed up the autumn bye-elections in these words: 'The bye-election results may be Delphic in some of their implications but their general message is anything but obscure. It is a restatement of the alienation of a large section of public opinion from both the major parties.' More significant than the unpopularity of the Conservatives 'is the demonstration in all four contests of the total lack of any public enthusiasm for the Labour Party as a beneficial alternative to the Tories'. He concluded his survey by saying: '. . . we may be faced with the prospect of a period of unstable government, for lack of a clear parliamentary majority, such as Britain has not experienced since the twenties'. (The remarkable success of Scottish and Welsh nationalist candidates in the election four months later confirmed his diagnosis.)

Politicians themselves are beginning, at last, to become dimly aware of the contempt in which they have so long been held by much of the population, though it has taken a long time for the acid to penetrate their armour of complacency. Labour Minister Anthony Wedgwood Benn actually wrote a worried pamphlet about it for the Fabian Society in 1970, and by 1974 Home Secretary Roy Jenkins was complaining that 'the effective working of our democratic institutions is aggravated by a widespread cynicism with the processes of our political system.' Similarly in the US, Presidential candidate Henry Martin Jackson told a *Time* reporter: '. . . the voters now are really much tougher in evaluating appearances. . . . They are not cynical, they are sceptical. . . . They are really looking for answers.' At the end of 1974, only 12 per cent of Americans said they had much confidence in the ability of the Senate or House of Representatives to solve the inflation crisis, while nearly a quarter of the population sampled had no confidence at all.

One consequence of this despair at Parliament's tackling the problems about which people feel deeply has been the growth of pressure groups. As Benn notes 'thousands of such pressure or action groups have come into existence: community associations, amenity groups, shop-steward movements, consumer societies, educational campaigns, organisations to help the old, the homeless, the sick, the poor or underdeveloped societies, militant communal organisations, student power, noise abatement societies, and so on'. He might perhaps have added: conservation societies, birth control and abortion groups, women's lib and gay lib, and actual political pressure groups.

A writer in the *Guardian*, reviewing a book on community work, noted, 'The revival [of community action] comes at a time of massive disbelief in the ways and whims of those in power, and in their solutions for involving us.' Community action 'has been trying to breathe some life back into groups of people, living in the same place or having the same problems, who have been winded by body-blows from bureaucracy, whether it is the local council or central government'.

Where people are united by a common culture, and especially if they are separated from other groups by a clearly-marked boundary or border, a possible course to allay dissatisfaction is to secede and set up one's own government. Significantly, secession is popular now as never before.

3 The 'New Tribalism'

In my youth it was a popular idea that the world was joining together into larger and larger units and that eventually, therefore, there would be a world state, with a world government, and peace would reign for evermore. Movements, of which Federal Union was perhaps the best known, were formed to promote this process.

Anyone looking round today could hardly fail to note the ever more rapid growth of just the opposite trend: the splitting of large units into smaller ones, and the subsequent further fission of these. Thus when India left the British Commonwealth, it split into two: India and Pakistan. Pakistan then divided, giving rise to Bangladesh. Nepal tried to split off but was forcibly prevented. Similarly in Africa, the half-dozen great states of fifty years ago have fragmented into a memory-taxing welter of new principalities, many of which are now busy crushing dissident minorities—and in at least one case majorities: the Sanwi, the Ewe, the Ovambos. Biafra is still fresh in memory. In Ethiopia, the province of Eritrea is riven by civil war. The Somalis in the south are demanding independence. (Amost unnoticed, an Eritrean guerrilla force, trained by Libya, did a million pounds worth of damage to Abyssinian copper mines.) In the Middle East, the Kurds are currently fighting for independence from Iraq.

When we turn to Europe, the picture is no different. In Britain, movements calling for self-government in Wales and Scotland are gaining strength. Eire of course has already left the Union, and Ulster seems on the brink. Cornwall is now beginning to raise its voice. In France, Bretons now place a B on the back of their cars to signify their desire for recognition as a cultural entity (and similarly in Languedoc), while when M. Messmer, as French Foreign Minister, visited Corsica in 1974, the crowds carried banners saying 'French out'. In Belgium, tensions have existed between the Flemings and the French-speaking population for centuries and show no signs of abating. Spanish Basques are fighting for their cultural identity. Canada faces the prospect of losing French-speaking Quebec. In Switzerland the Jura is demanding independence.

The basis of these movements is always awareness of the possession of a unique cultural identity. I can say from personal knowledge that the desire of the Scots or the Welsh for self-government is not based simply on the belief that a regional government would be more responsive to local wishes, but on pride in local uniqueness, which is seen to be threatened. This is why the use of Gaélic language is insisted on so strongly by Welsh, Scottish and Irish nationalists. The objections now being made by the Welsh to the growing number of English settling there also reflects a fear of their cultural impact. A similar fear is being voiced in the north of Scotland, as a result of the discovery of oil. Pride is also felt in other marks of community identity, such as special kinds of food or clothing (porridge and the kilt in Scotland) and cultural expressions, such as traditional songs and music (the bagpipes or the Welsh harp). It is important to understand that loss of communal indentity is felt as a loss of personal identity: the man who tells an Englishman with pride 'I am a Scot' thereby asserts a measure of individuality. He is that much less a cipher in an increasingly anonymous world.

This psychological need explains much of the opposition to the wave of immigration which has hit some countries, such as Switzerland (where there are 1.6m. foreigners in a population of 6.3m.) and Britain. When in any local community, the cultural strangers exceed some ten per cent of the population, communal stress is felt. Since many of the British immigrants have been coloured, the reaction is often seen as colour prejudice, and no doubt this is sometimes a factor. However, in Switzerland, where the foreigners are largely Italian, or in Wales, where they are mainly English, colour is clearly not the explanation; neither can it explain, say, Corsican separatism or the struggles of the Kurds.

I have little doubt that British hesitation to enter the European Common Market is mainly motivated by the feeling that national identity will be diminished (as indeed it has been already) and that decisions will be taken even further from the communities they affect by people with even less understanding of these deep-lying but poorly verbalised requirements.

Secession is only feasible where the cultural group has clear geographic boundaries. The American blacks' demand for recognition of their cultural identity is a clear-cut example of what happens when one cultural group becomes dispersed in another. Another is the Jewish Diaspora. One can hardly doubt that if American blacks had happened to live in a single area with a clear-cut frontier, they would by now have demanded independence. It is not impossible that in the future there will be a demand for the establishment of all-black areas, echoing the demand of many whites to preserve their neighbourhoods as all-white. One might also prophesy that Hawaii, as a culturally unique sub-area, will one day hanker for independence.

In the past, emigration was a possibility for dissatisfied sub-groups thanks to the existence of fertile, unoccupied lands in America. Today that solution is more or less unavailable. Hence trouble brews.

The USA, which has always had a high immigration rate and whose cultural history is relatively short, has much more experience of cultural and social fragmentation, which is why social pathology, as expressed in crime rates, etc., is worse than in Europe. But this has the result that Americans, being used to cultural chaos, often find it hard to understand what the fuss is about—why Europe is so slow to unite, for instance. These two not-quite-identical trends have been deprecatingly dubbed 'the new tribalism'. The term 'tribalism' implies, I take it, that they represent a return to a more primitive system, a swimming against the current, a kind of social Ludditism.

People's resistance to cultural break-up on the regional level is echoed by their resistance to the break-up of communities, where the preservation of group structure and local loyalties become the primary motive. It is an encouraging sign that ordinary people seem to be increasingly aware of the high social and personal cost of breaking up local communities and to be making active efforts to resist it. Strong opposition is now mounted to official plans to drive motorways through cities (the London ring-road scheme was a particularly crass instance) or to the placing of new airports in heavily settled areas. In France, the bitter local resistance to placing nuclear weapon silos on the Larzac plateau provides a perfect example.

Social cohesion is not something we can sacrifice blandly. If a man who is ill struggles to get back his health, we do not tell him that he is attempting to live in the past, to return to a golden age which has vanished, and enjoin him to resign himself to increasingly poor health as the price of progress. This misrepresents the issue. The key question is: can we actually hold an incoherent society together much longer by any means short of dictatorship?

In short, global disassembly is a more probable trend than the long-dreamed-of 'brotherhood of man, the federation of the world' of Tennyson's vision. In 1950 there were 90 nations in the United Nations; today there are 132. When shall we reach 200? A significant development to watch for will be the disintegration of the European Common Market (or Economic Community). Perhaps before then a new conqueror will have reversed the trend, extending the Pax Russorum' or Pax Sinorum over half the world.

4 A Guide to Governing

For a government to be 'legitimate' three conditions at least are necessary. As they don't seem very well understood, even by governments, I shall now enumerate them.

First, a leader must devote himself to helping people to fulfil *their* aims. (A leader, it has been cynically said, is a man who sees a crowd surging down a street and quickly puts himself at their head, crying 'Follow me'.) Our present leaders believe that the one and only objective is material prosperity. Right and Left are in full agreement on this and only differ about who is to get how much. 'You have never had it so good,' is how they bid for our admiration. Now of course material prosperity is important and our material standard of living is something of which we are all aware. But there are other less clearly expressed but nevertheless powerful demands: for liberty, for dignity, for national pride, for a pleasant environment, for public safety and much else. It is precisely in these matters that our leaders fail. It is the attempt to give expression to these non-financial desires which accounts for the countless amenity societies and pressure groups which have sprung up, and for the complaint of lack of consultation which we saw in the opinion-poll replies.

Some left-wing politicians have tried to claim that such demands are a pretentious middle-class form of selfishness: this is an insult to the humanity of the poorer groups. Poverty may force you to put up with your house being filthied by the smoke from a chemical works or made intolerable by the noise of a motorway carried overhead, but it doesn't make it any more agreeable. And the wish to be consulted is uncorrelated with class.

Even less do governments seem to understand such obscurely stated aims as the wish people have to preserve their own culture. Blind to this feeling, or regarding it as an obsolete sentiment, governments constantly act so as to invade and crush local culture, imposing standardised patterns for everything from telephone boxes to old-age pensions. But of all the demands people make, the most fundamental, if the least explicit, is the desire for a purpose in life. All that Right and Left, Republican and Democrat, have to offer is: more prosperity, more GNP. It is not the right bid.

Moreover, the commitment of governments to material growth—and more specifically to the desire of business to make profits—is shown by all sorts of actions: reluctance to restrict heavy commercial vehicles where they are destroying the life, and the property, in small villages provides a good example.

Even at a crude material level, governments show little ability to identify with popular feelings. In most countries, opinion polls show clearly that price stability and better housing are of vastly more importance to people than Channel tunnels, entry into the Common Market, the nationalisation of industry and all the folderol which takes up legislative time. A shrewd leader would make apparent his intense interest in improving housing. Having activated public opinion he would bring together builders and unions, planners and financiers, to arrive at a plan, create the means, and put it into execution. Shortages would be put under the spotlight and steadily eliminated. As it is, in most countries housing starts are declining.

This brings us to the second requirement of leaders: they must be competent. Mr Heath fell for the same reason as President Allende: he failed to solve the immediate problems. Good intentions are not enough. But while a leader may fall because he fails to cope with a specific challenge, the continuing dissatisfaction with government reflects their failure to cope with the on-going problems of war, public order, environment and other matters I have discussed.

Third—and this is almost always overlooked—people want leaders they can admire and look up to, which means leaders who are not merely honest but selfless. General de Gaulle, for all his quirks, was respected because he undoubtedly put France, and France's reputation, above all personal considerations. His own popularity, public honours, income were matters of little importance to him, as even his severest critics concede. Leaders are father-figures: they can be wilful, unfair, even arrogant, provided they are wholly devoted to their children's welfare; they must be brave and resolute; they can sometimes be petty if they are never mean.

But modern leaders, in addition, are under the mortal delusion that society consists simply of two groups: the electorate and the leadership—the masses and the elite. And that therefore their job is to engage in a dialogue of some kind with the masses. But, as we have seen, a cohesive society is organised into numerous overlapping groups, and decisions are dispersed and taken at many levels. As Patricia Elton Mayo commented, our social problems are not a question of 'the ownership of wealth but rather a crisis in the theory and practice of government'.

What people want, most of all, is a say in matters which affect them directly. They are perfectly happy to leave complex technical matters such as economic policy to experts, aware of their incompetence to judge, just as they do not ask to assist in the running of the power station which supplies their current. It is only when something goes noticeably wrong that, reluctantly, they begin to occupy themselves with these matters. As far as that goes, they are content to leave local administration alone too. The idea, popular in America, that all decisions should be referred to popular judgment (an attachment to the television set by which votes can be signalled back is the latest variant on this theme) is based on a misunderstanding.

Moreover, issues which affect a citizen directly are often local issues: the siting of a new road, for instance. The more such decisions are sucked up to national level, the more helpless the individual feels; and local enquiries, held by a national inspector, with the scales weighted in favour of those who have time and money to prepare their case, are very little satisfaction.

Governments, including the civil servants who take most administrative decisions these days, naturally tend to believe that they are more competent than local bodies; and they have an inbuilt preference for uniformity of treatment. But democracy means the right to take the wrong decision, sometimes, and certainly means the right to decide one's own affairs differently from other groups in a similar situation.

By centralising and imposing uniform practices, governments have not only undermined democracy and ensured their own loss of legitimacy; they have also destroyed social cohesion and made it increasingly difficult to govern. They have created ungovernability.

How have they got themselves into this unworkable position?

5 Sources of Illegitimacy

Legislative incompetence is not difficult to understand when we read the accounts of the shabby manoeuvres, personal vendettas, and open aggression in the memoirs of politicians. A man who has been unusually frank is Leo Abse, who regards much of the behaviour of British MPs as 'clearly pathological'. As debates approach their final stage they are punctuated by 'baying . . . I sit on the benches surrounded and fronted by men screaming puerile insults, distorting each others' motives, falsifying facts, and frequently creating an uproar totally disproportionate to the gap between the parties,' he writes in *Private Member*. But more serious than intramural ill-manners is the obsessive and vengeful attitude of many politicians, to say nothing of their willingness to sacrifice principle to expediency. Some effective filter to remove unsuitable candidates is desperately needed. Letting local party organisations decide favours the bigoted as against the open-minded.

When I first drafted this chapter I wrote many thousands of words analysing the defects of government and citing hideous examples. I spoke of its hypocrisy (e.g., in negotiating treaties and then failing to ratify them, or ratifying and then ignoring them). I mentioned its folly (e.g., in selling arms to countries who are all too likely to precipitate a conflict which could involve the seller). I gave examples of its dishonesty and broken promises (one British politician, when challenged, protested that the public did not *expect* political promises to be fulfilled). I devoted a whole section to its mania for secrecy, and its attempts to push its policies through without public debate when possible, for this is particularly relevant to public disenchant-ment. I also descanted on its incompetence: its readiness to pour public money into projects which no one really wants while neglect-ing those about which people feel deeply (Concorde versus housing). I discussed its tendency to favour one or other section of the com-munity—either capital or labour, as a rule—instead of governing impartially in the interests of all. It was satisfying to write and at the end I had a file of unused notes which would have enabled me to write another chapter equally long and just as scathing.

But anybody who reads the newspapers knows all this stuff—in fact the first mistake that politicians make is to imagine that no one notices what they are doing and saying.

Upon reflection it seemed to me to be more in keeping with the purpose of this book to point to two or three general trends in the nature and functions of government which suggest the conclusion that governments are decreasingly able to carry out their role, even when those they rule give them full cooperation.

Firstly, governments have gradually taken on more and more power. It started when governments arrogated to themselves powers hitherto exercised by universities, guilds, abbots, manors, etc. At the time this was welcomed because it seemed to free the emerging middle class from medieval restrictions. But the process has not stopped and now governments claim the right to legislate in every area of life—and the public accepts that claim, although it was never debated or agreed to. Thus the government takes it upon itself to manage the army and the postal service, once left to private initiative. The government runs education and levies taxes, once the prescriptive right of local bodies. And, another new development, it undertakes to function as the member of an international community.

As Drucker has pointed out, administrations now claim the right to withhold or censor information even in peacetime. They have the power, and use it to create and destroy profitability, to abolish or establish privileges, to seize property, and even to create it or annihilate it, as we see in the case of fishing rights, patents, satellite facilities and much else. Even when governments delegate decisions to local authorities, they do so on a provisional basis: the delegated power can be recalled at any time. (Hence the demand which is now beginning to be heard for the unqualified devolution of this excessive power from groups like the Basques and the Scots.)

Unfortunately governments have neither the time nor the skill—sometimes not even the wish—to wield so much power. 'No government functions adequately,' as Peter Drucker remarks, whether it be socialist, liberal, communist or democratic. All managements know that you must delegate if you are not to be swamped, but governments have no suitable bodies to delegate to, having emasculated local government and local organisations. (Technology, as we have seen, has contributed to this emasculation not only by destroying local communities but by creating urban constellations which have to be administered as single units—but which are already too large for an effective grass roots democracy.) It is this remorseless centralisation which makes the electorate feel helpless, ignored and out-of-touch.

This brings us to the second factor: the never-ending growth of bureaucracy. To an increasing extent decisions are being transferred from parliaments and senates, where there is at least a measure of public discussion, to 'faceless' bureaucrats whose decisions are seldom explained, much less discussed in public. 'Executive secrecy' is used as a weapon to prevent informed criticism of the decisions taken by the 'coalition between Ministers and the 3,000 or so members of the Administrative Grade of the Civil Service'. In addition, 'Parliamentary privilege' and the alleged inviolability of files and records are also invoked to this end. Anyone who has spoken to members of the dominant elite knows that they feel wholly confident of their ability to run the place if only the people being run would kindly refrain from arguing. Their job is to do as they are told without protest. Daddy knows best. It is a kind of crypto-authoritarianism.

As the sociologist Weber, whose analysis is the fountainhead for thought on the subject, realised, bureaucracy is indestructible and ever-growing. A military *coup* may change the nominal masters, but the machine has a will of its own. No one knows how to reverse the trend. No one knows how to make bureaucracies efficient in terms of human welfare rather than mere economics.

In reality, efficiency is not the point. Dostoevsky put his finger on the spot when he said: 'And how do these wiseacres know that men want a normal or a virtuous choice? What has made them conceive that man wants a rationally advantageous choice? What man wants is simply *independent* choice, whatever that independence may cost and wherever it may lead.' That is what secession is about and what communes are about. And it is also something that socialist reformers do not understand.

While the social process slowly bogs down in a self-sufficient morass the ever more rapid pace of events imposes on these hypertrophied structures the need to respond far more rapidly than in the past. I am thinking here not of political crises but of social changes. For instance, Britain continued to build isolation hospitals for tuberculosis patients long after modern drugs had begun to wipe tuberculosis out. An administration which applies corrections to trends which have already reversed themselves, as often happens in the economic area, only makes matters worse. Britain's vacillations of policy concerning nuclear power are a case in point. First, plans to build oil-burning power stations were cancelled, in the belief that nuclear energy would supply most of the power by the seventies, then restored when it emerged that this was a pipe-dream, then cut back, when oil grew more costly.

The life of parliaments is short compared with the twenty years or more of most social changes. This makes parliaments uninterested in changes which will only pay off electorally after their demise.

Having so much to do and under pressure to decide quickly, one might have expected parliaments (and bureaucracies, for that matter) to have streamlined their methods. Even in the simplest mechanical sense they are antiquated. Time is wasted in filing in and out to record votes which could well be recorded electronically. No industrial firm would tolerate the poor communications, office facilities, and obsolete ceremonial which distinguishes European, if not American, governmental processes. 'The working conditions in Parliament are grotesque' complained Eric Moonman, Labour MP for Basildon. 'I have spoken to many new MPs who felt that they were cheated; that they could not do the sort of job that they were able to do and felt that they had been elected to do, because of poor servicing.' But more serious than obsolete techniques is the time-wasting procedure.* Months of work may be done on a bill which

---

* A remarkable television programme, made by Britain's Granada Television in 1973, showed how the government of the day forced through a Fair Trading Bill, in defiance of criticism and objections by members of Parliament, while scrupulously observing the

is then dropped because the time available has run out—an abuse cheerfully referred to as 'the massacre of the innocents'.

Unfortunately, governments are unlikely to correct their faults. Whereas every other organisation has some superior to look at it dispassionately, there is no body with the authority to shake up parliaments, do time and motion studies, or devise better systems of recruitment. Upper chambers, which occasionally offer mild criticism, are being gradually enfeebled by governments too arrogant to accept even minor rebukes. The only control over governments is the power, still retained in a few democracies, to pass a vote of 'no confidence' in the whole boiling. And that is what is now happening.

6 Backlash or Crypto-fascism?

Governments, whether my analysis is correct or not, are certainly undergoing a steady loss of legitimacy. Coupled with the growing alienation of many people from society as a whole, this haemorrhage is likely to prove fatal. A system which can produce a leader of such little integrity as Richard Nixon can hardly retain respect. Even if industrial obstruction does not force an immediate issue, it looks as if, long before the end of the century, the remaining democratic governments may find that their mandate has finally run out.

We have already discussed one possibility: that a period of industrial chaos may develop out of which an authoritarian leadership could emerge to restore order. However, if industrial chaos is avoided, we might also see dictatorship achieved legitimately, by the election of a strong leader, as happened in Germany, or—and this is the most probable—we may see a 'creeping authoritarianism' in which more and more central control is gradually introduced and more and more liberties are eroded. While this would probably be backed by traditionally conservative and rightist feeling, the example of Sri Lanka (Ceylon) shows that it is not impossible to have a creeping authoritarianism of the left. A movement of this kind usually starts by restricting the freedom of the media, and by close control of personal movement; the power to deprive rebellious individuals of employment is a major weapon in countries where the state is the sole or main employer.

However, history suggests that left-wing movements arise where a working class is oppressed, and right-wing movements where a middle class is threatened. Today, in most developed countries, it

conventions of scrutiny and debate. None of the major amendments proposed in committee was accepted by the government, which sent the bill forward virtually in its original form. 'So you felt your four and a half months were wasted time?' one committee member, Mr Philip Whitehead, was asked. 'Totally,' he replied.

is the middle class which is under pressure, which suggests that the movement will generally be to the right. It is not only the financial squeezing which the middle class is suffering but the threatening of their entire value-system, now scathingly dismissed as 'bourgeois', which suggests to some that they must soon make a last-ditch stand. This is certainly the case in the United States, where strong rightist groups exist and the left is weak. In the event of a serious economic recession, outbreaks of violence will rapidly become serious—the days of oil shortage are proof of that. Violence, as everyone knows, evokes a demand for the restoration of 'law and order'.

Professor Stanislaw Andreski, who has taught in the US and in Britain, has examined the outlook in his *Prospects of a Revolution in the USA*. He considers that a revolution, in the proper sense, is improbable. The students are too undisciplined to offer any serious threat, the blacks and underprivileged too disorganised and disunited. He concludes that the privileged class should have little difficulty in maintaining its dominant position, but he takes very seriously the prospect of 'a long slide into totalitarianism'. Of course, no political party in America is going to claim to be anything but democratic—the Weathermen and the John Birch society, poles apart in everything else, agree on being in favour of democracy.

The machinery of repression is ready to hand. Given a decision by the two main political parties to collaborate in an emergency, the existence of computer and other records, together with the co-ordination of the FBI, CIA, police, security guards and vigilante posses organised by right-wing groups, would make it possible to impose control on the entire population. (John Brunner has imagined the details in *The Sheep Look Up*: curfew, surrender of all guns, seizure of food stocks, compulsory military service and so on.)

The computerisation of personal records has made the task of control vastly easier. Whereas Hitler had to go to devious lengths to identify those who had voted against him before he came to power, today the information collected in computer memory banks makes the task of supervision much simpler. (Britons protesting against census enquiries relating to their racial origins were assured that this information would never be misused. Apparently the possibility that a less nice government might one day come to power was not even considered by the Registrar-General.) As the computer security expert Peter Hamilton has noted, 'The greatest danger posed by people misusing computers is not intrusion into privacy, nor fraud, nor industrial espionage, but subversion—the overthrow of democracy.'

In America, 'the odds are that the social evils and disorders will grow until the strongest gang restores order on the basis of ruthless coercion,' says Andreski. 'Not forgetting what they have learned from the advertisers, they will, no doubt, invent for themselves a sublime-sounding name, like the New Democracy or the Revolution of Freedom, but, owing to the erosion of all ideals, the regime might resemble an enlarged Haiti with a vast corps of computerised Tonton Macoutes, rather than the doctrinaire totalitarianism of a Lenin or a Hitler.'

In France and Italy, while there are rightist groups, there is also a strong left, and democracy could fall off the fence on either side. Though Italy is the weaker economically, and will doubtless fall off first, France has a centralising tradition far stronger than Italy's, extending back to Napoleon, and might prove the pace-setter in such a movement.

Britain may be the exception, following the model of Ceylon, by combining crypto-fascism with a leftish ideology and industrial dystrophy. There are a number of right-wing groups, some primarily anti-Semitic, some primarily anti-Communist (but not fascist, being for economic liberalism rather than the corporate state) yet others patriotic in a traditional way. Others, however, are frankly fascist and are linked with fascist and neo-Nazi groups abroad. Many of these groups are at loggerheads: for instance, the World Anti-Communist League has been fighting against infiltration by anti-Semites and neo-Nazis. However, early in 1974, a number of rightist groups merged under the title The Independent Democratic Movement; behind this merger was Air Vice-Marshal Donald Bennett. But the leader capable of uniting these disparate gangs does not seem to have emerged and the £1m. fighting fund which Bennett controls remains uncommitted.

Thus the right does not, in Britain, constitute a faction as does the left. Though business interests can exert pressure on the government, there is no block vote by which the politically neutral can be entrained; no machinery for the open definition of rightist policy and strategy, such as labour has long had.

The situation is very different in Italy, where the right is much more active than the left. In addition to the extreme right-wing party, the Italian Social Movement, which is represented in Parliament by 26 senators and 56 deputies, and gets 10 per cent of the votes, there are extreme groups like Ordine Nero which claim credit for many of the recent bombings, including the train explosion near Bologna in which 12 people were killed. 'The Nazi flag did not die in Berlin back in 1945,' it announced afterwards. 'It still continues to live for a greater Italy, Fascist and Nazi.'

If the centre allies itself with the left, a protracted struggle seems probable, with rioting and street fighting as things go from bad to worse. The first street fighting is breaking out in Rome as I write.

Whether they understand what they are doing or not, governments are preparing the ground for the establishment of totalitarianism. As we saw in Chapter VIII, the preconditions for totalitarianism are the existence of a 'mass' dominated by an 'elite'. By redistributing wealth and income in the name of equality, by weakening local authority and by centralising power, by breaking up local communities in the name of slum-clearance or pushing through vast urban road schemes which split communities in half, by minimising class and cultural differences, governments, perhaps unwittingly, prepare the way for dictatorship.

Another of the tools of totalitarianism, as Hannah Arendt points out, is to create insecurity and uncertainty what to do. Governments contrive this by constantly altering the law, so that dispositions made one year prove inappropriate the next. Particularly objectionable is retrospective legislation, increasingly used in Britain. Governments tend to become increasingly authoritarian, overruling public opinion quite ruthlessly, as instanced by the introduction of 'comprehensive' schools in Britain, in the face of parental objections; or of 'bussing' in America.

Every society of which we have records has attempted to instill into the younger generation the sentiments necessary for social cohesion to be maintained. What worried Andreski (and worries me) is that for the first time in history we have, in the technological society, a system 'which has not only given up altogether the task of moral education, but actually employs vast resources and the means of persuasion of unprecedented power to destroy the customs, norms and ideals indispensable for its survival; and to implant fundamentally anti-social attitudes which are incompatible with any conceivable social order. It would be miraculous,' he concludes, 'if a social order which permits such massive anti-socialisation could fail to destroy itself.'

These are conclusions similar to my own, though I believe that it is Britain which will lead the way rather than the USA, both because its living standards are much more likely to suffer a decline than those of the US; because the destruction of 'intermediate structures' has gone further than in the States, where state and city managements are far stronger than county and city managements in Britain; and because the dominant elite in Britain, though less corrupt than in the US, is even less competent.

It is in conditions of social disturbance, then, that our less-than-competent governments will have to try to meet the external threats which will face them during the next twenty years.

They are not unfamiliar: in my estimation, the main problems will be a temporary resource shortage, third-world difficulties due to the onset of famine, and the pollution problems which will follow a solution of the energy crisis. But they need to be reassessed in the light of what we now know.

PART V

Practical Problems

XII

SCARCER?

*Central to our conception of the Prospects of Mankind
Study is an assumption that there are enough raw
materials for all, and (with reasonable decisions and
practices) no disastrous pollution problems either . . .
The first assumption was a fact.—Anthony J. Wiener
of the Hudson Institute, 1973*

1 Running Out of Everything

As I write this, my stationery supplier tells me he is out of shorthand
notebooks and expects no fresh stock for six months. My publisher
is uncertain when this book will be published, because of a world
shortage of paper. Of course, newsprint is not the only thing in short
supply. In late 1973 the National Association of Manufacturers in
America put out a poster: 'Yes we have no bananas, steaks, eggs,
blue jeans, candles, gas, tennis-balls, freezers, wheat, leather, air-
conditioners, fuel oil, pyjamas, floor-covering, sardines, chicken,
paper, hot-water bottles. . . .' In Europe shortages were beginning
to appear in some areas quite apart from wood-pulp—notably
plastics.

How far are these shortages temporary effects due to the fuel
crisis or to failure to foresee demand? Some of them certainly are.
Thus Britain's paper supplies are produced on half a dozen gigantic,
automated machines costing around £15m. apiece. Because of the
high capital cost, they must be run continuously. Moreover, once
stopped, the whole machine must be cleaned out, each of its 380 or
so rollers being removed and cleaned. The boiler which converts
wood fragments to pulp must be run for several days before the
mixture is smooth again and the paper which emerges of acceptable
quality. All in all, a shut-down and a restart can cost over £1m.

Naturally the management does not start up one of these machines until it can foresee a market for its entire output for an indefinite period ahead. As I have already indicated, the rise in commodity prices has been due in large measure to the fact that so many nations launched into a boom simultaneously. It takes time to expand mining and agricultural operations to meet greatly enlarged demand. If a simultaneous slump occurs, commodity prices, already on the downswing, could drop much further, causing serious problems to under-developed countries.

Other current shortages are due, at least in part, to the energy crisis; and since petroleum is the basis from which many synthetic materials are made, the crisis is two-edged. Thus American plywood firms were forced to lay off employees because they could not get natural gas or propane to dry the wood, nor the glue they needed owing to the petrochemical shortage. Packaging makes another bottleneck. Lipsticks are out of stock because plastic for the containers is unavailable. Toothpaste is difficult to get because there is no lead for tubes, Coca-Cola—no glass for bottles; tinned goods—no tins. The copper shortage, on the other hand, is due to failure to build more capacity because copper prices sank below the profitability point (around £500 a ton) in 1971. Five years ago copper stood at £250 a ton. Today, after soaring to a record £1,350 a ton, it is less than half that.

THE STOCK ANSWER

'I've tried five different suppliers for coloured Wellington boots and just cannot get them,' says a shoe retailer in Wales. A woman in Middlesex asked a chemist for a nail file. 'We haven't got them—it's the steel shortage.' A stationer reported a 50-week waiting list for manilla envelopes. A vicar of a Surrey parish has been trying for weeks to buy 100 cups and saucers for his village hall. Shops may be unable to get spare parts; a shopkeeper in East Kilbride has been waiting six months for a manufacturer to supply him with TV base panels. Do-it-yourselfers are finding it hard to get the screws and nails they need. . . .

Ronald Halstead, president of the Food Manufacturers' Association, has warned: 'If we do not have more cash to-day there will be a shortage of food tomorrow.'

Sunday Times 6 October 1974

But are current shortages really only temporary? Not only copper but a wide range of raw materials have risen in an unprecedented manner. Zinc, for instance, rose in a single year from £160 to £490 a ton. Tin hit £2,000 a ton in mid-1973. *The Economist* index of commodity prices, which started life in 1860 around 120 and which was fluctuating in the 350–500 range during the fifties and sixties, suddenly zoomed to over 900 and is still in the 800–900 range. Since industrialisation began, nothing like this has been seen except during the last stages of a major war. Some part of the rise is due to real shortages.

Experts are gloomy. 'As we approach the final quarter of the century, global scarcity of many important resources is emerging. The energy crisis has been occupying the headlines, but scarcity of other resources is now apparent too,' writes Lester R. Brown, a senior fellow of the Overseas Development Council and author of *Seeds of Change*. The fact is, the world's industrial nations are hungry not only for oil, but for copper, zinc and phosphates. John Morgan of the US Bureau of Mines was greeted with disbelief when he said that a US minerals crisis was 'only a short distance down the road', adding that the cumulative effects of current trends 'deserve far more attention from the industry powers than they are receiving at present'.

Other experts, naturally, are optimistic. The American Institute for Resources for the Future sees no immediate crises in view, with the possible exception of water supplies, arguing that greater economy of use and substitution of alternative materials will solve all problems. (However, as Lester Brown points out, in today's world the attempt to make substitutions frequently ensures only that scarcity is contagious.) Senator John Tunney (California) who chaired the subcommittee on Science and Technology, has attacked those who, like the economist, Professor Beckerman, dismiss the materials crisis as 'ecodoomsters', saying that expert after expert has warned his committee that a disastrous materials crisis is looming.

Euphoria reached a peak in *The Economist* which solemnly declared in mid-1974: 'Even if there are no improvements in existing technology, the world is not likely to be threatened with a physical shortage of raw materials until about AD 100,000,000.' The rapture induced by this news is qualified by the warning that one will have to mine the entire surface of the earth to a depth of one mile for this purpose, which surely will call for some novel technology—even if only with respect to growing food plants on granite chippings.

Ignoring these unverifiable journalistic flights of fancy, let us concentrate our attention on the next twenty years or so. The question which matters is: shall we actually succeed in mining and refining the metals we need, and in growing the timber, etc., in the face of the technical, economic and political obstacles which confront us?

2 Access is the Issue

The optimists base their optimism on the assumption that there is always plenty more of everything to be discovered. Thus Professor Beckerman dismisses the copper shortage, saying that thirty years ago reserves were estimated at 100m. tons; since then we have consumed 80m. tons, but reserves stand at 300m. tons. 'Known reserves' are, it is quite true, a poor guide to the future, because there are generally unknown reserves too—though as we shall see in the next section, there are many minerals further supplies of which are failing to materialise. But where the optimists really seem to be going wrong is in assuming that the countries which own these reserves will be willing to make them freely available. The good old days, when mining companies could move into a foreign country, buy a concession and start work with cheap local labour (and be thanked for providing employment) are now over. Owners of resources, like Canada, ask themselves at what rate it would be wise to deplete those resources. Others, like the Arab states in the case of oil, see the opportunity to force prices up by creating artificial scarcities, while husbanding resources at the same time.

For instance, producers of bauxite, from which aluminium is made, have been putting their heads together. At a conference in Conakry, the capital of Guinea, early in 1974, President Ahmed Sekou Touré of Guinea proposed an international association of bauxite producers 'to achieve a review of the prices of our raw materials'. Furthermore, he said, they should refine the bauxite to aluminium in their own territories and sell the finished product. The four copper-producing countries are already following the Arab example, while Chile, Peru, Zaire and Zambia are believed to have asked the Arabs to stockpile copper in order to ensure that current sky-high prices are maintained, which provides a model for another kind of third-world cooperation.

Phosphates and rubber, not to mention soft commodities such as coffee, cocoa and sugar, have also been mentioned as possible subjects for cartellisation. Currently, North African phosphate producers are forming a cartel to restrict exports of this indispensable fertiliser; coffee exporters are bargaining collectively while Brazil has restricted coffee production to the point where she may actually become an importer!

In January 1974, President Mobuto Sese Seko of Zaire put the whole thing in general terms, calling bluntly for African solidarity to force up the prices of raw materials. Pointing to the success of the Arab nations in imposing higher prices for oil, General Mobutu

declared: 'We have our copper, potash, our diamonds, gold and our
cocoa. If we agreed that the prices of all these raw materials should
be fair, we could impose our view.'

The Brookings Institute sums the situation up thus: four countries
possess 80 per cent of the world's copper; two countries possess 70 per
cent of the tin; four countries possess 50 per cent of the rubber; and
four countries own over 50 per cent of the bauxite.

Asia is rich in tin, in which the US is very poor. (But as against
this, Asia seems short of molybdenum, in which America is rather
well supplied.) Russia has nickel, manganese and lead, but imports
bauxite and has no natural rubber. Again, most of the world's
mercury is in Spain, Italy and parts of the Communist countries;
industrial diamonds come mainly from the Congo, and over half the
world's recoverable reserves of tin are in Indonesia, Malaya and
Thailand—and most of the rest in Bolivia and the Congo. Another
metal which could be used as a bargaining counter is nickel; well
over half the world's known reserves are in Cuba and New Caledonia.

Counterpointing the strength of many under-developed countries
is the resource-weakness of the leading developed nations. The worst-
placed of the industrialised countries is certainly Japan. Although
Japan only holds three per cent of the world's population, she buys
about a quarter of the world's exported natural resources. The rate
has been increasing by about 20 per cent per annum; if this continues, by 1980 Japan will be taking half the world's marketed
resources, and that would go for oil too. 'This is absolutely impossible,' says the Study Group for International Planning in Japan
which has produced a report calling, in view of these facts coupled
with the pollution situation, for a complete rejig of Japan's industrial structure. It says that many industries should be abolished,
including: oil refining, petrochemical fertilisers, primary steel-
making, light passenger car manufacture, except for export; pulp
and paper production; and chemical processes liable to discharge
mercury, arsenic and other dangerous effluents. This amounts to a
complete reversal of Japanese industrial policy. Japan's Federation
of Economic Organisations, deeply shocked, has set up a committee
to study the question.

The position of the USA is becoming hardly less critical than that
of Japan. It now imports all, or nearly all, of its platinum, mica,
chromium, strontium, cobalt, tantalum, bauxite and manganese. It
imports more than half of its fluorine, titanium, asbestos, tin,
bismuth, nickel, columbium and antimony, and more than a third
of its iron ore, up from eight per cent in 1950, according to Carroll
Kilpatrick in the *Washington Post*. By 1980 the list will be longer.
This need for minerals will play an increasing role in the balance-of-

payments situation. Sherman Clark, director of Energy and Resource Economics at Stanford Research Institute, estimates that 'between 1969 and 1980, the total annual mineral imports may nearly quadruple, going from about $8 billion in 1969 to as much as $30 billion (in constant 1969 dollars) by 1980'. This is not far from the value of *all* US exports today.

According to Maurice Strong, Executive Director of the UN Environment Programme, 'In one decade, 1959–68, the United States used more resources than all the world's people in all previous years. From the beginning of mankind to the end of World War II, the output of all the world's industry totalled less than will be produced by the next three years of industrialisation.'

The optimists speak of resource substitution and point to plastics as the substitute for traditional materials. Unfortunately plastics are already in short supply—as LP collectors know all too well—because most of them come from petroleum, via benzine. The immediate shortage is due to failure to commission enough plant, but, in an article titled 'Chemicals and the Oil Crisis', Martin Sherwood tells us: 'There is also no doubt that in the future organic chemicals—and ultimately everything that is manufactured from them—will cost significantly more.' Whereas the United States uses at present mainly natural gas as a feedstock, Europe, having far less gas, is obliged to use naphtha, in rapidly rising quantities. Britain, which now consumes about 45 million tons a year, is expected to need 80 million by the end of the decade for petrochemical purposes, while the need for naphtha for petrol will be 184 million tons—or, if lead-free petrol becomes standard, as much as 196 million tons.

And for certain materials there *are* no substitutes. Mercury and helium are unique; so are thorium and uranium. Platinum is virtually irreplaceable. Aluminium can substitute for copper in cables but not easily in electric motors nor as piping—and has the extreme drawback that it cannot easily be soldered, welded or brazed. We must face the fact that many essential raw materials are going to be scarce or expensive or both.

3 'Vitamin' Metals

The argument that substitutes can always be found if resources really run short is not always valid, and in particular it is untrue for certain metals only required in small quantities but essential to the making of alloys with required properties. Chromium, vanadium and molybdenum, needed for making special steels, are an obvious example and have been called the 'vitamin' metals for this reason. The US is already so short of chromium that it has had to import it from Russia, which is plentifully supplied, and it is an irony that some of the US bombs which fell on Vietnam contained Russian chromium.

Another unique resource is mercury, the only metal which is also a liquid, which is essential for various kinds of switchgear, certain industrial processes, and where its high coefficient of expansion is important, as in thermometers. Most of the world's high-grade mercury mines have been worked out—some large deposits remain in Spain and Italy. World reserves at $200 a flask were estimated to last until 1980 only, at current consumption rates. But consumption in the US has been increasing at three per cent per annum. At $1,000 a flask, the supply might be stretched to fifty years or so.

A further vital resource is helium, needed for arc welding, to pressure fuel tanks in rockets, and for the helium–oxygen mixture breathed by deep-sea divers—but much more importantly in the near future for cooling nuclear reactors, and for the transmission of electricity by superconductive techniques. It also has many uses in research and provides the inert atmosphere in which crystals are grown. So crucial is it that the US Department of the Interior set up a conservation programme to store the helium produced as a by-product in the extraction of natural gas. In 1974, however, the unbelievably stupid course of scrapping this programme was taken, on grounds of economy, and this irreplaceable substance now bubbles off into the sky.

Helium demonstrates the weakness in the argument that a rising price evokes further supplies. Helium is present in natural gas— sometimes. In the US there is one field, Pinta Dome, which contains helium at a concentration of 8.2 per cent by volume. Then there are a few small fields (Mesa and Hogback, in New Mexico) which contain helium at about 5.5 per cent. When this has gone you have to move to fields where it ranges from 0.3 to 1.0 per cent, such as those at Hugoton and in the Texas Panhandle. Other fields contain either no helium or less than 0.05 per cent. Finally, you can try to wring it out of ordinary air where it is present at 0.0005 per cent— and no one ever thought of a way to make *that* commercial.

Aside from small amounts of heavy helium produced in reactors, by the end of the century we may be desperately trying to synthesise it from hydrogen—'a process,' comments Professor Preston Cloud dryly, 'whose practical feasibility and adequacy remain to be established'.

The weakness of the higher price/increased supplies argument is also shown in the case of mercury. In the US consumption has doubled every 23 years, but the price increase needed to ensure that the demand was met was more than 500 per cent. In fact, in 1965 when prices soared to $800 a flask (and averaged $500 over the year), slightly *less* mercury was produced than in 1947 when the average price was a beggarly $83.

It is too often assumed that lower grades of ore are present in much larger amounts than the high grades, so that to get a given amount of metal one simply has to process more. That this is not necessarily so is also shown by mercury. Thus, during World War II, the us Geological Survey, investigating mercury resources, reported that it had found 370,000 tons of rock containing nearly 3,000 tons of mercury. After this, there was an ore-body of 1,220,000 tons, containing only 1,500 tons of mercury (that is, 2.5 lb/ton as against 16.2 lb/ton in the richer rock). Then, and this is the joker, there was 285,000 tons of rock containing a mere 228 tons of mercury, less than one ton in every thousand tons of rock.

Let us try to quantify some of these resource-scarcities.

According to the us Bureau of Mines, the lifetimes of 'apparent recoverable reserves' at currently minable grades and at existing rates of consumption for a number of common minerals are about as follows:

	us	World
Lead	1976	1986
Platinum	1970	1987
Silver	1974	1987
Gold	1975	1987
Zinc	1982	1988
Copper	1990	2001
Tungsten	1979	2002

Note the qualifications: 'currently minable grades', which means that lifetimes can be extended by turning to poorer grades, but these are harder to refine, which implies higher prices; 'apparent reserves', which means those known to exist—but new ore-fields may well be discovered in remote parts of the world, notably Australia, China and Russia; and 'existing use rates', which will certainly be exceeded as the third world industrialises and the rich world gets richer. The first two extend lifetimes, the third reduces them.

However, there are large quantities of lead, zinc and copper at grades which are not currently economic. The us Geological Survey estimates 1.275 million tons of zinc if money is no object—a 25 per cent price rise would increase resources by 30 per cent.

It is also interesting to note some minerals of which the us is now extremely short (as are some other industrialised countries) although world supplies are still adequate:

	US	World
Tin	1970	1990
Nickel	1972	2085
Manganese	1970	2100
Cobalt	1989	2120
Aluminium	1974	2140
Chromium	1970	2500

It is quite clear that nations which have largely exhausted domestic supplies will be very much at the mercy of the latecomers in the industrial race who still have the desired materials.

While no one can tell what new ore-bodies will be discovered, we can be quite sure that demand will increase dramatically, since virtually all estimates up to now have been far too conservative. Thus the Paley Report on resources published in 1952 forecast that consumption of lead in the non-Communist world would rise from 0.8 million tonnes in 1952 to 1.3 million by 1975. In actual fact, it passed the 2 million mark as early as 1969. Similarly, zinc was expected to rise from 1.0 to 1.5 million tonnes but hit 2.8 million, while steel was to go from 63 million to 127 million but has reached 289 million. A. G. Charles of the British Metal Corporation believes that by the end of the century annual demand for copper (which was 5 million tons in the late sixties) will have reached no less than 20 million tons, while that for aluminium (8 million in the late sixties) will attain a startling 70 million tons.

But it is not simply the fact that income per head is rising—equally important is the growth of population. India's population is expected to double in the next twenty-seven years—as, indeed, is the world's population. Even if income per head does no more than double, that means a quadrupled demand for raw materials, at least.

It is this zooming demand which makes the argument 'more will be found' a weak one. In the next twenty years we shall have to discover more of these minerals than the whole amount discovered hitherto—and obviously the most easily accessible ore-bodies are exploited first. And even when the ore is found, production facilities will have to be built at a tremendous rate. Mineral economists talk about an investment of $6 billion a year. If the new ore-bodies are in remote places, new railways, freighters, ports and other transport facilities may have to be created. It is evident that shortage and higher prices are inevitable in the near future, whatever the further future may hold and even if no difficulties are made by countries possessing the wanted minerals.

A balanced view comes from Professor W. O. Alexander, head of the metallurgy department of Britain's University of Aston, who thinks that in general the basic metals, along with concrete and timber, will be in adequate supply at least until the year 2000, provided the have-not nations do not jump ahead. Even so, he predicts that 'copper will become almost a precious metal, and its use for electrical applications will give way more and more to aluminium, sodium and possibly even iron'. And while steel will remain the metal used where large quantities of metal are required, it may have to yield to reinforced concrete where large structures are concerned. In the second half of the next century, however, 'timber and concrete may be all that is available in sufficient quantities' for building construction.

4 Wealth from the Sea?

A vast submersible barge, built behind locked doors in California by Lockheed, appeared off the coast of Nicaragua in 1973, together with its mother ship, the *Glomar Challenger*, the world's most advanced marine mining vessel. They were the spearhead of millionaire Howard Hughes' attempt to harvest the rich mineral nodules which strew the sea-bed. The potentialities of the sea-bed as a mineral resource have been described in glowing terms: 'Enough strategic minerals to supply man's needs for as far into the future as we can see,' rhapsodised the *Observer*'s correspondent Charles Foley, 'and at a fraction of today's prices . . . The nodules . . . carpet the ocean in concentrations of 60,000 tons per square mile.' Meanwhile rival companies are building similar ships and are prospecting in the Pacific, Atlantic and Indian Oceans, where the Russians are also at work. The *Los Angeles Times* calls it 'a new gold rush', with fortunes to be made overnight.

Lord Ritchie Calder fears that we shall see private navies operated by giant corporations to protect their claims, like feudal barons, unless an effective law is worked out. 'It isn't hard to see armed conflict between nations as a result. Chile, Zambia and Peru have already denounced this scramble.' In addition there will be serious pollution problems. 'These industrial privateers are going in for a system much like open-cast mining. Some will do their primary refining at sea, dumping acid and alkaline wastes and tailings overboard. Nobody knows what effect this will have on ocean ecology.' No doubt nuclear power will eventually be used on the sea-bed for these mines, while there are plans to build whole cities there—and cities, as we know, produce streams of wastes. 'The Law of the Sea Conference is our one hope,' Calder added.

However, the truth of the matter is that the ocean bed is a good deal less of a bonanza than the optimists claim. Preston Cloud declares: 'a "mineral cornucopia" beneath the sea exists only in hyperbole . . . minerals from the sea-bed are not likely to compare with those yet to be recovered from the emerged lands.' John Mero, president of Ocean Resources Inc. and a deep-sea mining expert, estimates that 100 million tons of nodules would yield, after processing, about 1.5 million tons each of copper and nickel (which are what we need) and about 240,000 tons of cobalt. This would supply a third of the non-Communist world's copper needs, more nickel than it could use and would swamp the market with cobalt and manganese. But it will be many years before ocean mining can recover 100 million tons a year. Most of the known deposits containing more than 1 per cent of copper and nickel are 4,000 to 5,000 metres down, far too deep to mine by any currently available technique, and many of the nodules contain so much silica that they cannot be purified by known methods. If there were such methods, there is plenty of silicaceous manganese rock on dry land which could be exploited.

It has also been alleged that millions of tons of fresh nodules are constantly being formed, but recent work suggests the accretion rate may be only one millimetre in a million years.

Metals are also present in sea-water itself, but the cost of extracting them is prohibitive, even in the case of gold. (The one exception is magnesium.) Eventually some minor elements may be worth extracting (sodium, iodine, etc.) but the outlook is poor for things we really need, such as molybdenum, nickel, tungsten and mercury. Take zinc: you would have to process nine cubic miles of sea-water to get a mere 400 tons of the metal. Says Cloud, 'The practicality of such an operation is not impressive.'

5 Inflation and Inflation

Just as serious as the delays and shortages will be the monetary and financial effects of all this, in every country which has to import a significant fraction of its raw materials. That means Japan above all, Britain close behind, and the us, with France, Germany and many other countries also affected.

If raw materials cost more, the prices of manufactured goods obviously have to rise. Already in October 1973, in Britain the cost of raw materials had risen in one year as follows: electrical engineering 26.2 per cent; mechanical engineering 14 per cent; textiles 32 per cent; timber 54.5 per cent; chemicals 24.5 per cent. Even steel from home sources was up 11 per cent. This was partly due to wage increases, dearer energy and perhaps the reduced working week. Now if we have to add to these trends dramatic increases in the costs of imported materials, probably compounded by working below capacity due to delivery delays, it is clear that prices must rise by several hundred per cent before the situation stabilises.

Behind these price rises lie the price rises of the raw materials themselves: lead up 53 per cent, tin ingot up 45 per cent, zinc up 288 per cent, natural rubber up 73 per cent, raw cotton up 188 per cent, raw wool up 207 per cent, and so on, as against the 1970 levels.

Misleadingly, we use the word inflation to describe two distinct processes. On the one hand we have wage inflation—too much buying power chasing too few goods. Quite a different situation prevails where the cost of purchasing materials from other countries is increasing. To offset these purchases, larger quantities of goods must be exported. In other words, the home population gets less of what it makes. In the economists' phrase, the terms of trade become adverse. Hence, unless internal buying power is cut back somehow, inflation will occur. But we have seen how difficult it is to reduce wages, especially when they are keyed to prices. Yet if prices are allowed to rise, exports become dearer and fail to compete.

In short, raw materials shortages cause internal inflation and adverse trade balances, leading to frantic attempts to find a new level of adjustment. Since many countries will be simultaneously involved in these struggles, their manoeuvres will be mutually defeating. Only real economies in raw material use will have any lasting effect, and the biggest economy of all is to manufacture less. Either way, the standard of living, in conventional material terms, will fall.

6 Survival Plan

As prices of raw materials rise and as inflation bites deeper, economy will become the watchword. The 'throwaway' society will have to rediscover pride in prudence and pride in quality. The currently fashionable disposables will have to be replaced by re-usables. In our grandfather's time, even a bent, used nail was laboriously straightened for use—indeed, I have seen this done myself in my youth. Artificial changes of style intended to make last year's model look obsolete will have to stop. As many writers have documented— notably Vance Packard in his admirable *The Waste Makers*— manufacturers have found many ways of making goods obsolete before their time, such as discontinuing the supply of spare parts or producing attachments which can only be attached to new models. That such shabby methods of marketing are unnecessary is shown by the Polaroid Camera people, who still manufacture their original 95 model, though with many improvements incorporated, and all of whose attachments will fit even the oldest model of camera.

How such changes in long-established marketing policy are to be introduced is an unsolved question. One line of approach would be to oblige manufacturers to give effective guarantees of the life of their products, with penalties for non-observance sufficiently severe to achieve the desired effect. The notorious waste of non-returnable bottles should be corrected: 25 million *returnable* bottles were never returned in Britain last year. But how? By charging much more for them. It has been suggested that old cars would be abandoned less often if a quantity of gold was incorporated in the metal of which they are made, making them really worthwhile turning in. Longer life of products also yields an energy saving. To make a car consumes perhaps 5,000 kW. To make a car which lasted three times as long might take 6,000 kW, thus saving 9,000 kW over the period, whereas recycling would only save about 10 per cent.

The scrap industry, faintly disreputable at present, will need to be seen as a vital activity, as it was in wartime. Britain, in fact, is ahead of many countries in this respect: over half UK steel is reclaimed annually, a similar proportion of lead, and about 40 per cent of the copper. In the US, despite the fact that the railways give more favourable rates for the transport of iron ore than they do for scrap, out of about 35 million tons of ferrous material thrown away annually, some 16 million tons is recycled (46 per cent). Technical considerations limit the amount of scrap a furnace can accept but modifications are possible which would raise the proportion.

Most wastes consist of an awkward mixture of glass, steel, non-ferrous metals and plastics. However, magnetic separators which remove the ferrous constituents have been developed: at present only twenty US cities operate them, and less than 8 per cent of the 48 billion steel cans discarded annually is recovered. Tin is hard to recycle, and only 10 per cent of US tin comes from this source.

However, iron ore is relatively plentiful and it is the non-ferrous components which will become increasingly worth recovering. Government incentives to local authorities to install such plants are needed and would also help to solve the growing problem of finding space to put human wastes. A further bonus would be in energy saving. To make a pound of aluminium from ore requires from 25 to 35 times as much energy as to make it from recycled material; for copper, 18 times; for steel, 5 times as much. Depletion allowances to producers of raw materials are another factor favouring use of primary resources: these might have to be scrapped.

Newsprint can also be recycled and in the US 400,000 tons comes wholly from recycled papers, and the figure is rising. Not so in Britain, where a government-backed attempt to raise capital for a recycling plant failed.

Another area where enormous economies are possible is in prevention of corrosion. A committee set up by Britain's Ministry of Technology in 1969 reported in 1971 that the annual cost of 'industrial' corrosion in the UK was then around £1,635 million; they computed that over £300 million of that figure could be saved by the proper application of *existing* knowledge, such as the use of inhibitors and the cleansing of corrosive environments.

In short, while many basic materials such as iron, stone, and timber will remain plentiful, it seems certain that a wide range of essential materials will be scarce, either in absolute terms or because the countries which possess near-monopolies will exploit their privileged· position. Japan, in a particularly weak position, has started making long-term contracts for the supply of ores in return for capital, equipment and know-how. Thus she is building a 50,000 tons per year ferrochrome alloy plant in Turkey in return for a guaranteed million tons of ore spread over 11 years. We shall see many more such contracts. Conversely, poor countries are beginning to insist that processing of ore be done in their territory, thus creating jobs, instead of exporting raw ore. Being scarce, the prices of these products will remain high or will rise further. The familiar situation of poor countries welcoming foreign exploitation of their resources has vanished forever. It is vital that Western governments wake up to this fact and make a real drive, not just a few gestures, on the kind of economy measures I have just indicated.

XIII

CLIMATIC THREAT

*He who would do good to another must do it
in minute particulars.*
—Alexander Pope

1 Evidence of Cooling

The Snowy Owl and four other arctic birds have started to nest in north Scotland. In America the armadillos are moving south. They are fussy about the temperature of their surroundings and during the early part of the century they moved gradually northward from Mexico into the south-western United States. But in recent years they have been gradually moving back to Mexico. They have noticed that the climate is getting colder. Birch trees are also temperature-dependent, and in their more leisurely way have been changing their ranges. The balance between softwood and hardwood trees is changing, as is the balance between forest and prairie. In the forests of Central Europe warmth-loving snails are disappearing. The fish, too, have noticed that something is happening and, at least in the Atlantic, are changing their ranges. In California, thousands of eucalyptus trees, which had flourished since the turn of the century, were killed by frost in 1972.

It is certain that the world is gradually getting colder—sunnier and drier perhaps, but colder. Most meteorologists believe that this trend will continue at least until 1985 and some say until AD 2000. A few foresee a new ice age.

If the climate is really going to get appreciably colder this could prove the most important single factor in our material future. It would reduce crop yields, making widespread starvation almost inevitable. And it would increase the drain on scarce energy resources, which in turn would react on agriculture, making it harder to win new resources and lowering the standard of living everywhere. A one-degree drop in average temperature means a fifteen per cent fall in crop yields. How seriously, then, should the forecasts of the meteorologists be taken? And what should we do about it?

Meteorological data confirm the armadillos' good sense. Thus, while the summer of 1972 was extremely warm and dry in European Russia and the following winter was so mild in Scandinavia that roses flowered in Copenhagen in late January, yet the temperatures in places like Sverdlovsk matched the lowest in the past two hundred years. In Franz Joseph Land, where the most northerly recording station is situated, the temperature from 1963 to 1972 averaged 5°C lower than the average of the preceding forty years. The Labrador icebelt has slowly extended east of Newfoundland beyond its previous record limit, and over four hundred icebergs were counted in the Atlantic south of latitude 48° (say, from Newfoundland to Brest).

Meteorologists are worried, too, by a substantial rise in the levels of the great lakes of eastern equatorial Africa, which has now been followed by a rise in the levels of the Great Lakes of North America.

For a hundred years or more, up to about 1940, average temperatures had been rising; the snowy Christmases described by Dickens were seldom seen. It was not until the late fifties that it began to become clear that the trend had flattened out and then started to reverse. In Britain, between 1910 and 1937, in low-lying inland areas, there were only five to seven days a year on which snow lay on the ground and many local authorities ceased to maintain snow-clearing equipment. But since 1950, the average has been ten to fifteen days a year, with fifteen to twenty days in some places. Though southerly winds have given a few mild Januaries, in general the winds have been cold and from the north. Mean winter temperatures were 0.8°C down from the level of the previous half-century. June 1973 was the coldest June since weather records started in England.

People sometimes object that winters have recently been milder in many areas. But it is not cold winters but cold summers which make ice-ages. What matters is whether the summer heat is sufficient to melt all the snow and ice which accumulated during the winter. And it is the polar regions rather than the middle latitudes which are chiefly important.

In 1969, Jerome Namias of the Extended Forecast Division of the us Weather Bureau, proposed the idea that a new climatic regime had been established over the North Pacific and North America since 1961, due to the presence of unusually warm water in the central Pacific Ocean. Prior to 1961 the north-eastern Pacific had cooled over a vast area and to great depths. Namias is probably the world's leading expert on the interaction between the oceans and the atmosphere, a subject which is gradually emerging as a crucial factor in weather forecasting. Although this idea was advanced in the 1920s, until recently its application was hampered by lack of data; today satellites and floating weather stations have transformed the situation. The complex processes by which the ocean masses generate depressions and anti-cyclones and influence climate are still being worked out. However, it is already clear that such patterns change abruptly and then last for several years.

As time wore on, the evidence became steadily firmer. For instance, in 1972, R. S. Bradley and G. H. Miller of the University of Colorado reported that Baffin Island seemed to be moving towards more glacial conditions. The total snow cover had increased and two new glaciers had appeared since 1960. There was 'a marked increase' in sea-ice in Baffin Bay and the Davis Strait. What puzzled them was the fact that, although the temperatures were below average by 2.1°C for June, July and August, for the remaining nine months of the year they were 2°C above normal! Airflow measurements showed that this was due to warm southerly air arriving in winter and cool east and north-easterly air arriving in summer. Mystified, they concluded that a decrease in mean annual temperature does not seem to be a prerequisite for glaciation!

Meanwhile a computer at Massachusetts Institute of Technology was chomping through a vast mass of figures: some 200,000 individual temperature and humidity readings taken at many points and heights between May 1958 and April 1963. It was calculating, by interpolation, the temperature at various standard points. When the task was finished, it revealed that the mean temperature of the atmosphere in the northern hemisphere had fallen by 0.6°C during the period—and if attention was confined to the band between the Equator and 30°N, the temperature fall was 0.81°C. This may not sound much but, in fact, it is remarkable. The temperature difference between summer and winter, in the UK, when averaged out, is only 4°C, so that a permanent decline of four or five degrees would mean the arrival of an ice-age. The MIT computer is now tackling the figures for the period 1963 to 1968. They may show that the atmosphere warmed again, but if, as seems probable from what we already know, the temperature has fallen further, the prospect is ominous. At that rate forty years would bring an ice-age.

The clinching evidence was uncovered in 1973 when an analysis of satellite observations disclosed that the snow-cover of the northern hemisphere had increased by no less than 4m. square km.—more than 11 per cent—between 1968 and 1971. This change is calculated to have decreased the amount of solar radiation absorbed by 0.24 per cent, causing a temperature drop of 0.2 to 0.3°C. The trend continued during 1972.

The figures just cited are for November, because they give the best indication of what conditions will be during the subsequent winter, but the satellite data revealed a marked increase, in point of fact, at all seasons of the year.

To what, then, is this remarkable and even alarming cooling of our climate due? More important, how long is it likely to go on getting worse?

2 Exceptional Episodes

The earth's climate, which we tend to think of as stable, actually moves in a complex system of cycles. For instance, there is a clearly-marked cycle of 13,000 years, almost certainly due to the 'wobble' of the earth's axis, which has a similar period. The shortest is eleven years and is linked with the sunspot cycle. The most obvious effect of these cycles is the advance and retreat of polar ice, the cold phase being known as an ice-age and the warmer phase as an interglacial.

Past temperature changes can be studied by various methods, such as identifying the different kinds of pollen found in the successive layers of silt at the bottom of lakes. There is a tiny sea creature which has the peculiarity of building its shell in a right-hand spiral if the temperature is above 7.2°C and in a left-hand spiral if it is below. By spotting where the spiral changes type in successive layers of ocean silts, a line can be drawn on the map for different dates which shows whether the ocean was warming or cooling. But perhaps the most informative method has been to study the oxygen trapped in the shells of minute sea-creatures known as foramenifera, or in the ice of the polar ice caps.

Oxygen exists in two forms, known as O-16 and O-18. The ratio of one to the other is dependent on temperature at the time the molecules were embedded in the ice or the shells. Hence, by studying the oxygen in successive layers of ice or silt, it is possible to produce charts showing the temperature changes going back half a million years or more. There is an element of uncertainty: one has to assume that the air in the past was similar to the air today. If it slowly changed, this might distort the results. But there are several ways of checking. For instance, the dating of some coral reefs of great age is known, and they must have formed during warm periods.

In 1969 Danish scientists from Copenhagen University, with American cooperation, took ice-cores in Greenland which yielded a temperature record going back a thousand centuries. It showed that temperatures had fluctuated with some regularity and startling abruptness. At least one full ice-age succeeded an era warmer than today in a period of one hundred years at most, and the switch may have been instantaneous. The conclusion which these curves suggested was that the earth's climate exists in two rather stable states but sometimes flips from one to the other, for reasons which are still to be discovered.

Ice-age cycles appear to last about 13,000 years. It is about 14,000 years since the last ice-age maximum (known as the Würm ice-age) and we are rather overdue for another. At a symposium at Brown University in 1972, it was generally agreed that the present interglacial could not last more than a few more centuries.

Professor Cesare Emiliani of the University of Miami studies temperature changes by studying the oxygen balance in the shells of marine creatures. In 1955 he published a temperature curve based on two cores taken in the Atlantic, extended it in 1966, and in 1972 published an improved version based on the analysis of two more cores. The curve which covers the past 450,000 years shows within each major warming three minor warmings and coolings ('little ice-ages') and implies that it is more than 60,000 years since the temperatures were as high as they are today. Pollen studies confirm this.

As Emiliani says, epochs like the present, far from lasting 100,000 years as the textbooks say, now appear to be 'short, wholly exceptional episodes'. He adds: 'New evidence from land deposits supports this view, strengthening the warning from the deep sea that the present episode of amiable climate is coming to an end. In this context, man's interference with climate through deforestation, urban development and pollution must be viewed with alarm. If the present balance is not maintained, we may soon be confronted with a runaway glaciation or a runaway deglaciation, both of which would generate unacceptable environmental stresses. A clear, quantitative understanding of man's effect on climate must be obtained.' (Emiliani's comments apply to the last half-million years. On a multi-million year view, the earth has usually been warmer than it is now.)

The part that man is playing will be considered in the next section. But first let us consider further the evidence concerning cyclical changes.

When it comes to the shorter cycles, the work of Professor Gordon Manley is classic. He has collected old diaries, the logs of ships' captains, and much other evidence concerning the British climate. When a few years ago he discovered in the Bodleian Library at Oxford a half-forgotten store of manuscript weather diaries he was able to push his series of data back to 1669, giving London the longest daily weather record of any place in the world.

It is now well known that, at least in Europe, the climate was rather warm in the thirteenth century, when grapes were grown as far north as York, but deteriorated until the 'Little Ice-Age' of the seventeenth century, when the Thames froze over. After that it grew warmer again until about 1920 and in 1940 temperatures started to decline once more. These facts imply a cycle of some 700 years, which suggests that the down-phase which started in 1940 will run to 2240 or so. So, whether or not a 'climatic flip' to an ice-age occurs, it seems highly probable that Britain at least (and that certainly means most of Europe too) must reckon with a steadily cooling climate for some time to come.

Recently, the whole subject has taken a new turn with the discovery that the weather is affected by changes in the magnetic field of the earth. It has long been known that the weather is linked with the eleven-year sunspot cycle; when sunspots are few abnormally dry or abnormally wet summers and winters occur, and it has recently been established that the temperature and density of the high atmosphere is associated with sunspot activity. But the eleven-year sunspot cycle itself forms part of a larger cycle, in which the peaks of activity grow steadily higher for 44 years and then decline again. Thus the number of sunspots at the 1923 peak was 75, against 120, 150, 190 in the three subsequent peaks. Dr J. W. King of the Radio and Space Research Station, Slough, made a study of the length of the growing season at Eskdalemuir in Scotland and found it varied from 186 days at the sunspot minimum in 1923 to 237 days in 1959, two years after a sunspot maximum. (The growing season was defined as the number of days on which the average temperature exceeded 5.6°C.) In short, this trend also suggests a cooling phase at least until the 1990s.

This short-term approach complements long-term studies made by workers at the Lamont–Doherty Observatory in New York, some going back half a million years, from which it emerges that where the magnetic intensity is decreasing, it is getting warmer, where it increases it gets colder. This may explain some of the puzzling regional variations which have long baffled meteorologists. Thus in Norway, Germany, Sweden and Russia, the field is increasing (=climate cooling). In Brazil, South Africa, New Zealand and Samoa it is decreasing (=climate warming). (Exceptions occur in places where strong ocean currents overrule the effect, such as Gibraltar, Tokyo or Lima.) And abrupt changes in magnetic intensity are followed, one year later, by abrupt temperature changes.

In short, a new branch of science, which King has christened magnetometeorology, has been born and promises to transform the whole status of long-term weather prediction.

Finally, John Gribbin of *Nature* has drawn attention to a 179-year cycle, corresponding to a similar cycle of solar output, possibly due to changes in the alignment of the various planets causing tides on the surface of the sun. On this cycle, likewise, the climatic optimum coincided with a sunspot minimum, in 1923. So on this data we can expect cooling for 90 years from that date, i.e., to 2013.

To sum up, the evidence from many different sources converges to the conclusion that, whatever the long-term prospects, the immediate future will get steadily colder.

But how will human activity affect this trend?

3 Impact of Man

Before 1940 world average temperatures had been rising, thanks to the 'greenhouse effect' of the carbon dioxide produced by man's activities. In the fifties, it became obvious that the climate was actually cooling. Attention shifted to explaining this. It was Professor Reid Bryson of the University of Michigan at Ann Arbor who (as I described in *The Doomsday Book*, 1970) first attributed the cooling to the increase in 'particulate matter'—or, in unscientific terms, dust and droplets in the atmosphere. A haze or dust veil, by obscuring the sun's rays, could cool the earth. Subsequently S. I. Rasool and S. H. Schneider of the Goddard Space Flight Center analysed the problem mathematically and concluded that, while the effect of carbon dioxide would be insignificant, the effect of particulates might be dramatic. Man's power to pollute will increase six- to eight-fold in the next fifty years. An increase in the opacity of the atmosphere by a factor of four might reduce the temperature 3.5 degrees. 'Such a large decrease in the average surface temperature of the earth, sustained over a period of a few years, is believed to be sufficient to trigger an ice-age.' 'However,' they added soothingly, by that time nuclear power may have replaced fossil fuels as a source of energy.'

In the following year, two workers at Ohio State University confirmed Rasool and Schneider's interpretation, though they found, on the basis of cores taken at 'New' Camp Byrd in Antarctica, that the cooling would decrease at higher levels of turbidity. And in 1973, L. Machta of the National Oceanic and Atmospheric Administration (NOAA) reviewing the evidence, concluded that the greenhouse effect would be negligible but that the cooling effect was more probable. He cited Russian figures showing a ten per cent drop in solar radiation at the earth's surface over the past fifty years. Measurements made at Mount Wilson Observatory in the sixties, compared with fifty years earlier, showed a drop of eight to nine per cent at longer wavelengths, but a drop of as much as twenty-six per cent in the ultra-violet.

Thus the evidence from this source too points towards the climate becoming colder over the next twenty-five years.

After a certain amount of argument it is now generally agreed that volcanic dust can cool the earth by cutting off the sun's radiation. The wave of volcanic eruptions which started in 1947 and culminated in the eruption of Mount Agung in Bali in 1963 certainly contributed to recent cooling. Professor Reid Bryson considers that about 70 per cent of recent temperature variance due to turbidity has been due to volcanic dust, the other 30 per cent to human activity. In 1972, the Mauna Loa Observatory—situated far from man-made disturbance—reported that the air there was free of volcanic dust once again. Volcanic dust is hurled up into the stratosphere, where it remains for several years and tends to collect in a band over the middle latitudes; whereas human activity—except for high-flying aircraft—tends to pollute much lower layers.

There is no question but that turbidity is increasing at lower levels: for instance, at twenty non-urban sites studied by an American team, the concentration increased by twelve per cent in the four years 1962–6, while observations of the sun's radiation show a four per cent decrease between the late thirties and the sixties which appears to be due to human activity.

Stimulated by the new interest in the topic, the NOAA is now setting up a global system of stations to monitor not only dust in the atmosphere but also carbon monoxide, carbon dioxide and ozone levels, the programme being known as Global Monitoring for Climatic Change. America will maintain stations at Barrow, Alaska and the South Pole, as well as the main station on Mauna Loa, and possibly one in Samoa. Russia has mentioned three possible sites, in the Caucasus, Central Asia and North Siberia. Sweden and Britain have agreed to help. The project will last for several decades.

Thanks to weather satellites and computers, the whole character of meteorology is changing. Satellites provide daily reports of temperature changes on a world-wide basis and are capable of measuring the temperature at different heights in the atmosphere; they can also report the amount of cloud cover and the extent of ice-fields. Computers can make sense of this mass of data which would take lifetimes to analyse by ordinary methods. From these reports it has emerged that two factors are unusually important: the extent of snow and ice-cover and the extent of cloud-cover. Fortunately, cloud-cover appears to be self-limiting.

In contrast, the ice-cover situation is unstable. For if the ice extends, more heat is reflected and less absorbed, lowering the temperature. So the ice extends further. Scientists find that ice reflects a hundred times more of the sun's energy than open water. The Russian meteorologist, M. I. Budyko, has calculated that a two per cent increase in radiation falling on the earth would produce a runaway glaciation, leading not merely to an ice-age but to glaciation of the whole earth. Correspondingly, if the ice decreases, the globe heats up and it has been suggested that if the ice-caps once melted they would never return (short of some catastrophic change in the overall situation). Here, it seems to me, we have a mechanism which could account for the suddenness of the climatic flips between ice-ages and interglacials. Like a ball poised on top of a hill, the slightest disturbance will cause it to run down one side or the other. The initial disturbance could be a train of volcanic eruptions, a change in cloud-cover due to the earth's magnetic field or the solar wind, or—today—the activities of man.

Obviously, some slower-acting mechanism must be present to limit and reverse these trends. And these movements are damped by the fact that it takes about a century for the oceans to warm or cool in response to changes in air temperature. Ice-sheets, too, can only develop as fast as rain or snow falls upon them.

This is why scientists have become intensely interested in the transfer of energy between sea and air, and in changes in snow and ice-cover. 'On the whole, it appears that sea-ice cover is one of the greatest variables in the environment of the earth's surface,' says Dr Joseph O. Fletcher, of Washington University.

Accordingly, an enormous experiment has been launched known as the Arctic Ice Dynamics Joint Experiment (AIDJEX) at the initiative of the Office of Naval Research and involving the collaboration of the Naval Oceanographer, the Advanced Research Projects Agency, the National Science Foundation, the National Aeronautics and Space Administration, the NOAA, the Coast Guard and several universities. Canadians, Russians and Japanese are also expected to take part. Pilot studies were run in 1970, 1971 and 1972. The main AIDJEX experiments were carried out in 1973 from drifting stations, five of them manned. Four stations were placed on the corners of a square, 100 km on a side, with the fifth in the centre. In addition, there was a microwave imager on satellite Nimbus F to detect cracks in the ice and estimate its age. It will take six years to analyse and interpret the data gathered in this year of field-work.

It is hoped to lead to a model of ice changes which can be dovetailed into models of the whole atmosphere/ocean relationship.

These are only two of the many initiatives now being taken, ranging from the placing of hundred-ton weather buoys in the ocean, which automatically signal air and ocean conditions, and the launching of fixed-height balloons, to the setting up of a southern hemisphere monitoring system by Australia, and joint USA–USSR studies in the Bering Sea. And 1976 has been designated Global Observing Year. Most of these are components in the Global Atmospheric Research Program which is working up to a colossal year-long experiment known as FGGE, involving no fewer than nine satellites, and covering the entire planet, in 1977.

4 Likely Consequences

'How long the current cooling trend continues is one of the most important problems of our civilisation,' says Dr Murray Mitchell. 'If it continues for twenty more years an icebreaker like the *Manhattan* couldn't even begin to get through the north-west passage.'

The consequences of a prolonged temperature drop are far-reaching, the effect on shipping being only one. Almost all Russia's ports are in the north and are closed by ice for roughly half the year. It wouldn't take a big temperature drop to close them entirely. Exploitation of North Slope oil in Alaska, and of Russia's northern oil fields would become even more difficult. Countries like Iceland would probably have to be evacuated, since its main industry, fishing, would cease.

Land transport would also be affected. Railways, even in Britain's mild climate, are slowed by fog and halted by iced-up points. Electric warming of switches would have to be made standard. Cars are also slowed or stopped by ice, fog and snow. Local authorities will have to hold snow-ploughs and snow-throwers, and will need places to dump the snow. Parking of cars which obstruct road-clearing operations may have to be prohibited. The market for power sleds and snowmobiles, however, will expand.

Aircraft likewise are especially vulnerable to fog and snow, while ice-forming on the wings can change their camber, destroying lift, as was demonstrated at the disaster in Munich in which almost an entire British football team was wiped out.

Industry will also be affected. Power cables sag when ice forms on them and also begin to vibrate in the wind. Currently they are commonly designed to work with an ice-coat of up to half an inch, but three inches has been known to accumulate. In Scotland, the use of nickel–chromium alloy coatings, lined with silicone insulation, is the subject of experiments. The metal becomes magnetic when the temperature falls below a certain point, and the resulting heat melts the ice.

Many currently popular tourist areas may cease to be attractive.

It may become impractical to store unsold products, such as motor vehicles, in the open. Ice pressure threatens hydroelectric and reservoir dams, especially when wind increases the pressure on them, but mostly due to the ice expanding. The maximum thrust which ice can exert has never been determined but the Hydroelectric Power Commission of Ontario has been making measurements on a completed dam.

However, it is agriculture, including market gardening, which is chiefly affected. As I have already noted, a fall in average temperature of one degree causes a crop reduction of fifteen per cent. Such calculations, however, tend to obscure the fact that some crops, and many other species of plant, will not survive continued or severe night frosts. Some areas will therefore have to abandon traditional forms of agriculture. In Britain the growing of peaches and other wall fruit in the open may have to be abandoned, and grape growing in the San Francisco area may fail. The great acreages under apricots, oranges and other fruit in Central California will have to be replaced by farms and ranches further south.

The Russians have devoted much effort to developing cold-resistant strains of wheat and other crops. Potatoes too are climate-sensitive: the yield can vary by as much as 30 per cent in two successive years. The temperature affects germination, and moisture affects bulking. Cold winds in June may ruin an entire crop.

A colder climate may also drastically affect fishing. Cod, for instance, are disturbed when the water temperature falls below 2°C. They appeared in large numbers off the coast of Greenland in 1917, having rarely been seen before, and by 1930 had reached a point more than 750 miles further north, well within the Arctic circle. Now they are moving south again. Sole are at their northern limit in the North Sea and soon the much-sought Dover sole will be a thing of the past. Again, insect life is affected, which could make artificial pollination necessary, or change the pattern of pest depredation.

Above all, a colder climate will drastically increase the demand for energy. Market gardeners will have to spend more on heating greenhouses, making tomatoes and melons (not to mention flowers of several kinds) more expensive. Energy will be needed for de-icing roads and runways, as well as for warming houses, although in summer the reduced use of air-conditioning will relieve the load.

In all the above I have considered only the temperature, but changes in the amount and distribution of rainfall could be of even more importance to agriculture, not to mention tourism.

5 Rain, Rain, go to Spain!

What goes up must come down, but not necessarily always in the same place. In recent years the distribution of rainfall has changed dramatically. Thus in North Africa and the Middle East, in the late sixties, the rainfall was the highest ever recorded. On the other hand, south of the Sahara in areas like Chad, Niger and Senegal, not to mention much of south-west Asia, the monsoon rains failed for seven successive years. Rainfall was less than half what it had been in 1957. In many of these areas agriculture is precarious and water-availability is the limiting factor. The result was disaster.

Particularly hard-hit was the area known as the Sahelian zone, comprising six countries: Mauretania, Mali, Niger, Senegal, Chad and Upper Volta. Here, thanks to international campaigns to eliminate disease, both human and animal, and thanks also to the plentiful rains, the population had risen explosively. So, when the droughts came, the situation soon became serious. In May 1973 the World Food and Agriculture Organisation appealed for immediate airlifts of supplies to this area, observing that 'in some areas there now appears serious risk of imminent human famine and virtual extinction of herds vital to nomad populations'.

In Asia the story was just as bad. In India, the harvest in 1972 was 60 per cent below normal, in Ceylon it was 30 per cent down. Simultaneously there were catastrophic floods in Pakistan, while, on the other side of the world, abnormally heavy winter snows and rain loosened the roots of giant sequoias in Yosemite and Sequoia National Parks, causing a number to fall. Chinese papers spoke openly of drought and famine. Central America was equally badly off. Was it Nature which had withheld the rain, or was it the activities of man?

Probably both.

There seem to be long-term cycles in rainfall just as there are in temperature, and Derek Winstanley has analysed these. Winstanley was by vocation an entomologist, engaged in studying the distribution of the locust, the breeding habits of which are temperature-dependent. So he was led to study African weather patterns in an attempt to explain the variations in locust populations. He looked at the trends in westerly circulation for the past thousand years, and projected them to 2030. The records suggest that there is a 200-year cycle, in which case we can expect the monsoons to decline for the next fifty years. If this occurs, the rainfall in Sahel and in the Rajastan of India will then be forty to forty-five per cent lower than the optimum. The Sahara will have advanced a further 100 km south. But the shakier evidence from earlier periods suggests that this pattern is superimposed on a 700-year cycle with a minimum in 1700. So if 1930 was also the peak of a 700-year cycle, these could be under-estimates. And that could be really serious.

A LAND DYING OF THIRST

For the last three years [Maharashtra] province has suffered one of the most severe droughts ever recorded, with an average annual rainfall of only three inches compared to the normal 25 inches.

The Bihma river was once 150 yards wide and 15 feet deep. It meant life for the villages along its banks. Now its dusty bed is being pitted with holes as villagers dig desperately for water, which sinks a little lower each week.

From Poona to Aurangabad, a distance of 125 miles, I counted 30 rivers that were absolutely dry.

Marine life in the dead rivers will take years to replace. Draught animals have also suffered badly. Bullocks, used by the peasants to plough the fields, once came to drink from the rivers. They are dying in thousands.

Villagers know that if the monsoon rains—due this month—fail them yet again, they may not survive. Continuation of the drought—which has been accompanied by a food famine —would mean certain death not just for a few, but for millions of people.

The Indian Government has been severely blamed by its own people for not taking adequate steps to cope with the situation. Riots have taken place in many towns, and police opened fire, killing at least eight people.

Serge Lemoine, *Observer Magazine*, 3 June 1973

North of the dry belt, however, winter-spring rainfall will continue to increase, making the Mediterranean climate (about which residents are already bitterly complaining) even worse.

The reader can keep tabs on these developments, in a rough and ready way, by noting the frequency of westerly winds. In Britain, and probably in the entire northern hemisphere, these have been becoming rarer since the 1920s.

Meteorologists have, by international agreement, selected 1930–60 as their base for comparison—or, in some cases, 1920–50. As it turns out, these periods, far from being typical, were in fact 'highly abnormal', perhaps the most unusual period in the last thousand years. World-wide industrialisation and expansion took place in a short-lived period of favourable climate—a brief interruption to the Little Ice Age of the preceding three centuries. 'When the earth entered that period between AD 1450 and 1600, the Mali Empire collapsed and the magnificent Indian city at Fatehpur Sikri was abandoned as its water supply failed,' notes Reid Bryson. 'Do such events lie ahead?' Bryson believes that the monsoon changes, at least, are due not so much to mysterious long-term cycles as to human activities.

In the northern hemisphere rainfall depends on two great air movements: the westerly air movement round the pole, and a south-north movement known as the Hadley Cell. Over the equator hot air rises, moves north (in the case of the northern hemisphere), cools and falls. A similar rotatory air movement occurs between the poles and the middle latitudes, but more erratically. The place where these two systems adjoin is known as the inter-tropical discontinuity (ITD), and it is just south of this that the monsoon rains occur, in a belt 800 km wide. North of the ITD there is no rain. It is this dry belt which produces the world's great deserts. What has happened in the Sahel and elsewhere is that the ITD has moved south. It has been shown that, in Nigeria, for every degree of latitude by which the ITD moves south, the rainfall declines by seven inches: a catastrophic decrease in areas which are already at the margin. And as Bryson has now shown, very small declines in Arctic temperature are enough to shift the ITD. Small changes in the temperature difference between the earth's surface and the high atmosphere will also produce the same effect.

What could produce such temperature differences? The first thing is an enhanced level of carbon dioxide, which raises the surface temperature. Bryson reckons that the increase which man's activities have caused since 1940 would account for about three inches of the lost Nigerian rainfall. The second factor is particulate pollution, and especially when the turbidity is concentrated in middle latitudes—which is precisely the case. Though we have no extensive measurements of turbidity, we do at least have temperature records, and we know that virtually all the temperature decline has been in the middle and upper latitudes. Tropical temperatures have hardly changed at all. This would be enough, he says, to cut Nigerian rainfall by fourteen inches.

Putting the matter in a nutshell, Bryson writes: 'My own analysis suggests that over the past century about seventeen per cent of the temperature variance created by turbidity has been due to agricultural, industrial and other human activities. However, it appears that in recent decades the human contribution has been closer to thirty per cent or so, the remainder being largely due to volcanic activity.'

So it seems that, whether carbon dioxide will make the earth warmer or particulate pollution make it cooler, in any event both trends are combining to suppress the monsoons of the world.

'If my analysis of the situation is correct,' Bryson adds, 'an unpleasant view of the future unfolds.' Man is unlikely to give up burning fossil fuels or amend his agricultural practices—and there will soon be twice as many men. Volcanoes are not particularly likely to quieten down. 'Will the monsoon return? Probably not regularly in this century.'

6 Survival Plan

In earlier days, the inhabitants of the Sahelian zone had a simple solution to the monsoon problem. When the rains moved south, they moved too. Today we have carved up the world with national boundaries and the problem is less simple. States to the south, such as Nigeria and Ghana, would have to absorb between ten and twenty million people. In any case the Sahelian states would certainly object. 'Are we prepared,' Dr Winstanley asks, 'to give massive international aid to maintain the independence and viability of the Sahelian states in the fact of increasingly adverse climatic conditions?'

An alternative possibility would be to attempt to provide water by massive irrigation schemes, perhaps coupled with desalination of sea-water. Apart from questions of cost, such schemes could not be put into operation, on any scale which would be adequate, for many years. And by that time most of the inhabitants may be dead or fled.

Finally, could we modify the climate, or at least the weather? Rainmaking techniques, when they work at all, only bring down in one area water which would otherwise have fallen in another. So unless we can be sure that we are not depriving one area in favour of another, rainmaking and climate alterations are unacceptable. At some future date it might be possible to ensure that rain which would otherwise have fallen on the oceans falls on land, but up to now, the science of meteorology, let alone the technique of rainmaking, has not progressed so far.

The problem is hardly less refractory when we turn to the temperature aspect. Basically, world temperatures are beyond our control. A colder climate is simply something we have to learn to live with. The challenge consists in finding ways to live with it.

It is true that the Russians have considered ways of melting the north polar ice cap, in the hope of freeing their ice-bound northern ports. Unfortunately a recent computer simulation suggests that though this might make the north pole bearably warm, the temperatures in middle latitudes—oddly enough—would fall. Air temperature might be $-2°C$ in Britain and Europe, and a chilly $-6°C$

in Siberia, said the computer. So plans for spreading black dust on the polar ice have been put back on the shelf.

First and foremost, we shall have to learn to husband heat—especially in the circumstances of an energy shortage. The wasteful system whereby power stations discharge waste heat into the air through cooling towers or into rivers by cooling water, will have to stop. The heat will have to be used for heating greenhouses or even exposed soil, and for district heating systems. Homes and buildings will have to be insulated to new standards. In Britain particularly, the wave of house-building early in this century capitalised on the fact that winters were rarely cold, in the way that they are in most of the US or even in central Europe and Italy. Windows were badly fitted, roofs leaked air and piping was installed outside. Countries like Sweden, which really know how to conserve domestic heat, will become the mentors of building construction. Governments, however, in such countries have so far done little to amend building regulation.

At the same time, we shall see intensive technical effort devoted to methods of snow clearance and ice removal. And as the ice-age closes in, and the sea begins to ice over, the demand for ice-breaking ships will rocket. The icing of masts and rigging also presents a technical problem. The Russians will be the teachers here. One of their new ice-breakers cuts the ice, transports it on moving belts and dumps it aside. Another forces slabs of ice under the ice sheet with a high-pressure water jet. The Russians have also attempted to prevent small lakes from freezing, using compressed air to bring relatively warm water up from the bottom to melt the ice and prevent more forming. They have at least twelve institutes studying such problems.

This, then, is the context in which we must set the practical problems of the next thirty years—the problems of energy supply and of feeding an exploding world population. It is a factor which governments and planning organisations have completely failed to take into full account up to now. It is of vital importance that they begin to do so.

All the arguments lead back to the supply of energy. To refine copper, aluminium, or titanium, to extract magnesium from sea water or make steel takes energy. A hundred tons of coal to get a ton of aluminium gives you the order of magnitude. Again, to make enough fertiliser to grow crops on a scale sufficient to avert famine could take one-fifth of the world's energy production: five tons of coal for one ton of fertiliser. Energy is also needed for pumping irrigation water and, lavishly, for desalination. And of course energy is needed for transport, for heating our houses in a cooling climate, for running industry and a hundred other things. What are the prospects of getting it?

XIV

ENERGETIC MEASURES

We do not predict a substantial price-rise in world oil markets over the coming decade.—U.S. Cabinet Task Force on Oil, February 1970. (The price of oil was then $1.80/bbl. Now: $11.68.)

1 Energy Demands

As recently as 1970 it was possible for Professor Ali B. Cambel, formerly director of President Kennedy's Energy Study Committee and a vice-president of the Institute of Defense Analysis, to declare: 'There will be no fuel shortage for centuries!' Even if there had been no squeeze by the Arabs he might have lived to regret the prediction.

While, thanks to the Arab stimulus, energy may become plentiful at some future date, the problem is really a different one. It is to decide how fast we are prepared to use up resources and what price we are prepared to pay in pollution. These decisions will determine our energy demands. The Arab squeeze has been called a blessing in disguise because it has forced the West to consider the whole energy question and to start developing alternative sources and novel technologies. If, as a result, we soon have energy coming out of our ears and use it to wreck the environment it may prove to be a curse in disguise. We desperately need a rational world energy policy.

Up to now world energy use has been increasing by about five per cent each year; on the assumption that this trend will continue, experts have been forecasting a doubling of energy use by the mid-eighties and a quadrupling by the end of the century.* The figure opposite

* However, there are indications that if the cost of electricity rises people will reduce consumption quite sharply. An American team which examined the question told a committee of the House of Representatives that the forecasts made by the Federal Power Commission and others may prove too high. Perhaps all those expensive power stations may turn out to be bad investments.

213

conveys what a fantastic increase this would mean and readers may
care to check back in a few years to see how we are doing.

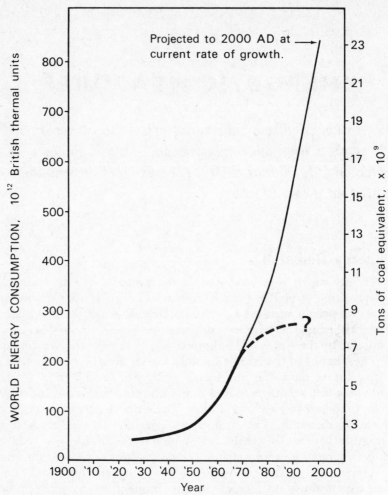

World energy consumption projected to AD 2000: diagram based on
Environment 1973 15 (8): 5.

Cambel's optimism may be justified in the long view, since in
principle energy can be extracted from low-grade ores and even
from sea-water. But in the short run of twenty years or so there is
more likely to be an energy-shortage and rising prices on a scale
which will affect our daily lives. The struggle to achieve the relatively
clean and efficient nuclear fusion process, which would solve most
of our problems, is something which in a more rational world would
be followed by everyone as closely as the sports results.

Energy, of course, comes in two distinct forms: large stationary sources and small portable ones. The first means, basically, electricity; the second oil. Cars, trucks, tractors, aeroplanes, motor-boats cannot run on atomic power—not to mention air compressors, chain-saws, concrete-mixers, brick-hoists, and much other portable equipment. (Electricity can be used for such jobs provided—but only provided— a source is near by, and at some loss of manoeuvrability.)

While the oil shortage of 1973–4 seems to have been created as much by the oil distributors as by the Arabs, the long-term outlook remains discouraging. Oil, and natural gas which Nature provides in conjunction with oil, will never be cheap again and the effects on agriculture and third-world countries may be quite serious. Indeed, the extensive exploration provoked by this crisis will probably advance the day of judgment. In the long run, there is a reasonably satisfactory substitute for oil: hydrogen. Early in the next century we may be attempting to switch over to it. But at present we do not have the techniques and we certainly need the oil, so let us start by assessing the prospects of getting it.

2 Black Gold

The world used, in 1972, seven million tons of oil a day, two million of them in the USA.* The experts seem to be agreed that US oil reserves will be exhausted by about the end of the century and world oil reserves by about 2050. How seriously should we take such forecasts? What precisely do they mean by 'reserves'? There have been many dire warnings in the past, which have proved wrong. An unpublished paper in 1967 alleged the presence of 'trillions of barrels', much of it in shallow water and coastal plain areas of southeast Asia.

In the case of oil, 'known reserves' means oil the presence of which has actually been established by test-drilling. In addition there are obviously unknown reserves in areas which have never been examined; until recently the shallow sea-beds had been hardly explored. (As in the case of minerals, reserves usually implies 'available at a price similar to the current market price'.)

But nowadays geophysicists have methods of estimating the amount of unknown reserves. You start by charting the amount of oil discovered for every foot of exploratory drilling. At first things are easy but as you exhaust the obvious oil-pools, it gets harder and harder to find more. In the US, for instance, the rate reached a peak of 276 barrels a foot (taking the average of 1929 to 1936). 'After that the rate declined precipitously to the present figure of about 35

* Oil-men measure oil in barrels and regard measurement in tons with disdain: but I have converted most of the figures roughly to tons, by dividing by 7.5, as many people find this simpler.

barrels per foot, notwithstanding the fact that 1936 to 1966 was the period of the most intensive research and development in petroleum exploration and production techniques in the history of the petroleum industry.' The quotation is from Professor M. King Hubbert, formerly Chief Geological Consultant to Shell Oil and Chairman of the Earth Sciences Division of the National Academy of Sciences.

This trend enables you to estimate the undiscovered reserves. With this in mind, if you now make a chart showing the amount of oil discovered every year since production started, you get a bell-shaped curve. By extending the curve, symmetrically, it can be seen that the USA, having passed the peak of new discovery about 1966, will have discovered 90 per cent of its oil by 1998. The remaining ten per cent will have been located by about 2060. Of course, the curve is not sent from heaven: the descending side might not be symmetrical with the ascending side. Extensive offshore discoveries might improve it. On the other hand, the depletion curve for the haematite ores of Lake Superior proved to descend more steeply than it ascended, and some computer studies suggest this may be true for oil also.

Naturally, it doesn't follow that the oil will be consumed as fast as it is discovered. Perhaps we shall develop enough sense to husband it. But up to now the rate of consumption has tended to overhaul the rate of discovery, new fields being exploited as fast as possible—as in the case of the North Slope and the North Sea.

King Hubbert, who made the foregoing calculations for the US, has also made a similar calculation for world oil reserves, but with less confidence as exploration has been much spottier and not much information comes out of China and Russia. However, geological knowledge makes it possible to guess, and estimates range from 1,350 to 2,100 billion barrels (180 to 280 billion tons). If a curve of production is drawn, in the same way as before, the lower estimate gives a production peak in the year 1990, with 90 per cent gone by 2025. The higher estimate only shifts the peak to 2000 and the 90 per cent point to 2032.

Similar calculations applied to natural gas give 1980 for the production peak in the US. For every barrel of petroleum you find, you expect to find 6,400 cubic feet of natural gas and about one-fifth of a barrel of natural gas liquids. World supplies are estimated, perhaps unreliably, by assuming that this ratio obtains everywhere. This suggests that the ultimate world production will be somewhere between 8,000 and 12,000 trillion cubic feet.

This does not mean that we are going to have to do without oil altogether before long. Oil can be extracted from shale and from tar-sands and it can also be made from coal. These resources are

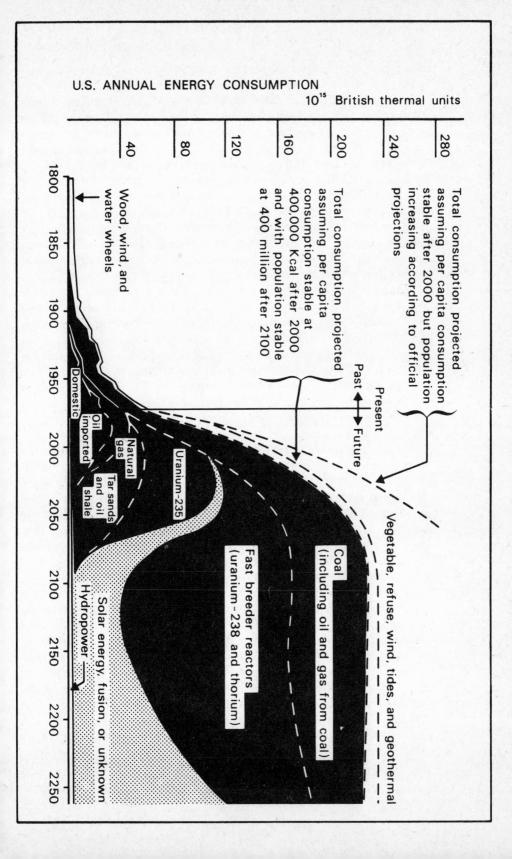

fairly plentiful, but techniques for extracting the oil at an economic price may take some time to develop. Some authorities think these sources will contribute little until after 2000. The most promising resource is the tar-sands of Alberta which contain about 40 billion tons of oil, so similar to crude petroleum that it can be refined in ordinary refineries without modification. It lies at various depths from zero to 2,000 feet deep: the upper layers can be 'mined' by ordinary earth-moving equipment and the oil extracted by treatment with hot water at a cost of about $4 a barrel. Since ordinary oil, until the recent crisis, cost about $2 a barrel, this was not competitive and no real attempt was made to exploit this resource. At today's prices, of course, the situation is transformed. How fast will Canada get moving? There may well be tar-sands elsewhere, but no world survey has ever been made.

Shale, though much talked about, is a rather less attractive proposition. It yields an oil which is harder to refine and to move and presents environmental problems. The oil content varies from 67 US gallons per ton down to zero, so it is hard to estimate the amount of worthwhile resources. Claims that shale oil will last for thousands of years are erroneous. Two American experts have put the recoverable oil at 190 billion barrels, world-wide, on the basis of a comprehensive survey of the known deposits. This is about ten per cent of the ultimate crude oil production, so it does not postpone the evil day very far.

Whereas tar-sands are soaked with oil in a viscous form, shale is quite different. Oil shale has a content of 'myriads of algal micro-organisms that flourished in ancient lakes, sank to the bottom when they died and were entombed in the muddy lake sediments'. This solid material yields oil on distillation. To distill the oil out, the shale must be heated to 800–900°F, which causes it to puff up like popcorn, so that it cannot be put back in the hole it came from. Enormous quantities of water are needed.

The US has set a target of 1m. barrels of shale oil a day by 1985; this will mean reaching a production level of 475m. tons of rock per year, starting virtually from zero. Incidentally, this means creating an undertaking equivalent in size to the entire existing US mining industry. And where are you going to put 475m. tons of popcorn?

Mined this way, the cost should be $7 a barrel. Where the rock is hard it is possible to fracture it by explosions and then to set the shale on fire with a propane burner, distilling the oil out of the surrounding rock. The fracturing is necessary as the rock is not porous. Late in 1973 came the news that Occidental Oil had succeeded in producing oil at $1 a barrel by this means. But many shales, including those in Britain, are too soft to work in this way.

Oil shortage does not only hit transport, electricity supplies and heating. It is the basis of the petrochemical industry; Britain uses nearly 6m. tons of naphtha annually. Costly oil means dearer lubricating oil for industry generally. British papermakers use 1.4m. tons of fuel oil a year; so does the textile and leather industry. Oil is too precious to use as fuel.

Natural gas presents an even darker prospect. Known reserves of us natural gas are sufficient for only ten years: what remains is very inaccessible. Outside America, the situation is obscure.

3 A Matter of Breeding

More and more, oil will have to be reserved for industrial feedstocks and essential vehicular use. So electricity will have to be made either by coal-fired plants or by nuclear reactors. Radically new methods will not make a significant impact during the next twenty years.

The popular idea that uranium is a limitless source of power is quite unfounded. Stories about a cupful of uranium propelling a liner across the Atlantic assumed one hundred per cent efficiency in exploiting the energy and were exaggerated even at that. In fact a 1,000-megawatt station needs a first charge of 220 tons of uranium, and has to be topped up every year with a further 110 tons. Current demand is for 19,000 tons a year, treble this by 1980, quintuple by 1985 and who knows what by the end of the century. Moreover, it is also necessary to maintain a forward supply for reactors under construction and R. L. Faulkner, in charge of raw materials for the Atomic Energy Commission (AEC), has put the 1980 requirement as high as 650,000 tons.

The growth of electricity consumption has been faster than the growth of demand for fuel generally. The American Bureau of Mines expects electricity generation to increase by 72 per cent in the years 1971 to 1980, and then by a further 78 per cent to 1990. Similar estimates have been made for Europe, while Japan's fuel consumption is expected to more than double by 1980. The current oil crisis and higher prices may make these estimates overstatements but the appetite for power is certainly there. Where will the power come from?

Known resources of uranium at around the present price of $7–$8 a pound are nothing like enough. Faulkner's estimate is 660,000 tons in the us and a total of 1,575,000 tons in the non-communist world, including the us. 'From these figures it is apparent that a very tight situation in uranium supply at anywhere near current prices is likely to develop within the next two decades,' concludes the oil expert M. King Hubbert. Faulkner adds that, in any case, existing mining capacity is only enough to produce about 210,000 tons by 1980 in the US or 550,000 tons worldwide.

Faulkner's figures may be a little overstated: according to the Australian AEC 'reasonably assured' world reserves of uranium at prices under $10 a pound are little more than a million tons, while world demand will be 79,000 tons a year in 1980, 200,000 tons a year by 1990, which would add up to a cumulative total of over three million tons by the end of the century. 'Consequently unless considerable quantities of new supplies are found, uranium will be in very short supply,' says the Chairman of Pancontinental Mining, Anthony Gray.

The Organisation for European Economic Cooperation (OEEC) though using somewhat different figures, comes to a similar conclusion: 'It is therefore essential that urgent steps be taken to increase the rate of exploration for uranium.'

On top of this comes the problem of 'enriching' uranium, since the reactors now being built are designed for uranium which has been purified, a process which adds about 50 per cent to the fuel-cycle costs. The demand is expected to outstrip enrichment capacity in the US by 1977 (these plants use one of two processes: diffusion or centrifuges) and if the AEC's forecasts are correct, America will be building a new diffusion plant every 1.7 years from 1981 or a new centrifuge plant every five months. Enriching uranium has been forecast to be a $5 billion industry by the end of the century.

Forecasts of this kind caused a minor panic when first published. Britain hastily launched a survey which uncovered a paltry few thousand tons of uranium minable at $15 a pound in the Orkneys plus a few hundred tons in England. It was in this mood of alarm that everyone began to pin their hopes on a new kind of reactor, the 'fast breeder', which, once primed and running, actually creates more nuclear fuel than it consumes. Something for nothing! 'Something resembling a crash programme' developed. President Nixon declared development of the breeders to be a 'national objective' and other countries did much the same. Currently over a hundred breeder reactors are in operation or on order, those in operation including Britain's Dounreay, France's Phoenix and Rapsodie, Russia's BN-350, etc. The AEC sees the breeder becoming the dominant source of power by 2020, and bringing the cost of electricity down as delivered to the transmission network, down to less than two-thirds the current figure—which means to say, below the cost of electricity from coal.

There are several varieties of breeder reactor, some using uranium, others thorium or plutonium as fuel; some cooled by helium, some by molten salt and some by liquid sodium, that cheap but alarming substance which bursts into flame when it touches water. This last variety, known as the LMFBR (Liquid Metal Fast Breeder Reactor) is the most favoured and my remarks apply primarily to it. Sodium boils at 800°C which makes it a more efficient heat extractor than water, but it is highly corrosive and experimental reactors embodying it have run into many problems. America's experimental Fermi I was closed down after only thirty days of full-power operation, when the coolant flow failed and most, if not all, the others are running behind schedule.

Unfortunately, there are serious objections to the LMFBR on grounds of safety, since it continuously produces the deadly plutonium-239, the intensely radioactive stuff from which nuclear bombs are made. Plutonium-239 is far more vicious than the other radioactive materials used as fuels since it is not only an explosive but also a poison, as I shall shortly describe; it has been said that a piece the size of an orange could kill every living person. To make a bomb you need only 5 kg (12 lb) of plutonium. An average power plant produces 200–300 kg of new plutonium per annum: enough for about fifty hydrogen bombs. And by 1980 there will be scores of such plants. According to an authoritative estimate, the amount of plutonium produced *every year* by industrial reactors will be enough to make 10,000 nuclear warheads. What is to be done with all this superlethal material? Is it to be bought by the International Atomic Energy Authority? No provision has been made for this. In a world riven by international stresses, the temptation to use this power for blackmail could become irresistible. In addition the breeder reactor produces other toxic wastes, as I shall describe. All this material will have to be transported from the reactors to the fuel reprocessing plants and back again. Apart from the danger of some being stolen in transit, most of it also has to be stored somewhere. And of course there is always a possibility, however remote, of an accident.

In the meanwhile, it has begun to emerge that the AEC's scare about running out of uranium is greatly exaggerated. The fuel charge comprises only ten per cent of the capital costs, which are 75 per cent of the whole. Hence uranium at $30 a pound (instead of, say, $8) would increase the cost of electricity by only 1.3 mills per kWh, while increasing US uranium resources from some 600,000 tonnes to 2.24m. tons. A further increase to $50 would raise resources to ten million tons and add 2.5 mills/kWh to the cost. But a price as high as this is never likely to be necessary. At Ranstad in Sweden, low-grade uranium (3 parts in 10,000) is being converted to pure uranium oxide at $10–$15 per pound, while experiments by Dr R. Spence and co-workers at the UKAEA, Harwell, suggest that

LOW MARKS FOR AEC'S BREEDER
REACTOR STUDY

The Federal Environmental Protection Agency has given a failing grade of 'inadequate' to the Atomic Energy Commission's year-long, $2 million attempt to assess the environmental effects of a commercial breeder reactor technology.

The AEC's first attempt to satisfy the requirements of the law was rejected as inadequate by the appeals court last year. In March, the AEC released a draft of its second attempt, a massive five-volume tome some 2200 pages long (*Science* 29 March). In this document, as in the first, the AEC concluded that plutonium-fueled breeder reactors could supply a large portion of the nation's electric power by the year 2000, without adverse effects on the environment and with a saving of billions of dollars over the cost of other technologies.

The EPA, in its critique, said it had not tried to render a 'final judgment' on these claims. At the same time, the EPA said the AEC's new statement 'does not support these conclusions'. The environmental agency gave the AEC report its lowest rating, a 3, signifying that the analysis was in need of 'substantial revision'.

Among its major points, the EPA said that the AEC provided vague and mostly qualitative indications of its approach to major problems of reactor safety; that it provided no assurance that plutonium fuel could be protected from theft at an acceptable cost; and that the volume of wastes produced by large numbers of breeders may have been underestimated.

Most of the EPA's criticism, however, centred on the Commission's optimistic analysis of the breeder's economic costs and benefits. The EPA points to half a dozen technical flaws or omissions, all of which have the effect of either inflating the projected benefits or minimising the costs.

In several instances, for example, the AEC seemed to count some benefits twice—including $67 billion that the AEC believes the breeder would save in capital investment that would otherwise go for uranium production and enrichment. At the same time, the EPA said, the AEC had neglected to add into the cost column the $1 billion that private industry is expected to spend on breeder R & D.

Science (1974) 184: 877

uranium could be got from sea water at \$20–\$40 a pound. Since the sea contains uranium sufficient for millions of years, the case for jettisoning the breeder becomes unanswerable. Clearly it is better to pay a little more for electricity, if necessary, than to endanger the future of the human race. The point is an ethical, not a technical, one, and only besotted technomaniacs could think otherwise.

It would make far more sense to develop the more efficient versions of the conventional 'converter' reactors (such as the High Temperature Gas Cooled Reactor). General Atomics has sold half a dozen round the world, but then dropped the project, as had Britain earlier, in favour of the fast breeder.

4 Faustian Compact

'Many knowledgeable observers believe that the hundreds of commercial LMFBRs that are projected to result from the LMFBR program represent the most serious long-term environmental threat facing our society,' says the National Radiation Defense Corps. At the 1972 Pugwash Conference famous scientists urged that all such programmes be stopped.

Despite the reams written on the subject, the public remains ill-informed about the dangers of nuclear wastes. Uneasily aware that they are a bad thing, they do not know how far to trust the reassurances of the nuclear-power people or the warnings of the environmentalists. Thus D. R. W. Marley at the first World Conference on such wastes, in 1973, said that by 2000 there would be 600 billion curies of waste (4 million being in the form of plutonium-239) but not to worry, as the average dose to the world population would only be 0.2 per cent of background radiation. This embodies two favourite bits of eyewash. The first is the implication that the natural background is harmless, since we all seem to have survived it. In fact it does produce measurable disease and genetic defects and any addition to it will raise the rate of such damage. The second is the trick of averaging the dose over the world population. If nine people receive a very small dose and a tenth receives a large one, he may die, even though the average for the group is reasonable. Thus you could have an acceptable *average* with a quite unacceptable mortality.

The risks from radioactive materials fall into four categories: those from the activity of power stations, from fuel re-processing, from the chance of mishap in transporting fuel to and from the power station, and from a runaway reaction leading to 'super-prompt disassembly' as the official documents soothingly call a nuclear explosion.

One of the most shattering analyses of the risks inherent in the nuclear programme that I have ever read is that made by Dr Alvin Weinberg, the Director of the Oak Ridge National Laboratory and a proponent of nuclear power since way back. He estimates that by 2000, the US will have a million megawatts of nuclear power, two-thirds of it coming from the dreaded LMFBRS. This, he says, will mean between 7,000 and 10,000 annual shipments of spent fuel, with between 60 and 100 loaded casks in shipment at any one moment. Each shipment would generate 75 megacuries of radiation and some 300 kW of heat energy. 'Design of a completely reliable shipping cask for such a radioactive load is a formidable job,' he says— perhaps an understatement, seeing the whole thing would have to be cooled continuously and screened at the same time.

However, the transit problem pales in comparison with the storage problem. Many of the wastes are very long-lived. Technetium-99 will have to be kept for many thousands of centuries before it becomes relatively harmless, and plutonium-239 is nearly as bad.* Weinberg estimates that the US will be holding about 27,000 megacuries of waste by 2000: they will be generating 100 megawatts of heat at that time. Between 1972 and 1985, shipments of 'the more hazardous types of radioactive materials in the US will rise from 1,800 tons to 32,000 tons a year'. As Dr W. Bennett Lewis of Canada's Chalk River facility has said, commitment to nuclear energy is a commitment in perpetuity.

Weinberg freely concedes this, saying: 'We shall never be totally free of concern over reactor safety, transport of radioactive materials and waste disposal.' 'We nuclear people,' he declares grandly, 'have made a Faustian bargain with society. On the one hand we offer . . . an inexhaustible source of energy . . . But the price that we demand of society for this magical energy source is both a vigilance and a longevity of our social institutions that we are quite unaccustomed to.' He concludes: 'Society then must make the choice, and this is a choice that we nuclear people cannot dictate . . . Is mankind prepared to exert the eternal vigilance needed to ensure proper and safe operation of its nuclear energy system? . . . What we offer in return . . . seems to me well worth the price.'

We non-nuclear people, while accepting Dr Weinberg's identification of nuclear people with the devil, may feel that mankind is not in a position to pay the price, whether it likes the deal or not. I for

* The full facts are: when the strontium-90 and cesium-137 have decayed to reasonable levels, i.e., after 600 to 800 years, there remain strong actinides, including americium-241 (half-life 487 years) and plutonium-239 (half-life 24,000 years). The latter will be at a safe level after half a million years. But there will remain plutonium-242 (half-life 380,000 years) and neptunium-237 (half-life 2,200 years) which must be cooled for some centuries and then isolated over biological time-scales.

one am quite unwilling to bet on the human race living up to Dr Weinberg's standards for a quarter of a million years.

Soon after Weinberg's offer was published in *Science*, the eminent biochemist John Edsall wrote from Harvard saying firmly: '. . . I draw the opposite conclusion: the Faustian bargain may indeed be a pact with the devil and we should reject it.' Edsall's letter is worth quoting more fully. He regards increasing social tensions as likely. 'Nuclear plants will be enormously attractive objects for sabotage and blackmail. A well-placed charge of explosives in the midst of one of these huge concentrations of radioactive material could blow into the air enough radioactivity to be carried by the winds over thousands of square miles, and perhaps render large areas uninhabitable for decades . . . only a tiny minority of such people need to exist to imperil all the rest of us.' I agree with the view recently expressed by Hannes Alfvèn (the distinguished Norwegian astrophysicist) in a most thoughtful article, that '. . . fission energy does not represent an acceptable solution to the energy problem. It would place an unendurable burden on the safety and health of future generations.' Edsall considers that we should therefore intensify research on new forms of energy, such as solar power and nuclear fusion, and meanwhile stick to coal and make every possible economy in the use of electricity. Unfortunately large sums have been committed to its development and the authorities seemed determined to force it through.

What is particularly alarming is the intention to recycle plutonium in the present generation of light water reactors. Plutonium is not native to earth. It is 'toxic beyond human experience' observes former AEC physicist Donald Geesaman. One millionth of a gram has been shown to cause cancer in animals. (A gram is one twenty-eighth of an ounce.) It is a bone seeker, but it is most dangerous when inhaled. Permissible air concentrations, under current standards, are one part in a million billion. The Natural Resources Defense Council, in a recent report, says it considers current exposure standards for the general public are 100,000 times too lax and the Council has petitioned the AEC to reduce them accordingly. In its report *The Plutonium Decision* (September 1974) it concludes: 'In sum, to accommodate plutonium, we shall have to move towards a more intimidated society with greatly reduced freedoms.' It urges that any decision to recycle plutonium be deferred until the whole issue has been publicly debated. The AEC's decision to launch what it calls 'the Plutonium Economy' is due to be taken, without debate, in mid-1975.

5 Fusion—Maybe

The ideal power source, the answer to all our energy problems—
or nearly—would be to use the trick the sun uses: fusion power.
The fuel can be derived from ordinary water and is available in
virtually unlimited quantities, at very little cost; and it is relatively
'clean' from the radioactive viewpoint. The only trouble is that no
one knows how to do it.

The atomic energy we have now is based on fission—that is, the
breaking-up of a large atom under the impact of neutrons. When
this happens, the fragments collectively weigh less (more accurately,
have less mass) than did the unsplit atom. The lost mass has become
energy, according to Einstein's famous law, $E = mc^2$. (In practice,
you can only induce a small proportion of the fuel to split, so the
efficiency is much lower than the theoretical maximum.)

Fusion is quite a different matter. Here you heat the fuel to
fantastic temperatures, until all the electrons are stripped from the
atoms, leaving the nuclei bare. This is called a plasma. All the
particles are whizzing about at terrific speeds. Finally the nuclei
begin to collide so violently that some of them fuse, forming different
atoms and exchanging some mass for energy as before. But whereas
in fission heavy atoms are used as fuel, and neutrons are the bullets
which fracture them, in fusion light atoms are used and no neutrons
are needed, though some emerge as a by-product. The most obvious
light atoms to use are deuterium and tritium, the heavier forms of
hydrogen, but others are possible. Deuterium can be extracted from
ordinary sea water quite cheaply—about one-hundredth the cost of
coal.

That such a process was possible was known before the war. The
invention of the atomic bomb (fission) provided a means of producing the fantastic temperatures required for fusion: hence the
hydrogen bomb, first demonstrated in 1951.

The temperatures needed are around 350 *million* degrees Celsius.
Obviously no material, known or unknown, could contain a plasma
at such temperatures: the only solution seems to be to contain it
with a magnetic field. It is fairly easy to make a magnetic 'tube'
but very difficult to stop up the ends. For more than twenty years
scientists have been trying out magnetic configurations which might
contain the plasma long enough for the temperature to rise to the
necessary level. A single second would be enough. Unfortunately
these fields are very unstable: the lines of magnetic force bulge and
squirm like demented elastic and speedily rupture. Coils shaped like
humbugs, coils shaped like the seam in a tennis ball, coils so com-

plicated that they have been called 'a mathematician's delight and a technician's nightmare' have been built in laboratories in the USA, the USSR, Britain, France and Japan. Several times success has seemed to be within grasp. As long ago as 1958 the ZETA system of the British Atomic Energy Authority was hailed as a breakthrough. But as the wilder instabilities were brought under control it emerged that there were finer-scale instabilities to cope with.

No one can say for sure that a solution is possible, but scientists feel they have made steady, if slow, progress and are confident of eventual success. Even if the feat is achieved in the laboratory, it will still have to be shown that the process is workable on a large scale and at a cost which compares with other sources of power. Currently it looks as if the power station would have to be a very large one, perhaps 5,000 MW (current fission reactors range between 1,000 and 2,000 MW).* Calculations made by P. Carruthers for the British AEA in 1967 suggested a capital cost of some £70 for each kilowatt of electricity produced, implying £350 million for each power station, of which a mere £10 million would be for the fuel. Such a station could produce electricity slightly cheaper than the best contemporary breeder reactors. Of course, these figures are outdated by inflation and will no doubt be even more unrealistic by the time such a station is attempted. In any case, they allow nothing for development costs, which may be considerable, and, I suspect, they underestimate the cost of containing radioactivity.

Certainly the fusion reactor is vastly cleaner than the satanic devices discussed in the preceding section and this has given it the reputation of being completely clean. Actually, however, it produces two forms of radioactive waste. These depend on the fuel used. Since the most likely fuel is deuterium, and this is also the most polluting, I shall consider this case. Deuterium gives rise to tritium, which is quite nasty. The molecule is so tiny that it leaks out of aluminium and even stainless steel containers by actually diffusing through the metal. It passes through most valves and seals. It can pass into the body either by being breathed or in water which is drunk, probably even by diffusion through the skin. Unburnt tritium from the fusion process will escape and must be recovered. Don 'Steiner of the Oak Ridge National Laboratory reckons that leakage would have to be limited to eight curies a day in a 5,000 MW reactor—that is to say, you could only afford to lose one ten-thousandth part of the tritium load. The cost of sealing the reactor

---

* Recently a new line of attack on the fusion problem has been launched which holds out the promise of a reactor small enough to power a ship or factory, perhaps as small as 20 kW. This involves firing pulses of coherent light from a battery of lasers at tiny pellets of fuel: each one implodes and this causes a spurt of heat, like a miniature bomb.

to such a standard may prove crucial. 'It is my opinion,' Steiner warns, 'that tritium release will be the primary concern in the event of an accident.'

As I have described in *The Doomsday Book*, tritium from fission reactors and fuel re-processing plants will probably already have reached alarming levels by the time fusion reactors are practical so that any addition to the existing risk may by then be regarded as intolerable.

Tritium has a rather short half-life of 12.3 years. (That is, it loses half its activity in twelve years, half of what remains in the next twelve, and so on.) The position is quite different in respect of the other radioactive risk, which arises from the 'blanket' of lithium coolant which surrounds the hot core and the structures which contain it. Lithium is corrosive stuff and must be contained in metals like vanadium and niobium. These become radioactive as a result of the bombardment coming from the core. Vanadium is less dangerous but is limited to lower operating temperatures, so probably niobium will be used. Now radioactive niobium has a half-life of 29,000 years and the disposal of these structures (which may swell or deform under the bombardment) is a problem which, though quantitatively smaller, is just as awkward as those we considered in the previous section.

Despite all this, fusion is a good idea if it works. But even if it is made to work in the laboratory before this book is published, it can hardly be less than twenty years before commercial stations begin to operate. At least one full-scale prototype will have to be tested, and it takes up to eight years to build a fission station today, with twenty years' experience to go on. Technologists always underestimate the difficulties, as they did in the case of fission. And until we have fusion power, we cannot have the hydrogen economy.

6 Hydrogen Economy

The nearest thing to an ideal fuel that man is ever likely to see is hydrogen: the simplest of all the elements. It is by burning hydrogen that rockets reached the moon. Hydrogen is readily made from water and when burnt the only waste product is water. There are no pollutants. It would revolutionise cooking and heating as no flue is needed. It could be generated by solar power in unattended plants at an efficiency of 60 per cent—far better than the 40 per cent efficiency of an oil-fuelled power station. With trifling modifications, it can operate an ordinary car engine, which is then pollution-free.

It could be distributed by existing pipeline, its heating value is lower than natural gas, but its lower viscosity and density compensate for this. Bulk storage is somewhat more of a problem than with oil, although NASA maintains a 900,000 gallon tank at Cape Kennedy and smaller ones elsewhere. All in all, it seems the answer to a prayer.

Everything has some drawback, and hydrogen's is its low ignition point. However, industry uses it without disaster, thanks to strict regulations, and the Space Agency has handled vast quantities without mishap. For domestic use, odorants would have to be added, so that leaks could be quickly detected. After all, household gas forms an explosive mixture with air, but accidents from this cause are not frequent enough to deter people from using it. Conceivably, however, it may be impractical to use it for private cars, for this reason.

The chief reason we don't have a hydrogen-based economy already is cost—the cost of manufacture and the cost of transmission.

To make hydrogen, the simplest course is to apply an electric current to water, which splits it into hydrogen and oxygen. It follows that hydrogen must cost more than electricity and, hitherto, that has also meant more than oil. Equally, it cannot compete with natural gas. If the price of electricity falls, as a result of using nuclear fuels, this could make hydrogen cheaper than oil and perhaps cheaper than gas. Hydrogen can also be made by the gasification of coal but this is only interesting if nuclear power is unavailable.

The problem is one of quantity: to change the natural gas system over to a hydrogen system would mean quadrupling the supply of electricity. To provide hydrogen for vehicles of every kind would mean manufacturing such vast amounts of electricity that questions of radioactive pollution and heat dumping would become serious. Hydrogen is only really 'on' when fusion power is available, if then.

As against this, the cost of transmission over any distance greater than 250 miles is cheaper than using electric transmission lines— and at a thousand miles or so, is only half as expensive. It is also cheaper than electricity from local distribution or the delivery of petrol by tankers. No unattractive space-consuming transformer stations are needed. Since the pipes run underground it does not spoil the scenery. In a century or so, perhaps our vast system of high-voltage transmission lines will prove to be a white elephant. Hydrogen could carry the energy from point to point and be converted back to electricity for local distribution.

It has been calculated that hydrogen would only be competitive as a fuel for vehicles if off-peak power were used to make it, at the present time. But a Mr Morris Klein of Miami has been running a delivery truck on hydrogen for less than half a cent a mile. However, while the cars themselves would be non-polluting, the total radioactivity produced would increase (owing to the increased electricity demand) by something like 60 per cent, assuming all cars were running on hydrogen by the year 2000.

Though no one expects immediate adoption, for the reasons I have given, a contributor to the British journal *New Scientist*, Mr Timothy Johnson, dismisses the enthusiasm for hydrogen as a fuel as 'nonsense' on the grounds that it is thermodynamically inefficient to use electricity to convert water to hydrogen, only to convert it back to electricity again. Consequently, it 'would do more harm than good, environmentally speaking, even if it shuffled the pollution around a little. For this and other reasons, one can feel fairly confident that the idea will be quietly forgotten about for another decade or so after the present flurry has died down.'

This is not the view, however, of Mr Francis Bacon, famous as the inventor of the fuel cell. The efficiency of the electrical decomposition of water could certainly be increased, he points out, and it is also possible to devise processes which depend on heat in the first place. A helium-fuelled reactor would be hot enough to decompose water to steam which could then be put through two or three chemical reactions to produce hydrogen. Hydrogen, with other synthetic fuels such as methanol and hydrazine, 'will not be mere luxuries but necessities of life,' he says. 'They may be needed in large quantities even before the year 2000.' This was also the view of several scientists who presented papers on the topic at the 1972 meeting of the American Chemical Society. 'Hydrogen could become the principal world fuel of the twenty-first century.'

An Australian, Professor J. Bockris of Flinders University, makes the further point that hydrogen is so light that it would increase the range of jet-aircraft and perhaps make a one-man helicopter practicable. And it could reduce the cost of many chemical processes from aluminium-making to the hydrogenation of fats. The cost of ammonia would be halved.

It seems a pity, therefore, that in 1967 Britain decided to cut back research on fusion.

7 Future Alternatives

Whether man goes ahead with the breeder reactor or no, it looks as if electricity will be short at least until 1985. Oil could be plentiful for a while, once the Arabs lift their restrictions (which they will probably do as soon as oil from other sources becomes fairly available) but it will become steadily scarcer as supplies are used up. If you choose to have the breeder, electricity might even get cheaper. What will happen after 1985 depends on whether a major accident or hijacking of plutonium occurs before the breeder program has gone too far to stop. Without the breeder, electricity could become slightly more expensive up to 1990.

Coal will enjoy a new lease of life, and will be converted to gas and oil wherever it can be mined freely. During this coal hey-day, miners will be able to dictate their own wages and coal will become dearer, rising to match the price of oil. But after 1985, as the nuclear stations begin to supply the bulk of current, the hey-day will be over.

Thanks to North Sea oil, together with plentiful coal, Britain should be relatively well placed by 1985—but back in trouble again by the end of the century. But Europe, except for Norway, will still be a big importer of oil in 1985.

Higher prices will mean more emphasis on economy. Many industrial processes are absurdly prodigal of energy. Charles A. Berg, a deputy director at the National Bureau of Standards, maintains that a quarter of total national energy consumption may be being wasted by correctable leaks at the point of use. The insulation of houses and offices, to say nothing of ovens, refrigerators, etc., is governed by initial costs: this also goes for the ventilation arrangements, type of heating installed and so on. Most insulation pays for itself in five years (sooner if fuel costs rise) and buildings now consume 40 per cent more energy than necessary. Perhaps huge picture windows are already obsolete.

Power stations are also profligate, discharging two-thirds of their energy into the air through cooling towers, or into rivers or the sea as waste heat.

The prodigal expenditure of energy on flood-lighting, illuminated advertisements, and the like, may have to be curbed.

Airlines will be forced to rationalise their services; it has been calculated that 800 million gallons of jet fuel could be saved annually in the us, without reducing the number of passenger miles flown, if airlines worked out optimum flight schedules.

But rising fuel costs will be reflected in higher prices all round. In particular, they will affect the balance of payments of all those countries which are obliged to import fuel, especially third-world countries which have not yet contrived their own fuel supplies. Above all, dearer energy will hit agriculture, as we have already seen.

What we have to do therefore is to make intensive efforts to develop new sources of energy and, especially, sources which are self-renewing. There is little doubt in my mind that the best course is to derive energy directly from the sun, or—since this may not be economic—indirectly from the temperature differences in the oceans. All other sources are relatively trivial, however useful they may be in special circumstances.

Geothermal energy could be important to one or two small countries, like Ethiopia, but would never be more than a drop in the bucket for a country like the US. The availability of tidal power is even more limited.

Solar energy is still far from being economic, except in such small-scale uses as heating homes or swimming pools. Aden and Marjorie Meinel (Aden Meinel is Director of the Optical Sciences Center of the University of Arizona) have calculated that to generate a million megawatts would require an area of 5,000 square miles even in the favourable conditions of Arizona, where the sun shines 330 days a year, and the cost would certainly be double that of the equivalent number of nuclear power stations. This may be too low, points out Paul Gast of the Argonne National Laboratory, since it allows insufficient margin for heat storage to carry you over cloudy days: probably three times nuclear would be nearer. And the Meinels assume the plant will last for forty years. However, no one knows what the life of these acres of lenses and pipes would be, baked by the sun and scoured by desert sand, or how much they would cost to maintain. This is even more likely to be a problem with the costly solar cells developed for powering space satellites. Nevertheless, international firms such as Minneapolis-Honeywell think there are possibilities. The Space Administration thinks solar power might meet 20 per cent of US needs by 2000.

A far more promising prospect is to exploit the temperature differences in the sea. A refrigerator uses energy to create a temperature difference; conversely one can use a temperature difference to create energy. This 'refrigerator in reverse' idea involves lowering pipes into the cold sea depths and circulating through them a fluid which vaporises when it passes through the warm upper parts of the pipe and condenses when it sinks to the colder parts. Its vaporisation can be used to drive an engine, just as steam, which is vaporised water, can. The idea is nearly a century old, having been suggested by the French physicist, Jacques d'Arsonval, in 1881. He proposed using ammonia as the circulating liquid. Clarence Zener, a professor at Carnegie-Mellon University, has revived the idea and calculates the capital cost to be about the same as a fossil-fuel plant. But, since capital cost only accounts for half the cost of electricity, fuel accounting for most of the rest, the fuelless 'reverse refrigerator' may be capable of generating power at half the normal cost. (Incidentally, it could also produce fresh water in quantity.) The main problem is getting the power ashore: the simplest course would be to send hydrogen.

Zener's personal conclusion is 'that the probability of economic feasibility is so high that advanced reactors, such as the liquid metal fast breeder reactors the AEC is developing, will be economically obsolete before development is completed'.

I believe there will be increasing interest in small, independent power sources, for two rather different but interlocking reasons. First is the romantic desire for self-sufficiency and independence, buttressed by the real possibility of shortages. Second is the increasing likelihood of large-scale public supplies being suddenly interrupted, whether by industrial action, by technical breakdown (as in the all-too-familiar 'brown-outs') or due to terrorism.

Here solar heating for houses has an obvious role to play: what is less well known is that these systems can be used even more effectively for cooling in summer. Also promising here is methane, otherwise known as marsh-gas, which can be made from household or farm sewage, at present commonly discharged into sewers and then into rivers or coastal waters, creating pollution. Using methane thus kills two birds with one stone. And it can be used to propel vehicles. Finally, the burning of waste to produce energy, already tried in London, Paris and other cities, could be developed much further.

In Haiti solar steam produced by solar heat is being used to cook the meals for 240 students in a school and to distil drinking water. In Syria, a solar hot-box costing only $14 serves to dehydrate and preserve vegetables. These rough-and-ready devices were developed by the Brace Research Department at McGill University; but this is only one of many organisations springing up to develop 'oil-drum technologies', 'low-impact technologies' and so-called 'intermediate technologies' intended as stepping-stones by which less developed lands can ease their way towards industrialisation.

If this view is correct, America's proposed distribution of funds for energy research and development needs revision. Le ing aside the large sums quite properly assigned to improving the fficiency of existing sources and to conserving energy, the expenditures on novel forms recommended for fiscal years 1975–9 by the President's Advisory Council on Energy were as shown in Table on page 234.

As can be seen, the breeder reactor is still 'the stellar attraction': most or all of that money should be switched to other programmes.

I have dwelt on the US proposals because no other country has even produced a ten-year scheme, and certainly none is committing a fraction of the resources the US is committing. This is true even allowing for the differences in GNP.

There seems little doubt that the money could profitably be made available. In July 1973, six international banks set up the International Energy Bank to finance energy development. A spokesman said that they estimated the world-wide capital requirements of the energy industry over the next decade at £500,000 million—that is,

	$m.
Fossil fuels	3675
Fission option:	
high-temperature gas reactor, safety and waste management	1660
breeder reactor	2730
Other programs:	
fusion	1550
solar	200
geothermal	185
ocean heat-pumps	0
small-scale sources	0
	$10,000m.

more than a hundred times the expected cost of exploration and development of North Sea oil.

But suppose we solve the energy problem, what then? Shall we proceed on our materialistic course, using up resources and polluting the environment with undiminished enthusiasm? It is all too probable. The question at issue is not: where shall we get the energy? but: do we want the growth society as we have known it? Naturally, growth is not without a good aspect. It would be folly to attempt to freeze the *status quo*. Any device which provides more human satisfaction, *provided that* it does not take away from other sorts of satisfaction (from clean air to social cohesion) is wholly desirable. The question is whether we are smart enough to be selective, instead of constantly giving the edge to material growth over other satisfactions, unthinkingly.

And if we do opt for material growth, shall we simply go on widening the gap between the rich and poor nations, providing ourselves with ever more ingenious gadgetry and scrapping many of our products long before they are worn out while more than half the world lives on the edge of poverty when not actually starving? It seems an unworkable scenario, even if the West is crazy enough to try to enact it. The countries of the 'third world' pose problems which we have not even begun to answer, but must at least face.

XV

CROWDED!

The scourges of pestilence, famine, wars and earthquakes have come to be regarded as a blessing to overcrowded nations, since they serve to prune away the luxuriant growth of the human race.

— Tertullian

1 Choking Cities

Take Djakarta, the capital of Indonesia, where new health centres have cut the death-rate by a quarter. Here five million people live in a space sufficient for two million. Ten years from now the population will be nine million. Or take Bandung, the fastest-growing city in the world at the moment. Bandung is expected to swell 242 per cent, from 1.2m. to 4.1m. between 1970 and 1985. Lagos, Karachi, Bogota and Baghdad, with growth rates of 186, 163, 146 and 145 per cent respectively, are the runners-up. As a consequence the list of the world's largest cities will look very different by 1985 (population in millions):

Tokyo	25.2
New York	18.8
Mexico City	17.9
Sao Paulo	16.8
Shanghai	14.3
Los Angeles	13.7
Bombay	12.1
Calcutta	12.1
Peking	12.0
Osaka	11.8

London and Paris will be thirteenth and fourteenth on the list, about to be overtaken by Seoul.

As cities begin to run together we can think more profitably in terms of megalopolises, such as the existing New York–Philadelphia–

235

Washington conurbation. At present there are about a dozen of these urban complexes, ranging from 1m. to 60m. in size, while six more are emerging. According to J. G. Papaiannou of the School of Ekistics, Athens, there will be a hundred of them by the end of the century, with populations running between tens and hundreds of millions each. They will contain nearly half the world's population—though Papaiannou thinks that the world's population will be greater than the officially predicted figure of 6½–7 billion; he puts it at 7–8 billion by that date.*

Well over half the world's population will be living in cities of over 100,000 by the end of the century and they will be living at high densities. In Calcutta, where already an estimated 600,000 people sleep in the streets, the density at the moment is 84,896 to the square mile. This is what creates the strain: not only the economic strain of providing water and drainage, houses, schools and hospitals (according to one estimate, 1.4 billion new houses will be needed between now and AD 2000) but the social strain of containing crime and integrating these uprooted people into communities.

In short, the overriding problem we have to solve is not merely the population problem—which we know about and are trying to tackle—but the cities problem, which we have not yet begun to tackle at all.

When towns grow at these rates, even the most efficient and well-meaning authorities cannot provide accommodation fast enough: shanty towns spring up—bustees, barong-barongs, callampas, favelas, villas miserias, barracas, barrios, geçekundu or bidonvilles. The choice of terms gives us a glimpse of the range of the problem. In some cities the misery-towns house as many people as the city proper. Soon these squatters will outnumber their hosts.

While some of them are disheartened or down-and-out, and others are more or less criminal, a considerable proportion of the inhabitants of these home-made suburbs are people of enterprise and public spirit, and some are well educated. They form committees to plan more logical development and make attempts to persuade the authorities to provide water and electricity, if nothing else, and perhaps to pave the streets. It has therefore been argued, rightly I am sure, that effort should be devoted to upgrading the communities which already exist as rapidly as may be possible, rather than clearing areas for elaborate housing developments. Lacking in community spirit from the start, these endure to become the slums of tomorrow, while the barriadas are easily torn down to replace with something better as opportunity permits. Moreover, the concrete blocks of

* While this book was in press it was announced that world population had passed the four billion mark early in 1974—sooner than expected.

which the planners are so proud can only absorb a fraction of those in need. If the butter is scarce, spread it thin.

It is, of course, grotesque that the rich world does so little to mend this situation. According to a press report, the Calcutta city corporation attempts to collect the 'night soil' from the city's 40,000 public privies with 22 trucks, 25 trolleys and occasional tractors: this force is able to cope with barely one-third. Almost half the central metropolitan area is without sewers, and when it rains the sewage in the streets is swept into basements and kitchens. The water supply system is as defective as the sewage system. When the Calcutta Metropolitan Development Corporation sought to clear the gully pits, it was told that the gully pits could not be cleared because the inlets were choked, the manholes could not be cleared because the sewers were choked, and the sewers could not be cleared because the pumping stations were too weak. It is beyond belief that the rich world cannot form task forces and provide pumping equipment and sanitation vehicles to improve the position.

Small wonder that many social analysts fear the collapse of public order in class and racial conflict, in riots and guerrilla warfare. We have already seen racial riots in Bombay, army evictions of squatters in Manila, Chinese/Malay massacres in Kuala Lumpur, shootings in Peru and bloody suppression of student protest everywhere from Seoul to Bangkok. Food riots are reported almost daily from different Indian provinces. If the rich nations do not wish to cope with a world aflame, in which bitterly resentful men indulge in dramatic acts of destruction—and as the Arabs have taught us, such acts may be directed at the West—they should, in their own narrow interests, begin to tackle such problems. The possibility of Communism being adopted is also a motive.

The International Labour Office has argued, in the person of one of its officers, H. Lubell, that these poverty-stricken areas are not dead, but are brimming with life, and that therefore one need not approach the problem in a doom-laden spirit. This is to miss the point. It is not the quality of the people but the failure to alleviate the misery which gives cause for trepidation. The vitality, if not given the help which could turn it into constructive channels, could well switch to destructive ones.

2 Dying Cities in the West

While the barriadas expand around the burgeoning cities of the third world, until their inhabitants outnumber those of the city proper, in the first world people are fleeing from the centre of cities, as much to escape from crime and violence as to attain the pleasures of a suburban or rural existence. Detroit is a horrific example of the future which lies ahead of the new megalopolises. More people were shot or stabbed in Detroit in 1973 than have been killed in four and a half years of civil strife in Belfast. The murder rate, one in 1,806 city inhabitants, was the highest in the US. The schools system is collapsing. Commercial development has ceased. The city has more abandoned and derelict houses than any city in America. The inhabitants are streaming out at the rate of 40,000 a year—to suburbs where they live in ghettos surrounded by high fences and protected by armed guards, night and day, if they can afford it.

Even in England, where violence is much less of a factor, the cities are under pressure from the outward movement. In 1973 one British paper carried the headline: 'Why Britain's Cities are slowly seizing up.' Another asked: 'Is London Facing Collapse?' Vital services are desperately short of staff. London Transport has only 80 per cent of the staff it needs to inspect tracks. Buses and trains supposed to run at ten-minute intervals may run an hour apart. In the borough of Greenwich, the housing programme has been 'virtually brought to a standstill' for lack of supervisors and crafts-men. Schools cannot find teachers, the health departments cannot find dustmen. The reason is that people find it cheaper and pleasanter to live in the suburbs, where they can find work readily, without facing a tiring and costly journey to the centre. An incomes policy which limits wages prevents any attempt to lure workers in by offers of higher pay. This is how the centre of great cities begins to die. Cities resemble a growing mass of bacteria. Those in the middle die because they are shut off from light and air by those outside.

'London's population needs to be brought below the 6 million mark,' says Professor Alan Day of the London School of Economics. Some hopes! The let's-not-panic brigade tries to argue that people really prefer urban living, and that is why the cities grow. The demand for country cottages is one of the facts that show how untrue this is. A Gallup Poll showed that 56 per cent of Americans would prefer a fully rural life if they could have it, while a further 25 per cent would choose suburban living. Only 18 per cent said they actually wanted to live in cities. Moreover the cost of running big cities compares adversely with small. Thus in the US education can be provided at $12 per head in cities under 50,000; the figure is double for cities between 200,000 and 300,000; it is quadrupled for 500,000 and rises to $85 per head for cities of a million plus. Similarly public health is twelve times as costly in cities over one million population compared with cities under 50,000, while welfare costs the rate payer 88 times as much. Again the crime rate shows

12.8 robberies per 100,000 population in cities under 10,000 against 117.6 in cities over a quarter of a million, while the capital cost of police services doubles. The case is unanswerable. Why don't we do something about it?

The death of cities is a theme now so familiar that it need not be embroidered, unless to say that in crowded animal populations fertility falls. Recently completed experiments by John Calhoun, whose populations of over-crowded mice have been widely written about, show that when these mice are removed to normal conditions they fail to recover their fertility. The damage to their systems is irreversible.

Some architects, with little knowledge of anthropological reality, have claimed that the megalopolis is perfectly viable. Cities will be divided into cells of 50,000 people, and they will preserve their own culture and a human scale. Richard L. Meier, of the University of Michigan has pushed this idea to the limits of euphoria. 'The kind of city that will be able to compete successfully in the future,' he says with true American faith in the dollar, 'is the one which generates wealth. Therefore planning will have to take a different tack,' that is, different from seeking to design a city in which one can 'find serenity'. He envisages cities partitioned into ethnic groups, speaking the same language or dialect, growing their own algae to provide protein, fertilising it with chicken-dung and reprocessing the water for drinking purposes. Since these 'urban villages' will have to be kept busy, they will have to find work which needs lots of labour but little raw materials; that is, they will have to make complicated gadgets. And, since no one will be living in the countries between these cities (which will contain 90–95 per cent of the world's population at densities of 100,000 to the square mile) airlines will be much more important than now, to link them together. One can hardly wait.

3 The People Problem

Population growth is of course the author of all these problems. India, for instance, succeeded in increasing agricultural output by 24 per cent from 1961 to 1971—but the population rose 24.75 per cent in the same period. So the inescapable question is: what progress is being made with population control? Who is right? The doomsayers or the optimists?

The population explosion has by now been written about to the point of boredom, and I discussed it in detail five years ago in *The Doomsday Book*. All I propose to do here therefore is to consider whether the situation has changed since then or shows signs of changing. The following table summarises the position:

POPULATION (millions)

	1950	*1970*	*Increase*
Latin America	162	283	75%
Africa	217	344	59%
Asia	1,355	2,056	52%
Oceania	13	19	46%
North America	166	228	37%
Russia	180	243	35%
Europe	392	462	18%

The places where family planning has been unambiguously successful are Japan (birth rate 9.4 per 1,000 in 1964), Hong Kong (18.9 per 1,000 in 1970), Taiwan (23 per 1,000 in 1969), Singapore (25–28 per 1,000 in 1967). It has been moderately successful in places like Sri Lanka (Ceylon) where the rate was down from 36 in 1960 to 32 by 1968, and Korea (33 in 1969). It is easy to contrast with these places like Kenya, where the government provides only insignificant funds and Mboya has said 'population growth is not particularly alarming to the government', and where a trade unionist attacked family planning as recently as 1970, saying it was asking workers 'to refrain from the only source of pleasure they have'. In Kenya, the birth rate is about 50 per 1,000, the crude death rate 20.

Particularly alarming is the case of the Philippines, possibly the fastest-growing population in the world. Average family size: 7. Fifteenth largest country in the world in terms of population, fifty-seventh in terms of land area. For every four Filipinos who die or retire from work, fourteen are waiting to step into their job. Twenty-five per cent of the population consists of working mothers. If this explosion continues, a century from now the Philippines will have the equivalent of the present combined populations of North America, Latin America, Africa and the USSR. Of course, it cannot continue. Already food is running short.

However, these are relatively small areas. It is vast countries like India and Bangladesh which really matter. The case of India is particularly instructive, since a major effort has been made. Despite the existence of more than 80,000 full- and part-time workers on family planning and the spending of almost as much money as on the health services, birth rates have hardly been affected.

A glance at the diagram opposite, which shows the change in India's population, reveals immediately that the situation there is worse than ever. The rate of increase is not tapering off, it is getting steeper: 24.75 per cent increase in the last census decade, 13.31 per cent in the decade before that.

Despite this the Indian industrialist, J. R. D. Tata, is one of the

optimists. 'In Family Planning,' he told the Nobel Symposium in
1969, 'there are unmistakable signs of a significant advance.' He
pointed to two industrial towns, Jamshedpur and Mithapur, where
the birth rate has been reduced to below 25 per thousand against
40 per thousand for the nation as a whole. But the fact is, family
planning has only proved effective among relatively sophisticated
urban populations, within near reach of clinics. In South India it

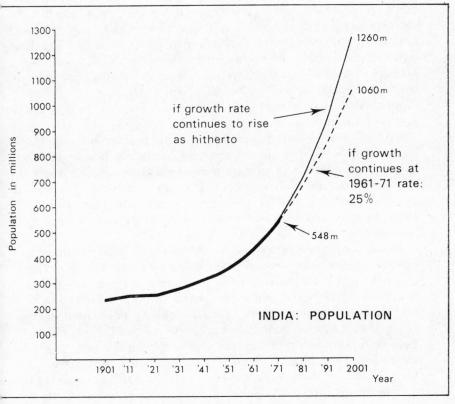

Projections for the growth rate of India's population.

has failed to bite at all. (Tata's optimism about agriculture is equally
unreliable: the Green Revolution has broken through, he said, and
food production has begun to forge ahead at 5 per cent per year!
In actual fact, the 1970 figure was about 2 per cent, the 1971 figure,
zero.)

Social custom is still against the limitation of families: more, social
pressure on a young married couple is to procreate. 'In the final
analysis,' says Tara Ali Baig in the Indian paper *Seminar*, 'nothing
but economic desperation makes a man or his wife in a traditional

home decide to be sterilised.' It is only when four, six or more children have been born that the family faces the fact that it cannot support more children and sends the ten- or twelve-year-olds out to earn their living.

In seven villages in the Punjab, an intensive effort was made over five years to spread knowledge of birth control, change attitudes to it and to reduce birth rates. It was a complete failure: all that this programme, known as the Khanna Study, achieved was to make about one-third of those couples already practising birth-control switch to more modern methods. The truth was, people had large families, not because they overestimated infant mortality, but because they *needed* large families. Eighty-five per cent were small or middling farmers who could not afford to buy a tractor or hire labour to farm their small plots, 16 acres or less. 'To farm at all they needed family labour. More sons meant only a marginal increase in household costs but a significant decrease in farm labour costs,' says Mahmood Mamdani in a devastating critique of this programme. 'Children were often the only means to prosperity.' In short, family planning is not just a question of education and providing contraceptives, as so many Western 'experts' believe. It means solving the problem of poverty. In India, at least, poverty does not come from high birth rates; high birth rates come from poverty. This vicious circle will not easily be broken.

India, displeased with the tactlessness of some international agencies, threw them out and decided to go it alone. For an example of what can be done with international help, we can turn to Java. Indonesia is the world's fifth most populous country at 129 million and doubling every 24 years. (Estimates of the population in 2001 range from 220m. to 300m.) But what makes this the world's worst population problem is that 70 per cent of the population (80m.) live in Java and the nearby island of Bali, an area hardly larger than Greece, which has a population of 9m. By 2000 there may be 175m.

The former president, Sukarno, was actually 'pro-natalist' and objected to contraception as conducing to 'moral laxity'. Indonesia could support 250m. people, he claimed. The new president, Suharto, reversed this policy: almost a million people were killed out of hand, mostly Chinese, and some 2,000 family planning clinics were set up. Field workers go to the villages to persuade the women to attend. Contraceptive devices are provided free (in theory; in practice the staff are apt to supplement their meagre incomes by charging). In Bali, mainly Hindu-Buddhist, acceptance has been high; in Java, predominantly Muslim, less so, for religious reasons. Strong motivation is provided: no promotion for soldiers or civil servants with more than three children, and no foreign travel.

Persuaded by these means, and aided by almost unlimited money from the World Bank, 20 per cent are now using birth control and an acceptance rate has been achieved which the World Bank did not expect until 1975.

But none of this means that zero growth is in sight. 'Forget about zero,' Dr Judono, a key official, told Jon Tinker of the *New Scientist*. 'If within a generation we can get it down to 1.5 per cent annual growth that would be tolerable.' But a rate of 1.5 per cent means 300m. people in Java by 2050. Such is the scale of the problem.

Westerners who like to reassure themselves that there is nothing to worry about often point to the fact that, when countries become industrialised, the birth rate drops. So it does, but they ignore the fact that the process has always taken several generations and that it has never gone as far as levelling off at replacement rates. Britain, after two centuries of industrialisation, still has a rising population. So does Japan, often cited as the star example of birth limitation.

They also point enthusiastically to falling birth rates, without asking whether death rates are not falling just as fast or faster. They leaped on the recent downward readjustment in Britain's population projections, which may well be due to couples starting their families at a later age, or spacing their children more widely, as a result of wider contraceptive knowledge, rather than to a genuine reduction in preferred family size. In any case, the girls who will be bearing the babies in the nineties have already been born, and we know that in every country they are more numerous than in any previous period. This is the origin of the famous 'demographic inertia'—it takes some twenty years before any reduction in the birth rate can begin to affect population size, even when death rates are constant. Thus in Britain (birth rate about 14.7), for every hundred women in their twenties in 1971 there will be 120 in 1991. The population is expected to increase by ten million by 2012.

Only in China, where the population is extraordinarily obedient, have there been dramatic results. In pursuit of Mao's precept, 'To allow anarchy to win in human reproduction is not to be tolerated. It is also necessary to practice planning-of-birth,' population is planned at the three basic levels of social organisation: the production team, the production brigade (consisting of seven to twenty teams) and the commune (10,000 to 60,000 members). In November, the teams sit down with the cadres of Party officials and work out how many babies will be born and who will bear them each year for the next five years. Newly-weds have first claim on the quota, then couples with fewer than three children, then women whose last child is four or five years old. If a woman is scheduled to conceive at a time when her husband will be away on a job, she can swap with another woman. Newly-marrieds are not expected to practice birth control until after the birth of their first child. Contraceptive pills are distributed free on a lavish scale and abortion is widely performed, on the mother's request alone.

While some communes are known to have cut the birth rate to 19 or less, how widely this system is proving effective is unknown, since China does not compute a fertility rate, and the census figures are highly unreliable. Even the Chinese government does not know the population count, which has been estimated at less than 750m. by the Chinese Planning Department but at 830m. by the Ministry of Commerce. The population is thought to be growing by 2 per cent per year.

But it is still the case that half the world does not know about scientific contraception and only one third practises it. Every second there are two additional mouths to feed. Every day there are 200,000 more births than deaths, six million more every month. The central problem of the day has not been solved and will dog us during the near future. The standard world population projections are still valid for twenty years ahead, if not longer.

The point emerges clearly in Bangladesh, with a population of 73m. in 1973. According to a report sponsored by the UN Relief Organisation, and on the basis of projections made at the Harvard University Center for Population Studies, it appears that, even if there is a drastic reduction in fertility from the present family size of 6.5 to 2.2 children, the population will be 153m. by 2003. If Bangladesh achieves replacement rate by 2000–5 and maintains it, the population will continue to grow until 2070, when it will be 234.6m.

This implies a density of population of 2,750 to the square mile, even on the assumption of reduced fertility, and 4,260 if there is no reduction—incredible figures. By 2003, also, the population per cultivable acre will be 6.8. How can seven people live off an acre of land? 'A fundamental revision of the landholding and settlement patterns will become essential, to make use of modern agricultural inputs,' says the UN Relief Organisation.

Even in Europe, if the reproduction rate were to fall as low as 0.9, the population would grow for some time and it would be 50 years before it would have sunk back to the present level.

In the face of such figures it is hard to understand how there can still be some countries where family planning is regarded as unimportant, if not indeed a Western ploy to preserve its dominance—and how Catholic interests can still oppose the implementation of family planning. Brazil plans to raise its population and the Argentine has mounted a campaign to double its population by the end of the century. Population problems are not discussed in the UN (and were ignored at the Stockholm Conference on the Environment) for fear of offending such countries.

EHRLICH WARNS ON UNDERPOPULATION

Emeritus Professor Paul Ehrlich, who at the age of 70 has embarked upon a world crusade to halt the population decline, announced at a press conference in Los Angeles today that a team under his direction are within sight of a technique to reduce the human gestation period to three months. He is levitating to New York next week to meet the Secretary General of the United Nations who has promised help in setting up the World Sperm Bank. The Bank project ran into trouble at the last session when the general assembly could not agree on the predominant pigmentation. Professor Ehrlich, who favours a light tan, said today that the colour squabble had been allowed to obscure the main issue. 'What we want is more people, no matter what colour they may be. More people, more quickly.' He said the situation in the Eastern States (England, Wales and Scotland) was becoming critical. There were now only four families known to be living north of Birmingham, England. He was also concerned about the pace of re-populating India through immigration; he urged that no further entrance permits to the lunar settlements be granted to women still capable of bearing children.

New Scientist 45 (682): 19

There is only one thing which, as far as I can see, would really change the position overnight: the discovery of a simple way of biasing the sex ratio towards males. Almost all unsophisticated peoples want sons, rather than daughters, because they can do agricultural work, so the method would be adopted very rapidly. But, it goes without saying, that, if fewer girls are born, the population must, within fifteen or twenty years, begin to fall. In a saner world, instead of pouring money into contraception we would be working on this problem.

4 Don't Make a Move

If you have a quantity of gas in a container, you can raise the pressure it exerts on the walls in two ways: you can pump in more gas or you can heat the gas which is already there. Then the gas molecules rush frantically about, impinging on the walls at higher speeds and also colliding with each other. In much the same way, members of a more mobile population have a greater impact on the environment, and each other, than members of a stable one. Since the world's population is both growing and more mobile, the impact is multiplied. It would be more to the point to reduce mobility. And this may happen.

Transport, cars especially, make it possible for people to flood into an area in numbers too great to handle. Towns like Florence, which everyone wishes to visit, become a misery. The Sistine Chapel in Rome is a shoving mass, a cacophony of voices in a dozen languages, from morning till night. In Westminster Abbey, London, as many as 3,000 people crowd into an area calculated to hold 700. The charm of remote villages is destroyed by gangs of youthful tourists with their guitars. (And too often they seem uninterested in what they have supposedly come to see.) In the US it is necessary to book months ahead to visit the more popular national parks, while the trails have had to be hard-surfaced to stand up to the wear. The introduction of snowmobiles, dune-buggies, trail-runners and other specialised vehicles has opened up areas previously immune, while fibreglass boats and outboard motors have enabled the rape of islands and remote lakes and beaches.

The area currently most threatened is the Pacific, easily accessible to those enthusiastic tourists, the Japanese. British airlines have been counting on increases in traffic of 100 per cent to the Caribbean, 150 per cent to Japan and 200 per cent to Australia over the next 10 years. (This was before the fuel crisis, which caused downward revisions. But, as I have said, fuel may be plentiful again in a few years time.) Local authorities are beginning to restrict the building of hotels and holiday accommodation in an attempt to limit the inflow of people.

The biggest increases up to 1980, apart from Fiji (500 per cent increase by 1980) and French Polynesia, are expected to be in New Zealand, Australia, Mexico, South America and the Magreb, in descending order; all these are expected to show annual growth rates of over 10 per cent. While these are the fast expansions, the numbers involved are small, and more than half the tourists will be going to Canada, the USA, France and Spain.

Hitherto, most forecasts of tourist traffic have been far too low. In 1968 the Austrian Institute of Economic Affairs predicted that tourists receipts would amount to Sch. 25,000m. by 1980. In the event, this figure had been passed by 1970. In 1962 the Federal Aviation Bureau of the US forecast 85.9m. air passengers for 1967–8 (I like the accuracy of the .9) but the actual figure was 153m. In Britain, the Roskill report (on the need for a third London airport) predicted 26m. visitors in Britain in 1991 and 40m. in 2006—compared with 7m. at the time of writing.

Tourists are welcomed by governments as bringing in money—but the realisation is dawning that they also impose concealed costs. For instance, if all those who wish to visit London in 1980 (15m.) are to be accommodated, London will need 220,000 more beds than in 1970. This means 100,000 more hotel workers, to say nothing of ancillary occupations, e.g., dry-cleaners. The demand for water, for transport, for medical services is affected, and this demand is seasonal. Car parking has to be provided—for which the residents have to pay. And when 40m. people descend on an island containing 70m. the economic impact is considerable. Yet in Britain the Department of Trade and Industry provided a grant of £1,000 per room to encourage hotel building. And in remote islands it can be much worse. A recent study, cited by George Young in his *Tourism: Blessing or Blight*, from which I have taken some of these figures, suggests that one tourist for fifty residents is a desirable limit, with a maximum of 3 in 50 for some areas. But in the Cayman Islands the ratio is already one to five. In St Martin, a resident population of 7,000 plays host to 130,000 visitors a year in an area of 16 square miles.

Not surprisingly, resistance is developing. Bermuda has frozen all new hotel development for five years; in Jamaica, armed guards patrol the hotel grounds; in Puerto Rico American-owned hotels have been bombed. In Santa Lucia, so much food is imported for tourists that the trade balance is out of kilter, while the banana industry has been ruined. In Greece, where the government has allocated vast sums to help owners improve their houses for letting to tourists, while leaving many Greeks in poor housing conditions, resentment grows. In Mexico, foreign ownership of land has been forbidden within fifty miles of the coast. A further problem is pollution: many lakes have died as a result of sewage from large hotels, and the whole Mediterranean is on the way to becoming a sewer.

Apart from the economic impact, more serious is the fact that the visitors break up the local culture. And too often they treat the local inhabitants as a Disneyland sideshow arranged for their benefit, wandering into their houses, offering to buy their belongings and posing them for photographs as if they had no lives of their own. This is the real basis of the new resentments.

Resistance is also developing to permanent migration, for similar reasons and not only where questions of racialism are involved. Thus in California some areas have attempted to establish quotas, similar to the quotas long set by nations. The Welsh and the Cornish are beginning to raise objections to the English residents and owners of holiday cottages. The Swiss, with over a million foreign residents in a population of 6,310,000, have virtually banned all further inflow.

The indications are, in short, for a more static world. It may also be one in which exit permits, temporary or permanent, are as hard to get as entry visas. It is significant that the European Common Market which was supposed to make travel within the area as free as within the member countries has had no such effect. In place of the traditional 'Come to Britain' campaigns we may even see posters: 'Please do not come to Britain this year', George Young suggests.

5 How not to Farm

The mad growth of cities in the third world is the product of a demented farming policy. We attempt to improve the food supply by encouraging third-world countries to use the labour-intensive methods of the West. Every tractor we send to the East displaces about five men from the land; every ton of fertiliser has a similar effect. In the West it is profitable, and possibly even sensible, to farm intensively since labour is costly and industry can easily absorb those who are displaced. In the developing world neither of these conditions obtains. Thus the more we do to solve the food problem by such means, the more we cause people to stream into the cities in search of work. Since few of them find anything really productive, they join the desperate throngs of dissatisfied slum-dwellers.

The rational policy would be to farm extensively: to increase the size of crops by ploughing up more land rather than by increasing yields per acre. In this way, more work would be provided to absorb those displaced: a movement from cities to countryside might even be initiated. I overstate the case, of course: we need to do both. But at present acreages are hardly increasing at all.

In some areas, to be sure, land is not plentiful. And to turn the jungle into arable land cannot be done overnight. But the real problem is land-ownership. In South America, especially, where the land is held in large estates which are either grazed, used for coffee growing or plain neglected, a policy of extensive farming is unwelcome to landowners.

The fact is, the approach of Western experts to the world food problem has been distorted by a gigantic false assumption, the nature of which is only now beginning to become clear. This is, in fact, to measure the efficiency of agriculture in terms of crop-yields per unit area—per acre, or per hectare. This has become the traditional method because, for the small farmer with a plot of land which he could seldom increase, the only road to a higher standard of living was to increase output per acre. More recently, in Western countries where land is becoming scarce, in the sense that it is in demand for many non-agricultural uses from roads to airfields, and from housing estates to reservoirs, the pressure to farm intensively has grown even greater.

But looking at the world food problem as a whole, we can see that extension of acreage farmed may easily be a better way to increase the total food supply than applying fertilisers and pesticides, and using costly machinery, on the existing acreage. In point of fact, though it has been calculated that the acreage of arable land could be doubled, world-wide, the proposed rate of expansion is a miserly 0.7 per cent per annum over the quarter-century up to 1985. The pressure has been entirely towards raising yields by introducing Western methods of agriculture—a policy perhaps connected with the fact that it enables developed countries to make profits selling equipment, fertiliser and farm-consumables to the undeveloped world.

Actually, there are two ways of looking at the problem which are more appropriate than yields per acre: they are, from the viewpoint of energy expenditure and from the viewpoint of manpower.

If you work out the energy expended in producing food—not only the farm machinery and petrol, but the energy which went to make the pesticides and weedkillers, to dry the crops, to make the barns and fencing, and finally to distribute the product, you find that you are actually putting more in, in many cases, than you are getting out. This is not generally true of grains, but it is very much the case for beet-sugar, battery eggs and chickens and especially for fish. Gerald Leach, in a study made for UNESCO, has shown that for potatoes, in Britain, the ratio of energy input to output is 1.0, but for sugar beet it is 0.5—that is, you are putting in twice as much as you get out. While for battery eggs it is 0.16, for broilers it is 0.11 and for sea fisheries as low as 0.073, i.e., nearly fifteen times as much energy is used (mostly in the form of oil) as is returned. In fact, it takes up to a gallon of petrol to get a pound's weight of protein. And Britons eat some 37 lb of animal protein a year. In fact, British agriculture consumes 6 per cent of all the energy used, and distributing food consumes another 8 per cent. Leach points out that, if you drive to the dairy to buy a bottle of milk, you use more energy than the milk supplies. Packaging is also wasteful of energy, and especially in the form of aluminium cans, which contain more energy than the food within them.

This squandering of energy is growing by leaps and bounds. An article in the American journal *Science* points out that over the period 1950 to 1970, the amount of fertiliser applied in growing maize increased by 7½ times; the amount of insecticide ten times, the amount of weedkiller 20 times; the use of electricity, six times. It takes 540 UK gallons of petrol (or equivalent) to grow an acre of maize in the US. While wealthy countries, especially those which are densely settled, may find such a mode of behaviour worthwhile, it is obviously crazy for those which are poor or have trade-balance problems.

Taken as a whole, it is clear that the system is ecologically unsound. The down-to-earth realist replies: 'Unsound or not, we can make it work for the next few generations, so what?'

However, even this seems to be uncertain when we look more closely at the world food situation. Famine may be nearer than you think.

XVI

FAMINE!

The growing disparity between the haves and the have-nots seems destined ultimately to bring the affluent society down to ruin.—Lloyd Berkner

1 Pseudo-food

In twenty years time, a steak dinner may be something you save up for once or twice a year, and all meat may be a luxury much as pheasant or venison are today. It may reach the point where restaurants serve meat only on one or two days a week, as happened during the war. In some countries meat rationing will be re-introduced. Since 50 per cent of Americans die of eating too much animal fat, the shortage may prolong the life-expectancy.

'The world food crisis is upon us,' declares the President of America's Standard Milling Co. 'We are actually on the verge of a panic.' Recent staggering rises in food prices are the first ripples of the new era of food shortage. Not only meat. By spring 1974, coffee, cocoa, sugar and other items had attained record prices: £576 a ton for coffee, £595 for cocoa, £209 for sugar. By October, though coffee had weakened to £455, sugar was £400 a ton and cocoa £870! In three of the world's four most populous countries, rationing is already in effect. Before the end of the century it is reasonable to expect food prices will be four or five times higher than they are now, in real terms, quite apart from monetary inflation. In the effort to alleviate the shortage, land will be diverted from growing non-food items such as cotton, rubber, sisal and hemp, so that there will be a textile shortage. Only if the oil shortage has been solved will there be an adequate supply of synthetics to fill the gap.

Research on the 'pig pill' which aims to enable you to eat as much as you want without absorbing any nutriment, may prove as unrewarding as it is irresponsible.

251

However, this disagreeable shortage will be alleviated by an enormously increased use of protein substitutes and filling agents, especially protein derived from soya and other beans. These meat-analogues are already in much wider use than most people realise and form 30 per cent or more of many meat-pies, sausage rolls, meat loaves, and the like. Since the law has not yet got around to specifying what kind of protein may be used, the limiting factor is usually whether the eater can detect an alteration of taste or texture.

Already we have the bacon-like Stripples, the ham-like Wham, and the sausage-like Prosage. By 1990, Britain's much-loved sausages-and-mash may have become Prosages-and-Smash. American hamburgers made from peanut protein are in the pipeline, according to the Food Sciences Department of Stanford Research Institute, and so is cottonseed 'chicken' and soya-bean 'ham'.

There are two ways by which chemists attempt to turn the bland powder which is the extracted protein into something resembling meat: one method turns it into a kind of foam, which is then coloured and flavoured, the other into threads which can be woven into something more closely resembling meat, which is fibrous. Kesp, made by Courtaulds, the nylon fabric manufacturers, is an example of the second. Despite the claims of SRI's Dr Herbert Stone that, whereas a few years ago such foods retained an aftertaste of the plant, 'now their taste as well as their texture can be made virtually indistinguishable from that of meat', the *British Nutrition Journal* is sceptical. The texture tends to become too slimy or too 'chewy' and in getting rid of the bean flavour the product becomes totally flavourless, it says. As the chef in one British industrial canteen where these substitutes have been introduced remarked: 'You have to go all out on the sauces. As it cannot be overcooked, you can go on cooking until it has absorbed the flavour.' The time taken in preparing the sauces, he added, absorbed any saving due to not having to trim off fat and gristle.

These plant proteins have been prepared to look like steak, brawn, ham, chicken and even fish (to be called, presumably, Artifish) but the cost of such window-dressing is high, and the main use will be in stews, mince, meat loaves and the like. Last year Britons ate a thousand tons of such synthetic meats. By 1980, according to one estimate, Europe will be consuming 750,000 tons a year. By 2000, one guess is that a quarter of the USA's needs could be met this way.

Quite different in origin from the foregoing are synthetic meats made from fungi (mycoprotein, being threadlike, has a texture closer to real meat, and mycoprotein can also be puffed up like rice), from yeasts grown on methanol, from bacteria raised on methane, or from pond plants, such as water hyacinth. Of these, yeast is the most promising. Factories producing 100,000 tons a year of yeast-protein grown on petroleum derivatives are being built in Europe; Japan is planning for 150,000 tons by 1974; while Russia is aiming at a million tons a year. However, as petroleum contains cancer-producing substances, and as the product is high in purines, which cause gout, some reservations may be in order, even though tests on animals have been encouraging. Yeast protein can be produced very cheaply—25 cents/kg is envisaged—so that it is competitive with animal feeding-stuffs. Since animals consume a lot of fish (in the form of fishmeal) which could be diverted to human use, no doubt they will soon have to put up with artificially-produced protein. BP is already marketing such a feed, named Toprina. In general, captive markets—such as old-age pensioners and school-children—will be the first to enjoy these new blessings of science. In the US, the law has already been modified so that 30 per cent of the meat in school-meals can be substituted.

All these meat substitutes differ from real meat in having no fat, and, while this may sound attractive to persons trying to slim, actually the situation is more complex. The so-called 'structural fats' are essential and form 60 per cent of the dry weight of the brain. (This is probably why herbivores have much smaller brains than carnivores.) It is only the saturated fats which are not essential, and which weight-watchers have to avoid. So fat-starvation could result.

Unfortunately, there is no 'miracle' version of soya bean—already America's largest earner of foreign currency. This plant is very sensitive to light and at present can only be grown in a narrow belt running across the US. But Brazil is expanding her crop and new genetic variations are being bred which will, with luck, establish it in Europe and Australia.

Naturally, the trend towards substitutes will not stop with meat. As grazing land is ploughed up to increase grain yields, milk may get scarcer. No matter: America has long had Coffeemate and Britain now has Plamil. Coffeemate claims no relationship with dairy products and is based on sodium caseinate; Plamil comes from soya and sunflower oil. 'Filled milk', in which the natural fat has been replaced with vegetable fat, is available for slimmers, and gives us a glimpse of the many ways in which food can be rejigged. Reconstitution of milk will surely come: since milk is mostly water, we presently waste money hauling tons of water about. In America, the Peter Paul company is now coating Mounds, Almond Joys and other confections 'with some undisclosed substance touted by the company as having "better shelf life" than chocolate'. The recent sharp rise in the price of cocoa beans is doubtless coincidental.

Company President Lloyd W. Elston says the brown stuff 'handles, looks and tastes' like chocolate. 'The difference is rather a technical one,' he urges.

As energy shortages and the opacity of the atmosphere combine to make market gardening unprofitable, the trend may spread to vegetables and fruit, giving rise to prefabricated lettuce and straw-berries made from real straw. Flavours too are beginning to be substituted and the tastelessness of substitutes is giving a fillip to the trend. 'Interchicken' is a blend of flavourings, artificial and natural, which can be injected into battery chickens shortly before plucking, and is said to make immature broiler chickens taste like mature, free-range birds. Tests in supermarkets show that shoppers are willing to pay 3p. a pound more for such chickens, once they have tasted them, though the cost of treatment is only about 1–2p. a pound. There are paprika, curry and American-fried variants. The next step is to extend the process to larger animals. At the White Tomkins laboratory, says Alec Gordon, the Chief Chemist, 'We are working on a cooked tomato flavour to add to hamburgers. . . . Often, to get a flavour we have to add elements which are not in the real thing.' A wood-smoke flavour is being developed for kippers and smoked ham. The chemists also have their eye on drink: gin flavour-ing has been contrived, whisky is still to come. The gin flavouring is for export only, at present: if you are East of Suez, according to an article in the *Farmers Weekly Guide to Synthetic Food* (from which I have taken many of these facts) you should stick to whisky.

The reasons for the Western world's coming food shortage are, basically, threefold. First is the fact that the developing world is no longer content to supply the developed world with cheap food, and is beginning to form producers' associations to restrict production and force up prices. Coffee producers have recently done just that, and Brazil has reduced coffee acreage so severely that—believe it or not—it may become a coffee importer! Sugar producers of 75 nations met in Geneva for nearly a month in 1973 to try to negotiate a new agreement, but failed to agree. Said M. Jacques Chirac, then the French Minister of Agriculture, 'A serious shortage of sugar is unavoidable in the years to come.' (Of course, this situation could change if a really safe sweetener were found.) Moreover third-world trade is expanding. If, as seems likely, sugar-for-oil deals are negotiated, the free market in sugar will be starved of supplies.

Second is the fact that as incomes begin to rise in the poor world, the very first thing people do is to begin to diversify their diet. People do not live on a bowl of rice from choice; they prefer to have a little fish or meat with it. They wish for sugar on their porridge and jam on their bread. The force of this is vividly shown by what has happened in Japan. Over the past twenty years, the consumption of rice has fallen sharply, while the consumption of wheat, eggs, milk, meat, beer and 'Western' luxury foods has rocketed. (The average Japanese ate 1.8 kg of meat a year in 1934–6: by 1963 the figure was 10.3 kg. In the same period milk consumption per head rose more than 800 per cent.)

But underlying the whole story is, of course, the world food shortage, which means wheat and rice. Paradoxically, if it is solved the Western world will be hungrier, but whether it is solved or not, the result may be 'a conflagration of violence that would sweep through millions of lives'. The words are those of Addeke H. Boerma, the Director General of the United Nations Food and Agriculture Organization (FAO).

Be that as it may, we have to try to feed the world's population. How is the battle going? Are there going to be great surpluses by 1975 as the optimists predicted?*

2 Thought for Food

When I wrote *The Doomsday Book*, the situation was dire. Now it is disastrous. According to Britain's *Economist*, in April 1974, 'The world's food supply has never been so perilous. Two years ago our granaries were bulging with surplus grain. Today they are touching bottom.' W. David Hopper, President of the International Development Research Center, says that the events of the past several months leave him with 'the sense of an impending cataclysm'.

Four years ago, although the poorer countries were barely holding their own in the struggle to increase food output faster than population growth, the great grain-producing countries—Canada, America, Australia and the Argentine—were producing surpluses: world reserves were over 40m. tons. When bad harvests occurred in the east, they filled the gap. Today, those reserves have practically gone, as a result of a series of bad harvests all over the world. In April Hopper warned his board of governors: 'I believe the world can no longer rely on the prospect that food reserves in the four grain-exporting nations will ever again be able to meet the short-term calamities that may befall the major populated areas of the world.'

The failure of the Indian monsoons for several successive years; the failure of the Russian crop in 1972; and, this year, flooding in Canada and drought in the US have ensured, despite record crops in 1973, that reserves are low. By June 1974, stocks stood at one-third the level of four years ago, while there were 300m. more mouths to

---

* Thus, according to Herman Kahn and B. Bruce–Briggs, 'We can confidently predict a world food surplus rather than a shortage for the mid-seventies.' *Things to Come*.

feed. The rise in oil prices, which has doubled the price of fertiliser as well as adding to agricultural costs, exacerbates the situation. The Indian drought has hit hydroelectric power needed to run irrigation pumps. Some hydroelectric power stations have closed down. In the late sixties, agricultural production in the third world seemed to be keeping ahead of population growth. In 1970, *Time* magazine had announced 'Plainly the Green Revolution has shown that the battle of food production can be won', and at the World Food Congress in The Hague that year the emphasis was on the problems of plenty. But in 1971 and 1972 the picture darkened. Wheat stocks tumbled from 49m. tons in mid-1972 to below 30m. tons in mid-1973. But in June 1974, Dr Boerma told the FAO Council that he had abandoned the hopeful views he had expressed the previous February. The wheat crop could not possibly cover 'the lowest foreseeable wheat requirements in the 1973–4 season' and a shortage of 2 million tons of rice was expected. The clock had only a year or two to run before Doomsday.

By April 1974, the headlines were shrieking: 'World Threatened by Famine.' The World Bank appealed to Russia which had bought up almost all the USA's grain resources to give aid to India, where grain stocks were almost non-existent. India would have to import two million tons of grain by October, and then two million tons every year for at least four years. It is hoped that grain production will reach 108m. tons—the same level as three years before, when there were 40m. fewer mouths to feed. The target originally set was 115m. India was not the only sufferer. In Ethiopia, for instance, deaths were estimated by the UN at between 50,000 and 100,000. In the June floods, in the streets of Wollo, capital of Dessie province, people drowned because they were too weak to lift their heads above water. Official predictions for 1974 were that at least 200,000 people would starve. Relief workers said that half a million was a more realistic estimate.

The Green Revolution—the name invented by America to advertise its 'miracle' grains—proved to be only one more Transatlantic advertising stunt. Optimists had claimed that not only could the world's population of $3\frac{3}{4}$b. be fed, but that 15 billion, 30 billion —at one euphoric moment even the figure of 157 billion was suggested—was not too much for the earth to support. Those who drew attention to the obstacles were doom-sayers, guilty of anti-social negativism.

No need to analyse in detail the errors in the academic calculations of the optimists. The facts are enough. The FAO prepares indexes of food output per head of population, which show clearly whether food production is expanding faster than population or not. I shall compare 1961 with 1971. In that time the Rich World (meaning Europe, Russia, North America and Oceania) expanded food per head from 97 to 115, but the poor world (meaning Latin America, Africa, Near East and Far East excluding China) expanded only from 100 to 101: virtually no progress in ten years of effort. When these areas are broken down by countries, the figures are more disturbing, since some countries are markedly worse off. Thus while Sri Lanka was 44 per cent up in gross output and Costa Rica a stunning 102 per cent, or 14 per cent and 40 per cent respectively when population growth is allowed for, Cuba was 14 per cent down, Afghanistan 16 per cent down, Syria 14 per cent down, Iraq 18 per cent down; even Argentina was 7 per cent down. Stranger still, Denmark was 5 per cent worse off. By 1972, the figures were worse. . . .

The star performer of the optimists was Mexico where, with massive foreign aid and advice, food per head climbed from 89 to 142. But in 1974, even Mexico had to import grain.

The FAO's Indicative World Plan called for an annual increase of output of nearly 4 per cent; the figure varied a little in different countries. In the event, of 92 countries, six were producing less absolutely at the end of the 1961–71 period; a further 36 had failed to keep pace with population growth; thus output failed to keep pace with population growth in more than half. Only 21 countries achieved the growth rates called for by the IWP. 'These results are most disquieting,' observes the FAO's latest report. 'Instead of revealing a small number of countries where the agricultural sector is making particularly slow progress, they indicate that the majority of countries are probably in this position.'

'Total grain production in every region increased less rapidly . . . than proposed by IWP . . . in Latin America there was a very big shortfall.' For meat the situation was no better. 'Beef and veal production increased more slowly than the objectives in every region except the Far East and the Near East and North-West Africa . . . the Near East and North-West Africa region was the only one to exceed the rates originally proposed for livestock production up to 1975.'

How is it possible that the optimists could have been so wrong? Without going into tedious detail, let me just list some of the things they overlooked:

1   the changing climate
2   the fertiliser shortage
3   the fact that 50 per cent of all crops is lost as a result of pest, fungi, damage in storage, etc.
4   corruption on the part of some administrators and officials
5   effects of war and civil disturbance

6   water shortage
7   lack of facilities for soil-testing and technical advice
8   need for roads, barns, silos, trucks and a distribution system
9   rigidity of food preferences
10   difficulty of getting money into people's pockets so they can buy
     the food
11   increased use of grain to feed animals by the rich nations.

(Of these the first and last are particularly important.) Some of their arguments verged on the dishonest: they pointed to small areas where results were uncharacteristically favourable, or contrasted years of exceptionally low yield with exceptionally favourable ones. They bear a considerable moral responsibility.

Back in 1969 when I was writing *The Doomsday Book*, the claim was being made that every developed country would have a food surplus by 1975. Lester Brown, at a conference in 1968, declared that the Free World would have an adequate food supply by 1975, except on the west coast of South America. Today he says we may be witnessing 'a fundamental transformation of the world food economy'. And he adds: 'The urgency of the food problem is underscored by increasingly frequent reports of starvation in sub-Sahara Africa and of food riots in Asia.'

Much was made of the case of the Philippines where self-sufficiency in rice was achieved during the sixties, after half a century's dependence on imported rice. But for reasons ranging from social unrest to the susceptibility of the new rice strains to diseases, this independence did not last.

The fact is, the long-prophesied world famine is here. Only in China, where stockpiles have been built up at national, provincial, village and farm levels, to an estimated total of 40m. tons of food grain, is the situation reassuring. Violence and political unrest are the inevitable consequences. Indian riots, in which the police shoot half a dozen ringleaders, are reported at frequent intervals. Anger over rising prices and the shortage of jobs adds fuel to the flames. The price of food grains has risen 50–90 per cent in two years; incomes have not. In the Philippines, where the population is obliged to supplement its much-preferred rice with corn and noodles, rationing is imposed and the military ensure that it is distributed to households and not diverted to the black market.

WORLD THREATENED BY FAMINE. *Observer*, 7 April 1974

STARVATION FEARS IN INDIA AS DROUGHT HITS CROPS. *Times*, 28 July 1973

10 KILLED AS POLICE FIRE ON RIOTERS IN BIHAR TOWNS. *Times*, 20 March 1974

HALF INDIA SINKING RAPIDLY BELOW THE POVERTY LINE. *Observer*, 16 December 1973

Nor is the situation yet at its worst.

Rising fertiliser use in the rice paddies of the Philippines is eutrophicating the nearby lakes and ponds, depriving them of fish. Irrigation canals are silting up in Java; overgrazing and deforestation are causing reservoirs to silt up in West Pakistan. As the demand for food grows, land too steep or too dry to sustain cultivation is brought under the plough. Result: erosion. Just as in the Middle East two millennia ago, the great deserts are beginning to form. Possibly one-third of farmed land in the us is suffering from erosion. According to Arthur Bourne, at the Man/Food Equation meeting in London in 1973, world agriculture 'is about to collapse'.

What can we do about it? World grain stocks would suffice if they were more equally distributed. As it is, grain consumption in the us is 2,000 lb a head, in India 390 lb. Distributed equally, there would be 695 lb per head. The reason for this discrepancy is that, in the West, most of the grain goes to feed animals, in order that people may eat meat. In fact, meat consumption is increasing, up from 55 kg/head to 73 kg/head in Europe, from 81 to 92 kg/head in the us, from 36 to 44 kg in the ussr and from 7 kg to 19 kg in Japan. Of the 1,000 lb/head of grain consumed in the industralised world, 880 lb goes to livestock production. Russia's massive wheat purchases, which did so much to deplete reserves, were to expand meat production—and perhaps to weaken America's position as saviour.

The us, seeing market possibilities behind the Iron Curtain, is now strengthening its representation in these areas at the expense of the third world. French farmers, to maintain food prices, threw meat into the sea. 'That sacred cow, the eec's Common Agricultural Policy, is an example of advanced irrationality,' says Dr Boerma. 'Sometimes I feel they are so mixed up with their own problems in Brussels that they cannot see the world problems at all.'

The Indus-Ganges-Brahmaputra plain is the most promising high-production area in the non-Communist world, capable of producing a billion tons of food grain a year, ten times India's present output. All adjacent states—Nepal, Pakistan, Bhutan, Sikkim, Bangladesh—should be joining in a cooperative effort to exploit it. 'It would be the most formidable task ever tackled by the world community,' says Hopper, 'and it will require relatively little of the world's resources.'

3 Fish failure

One other important source of protein exists, of course: fish. The optimists talk of increasing the world catch to 100m. tons from the present 60m. but in practice it is proving difficult to raise the figure any further, mainly because of over-fishing. Since 1968 it has

fluctuated unpredictably and many marine biologists believe we
have reached the maximum sustainable level. In three decades the
world catch has been doubled. 'Tuna has been overfished almost
everywhere, as we have cod and perch in the North Atlantic. The
West Pacific has been all but rid of bottom fish, the Bering Sea of
flatfish, and the North Atlantic of hake, to name a few,' writes
Carle O. Hodge of the University of Arizona's Environment
Research Laboratory. The Californian sardine industry has perished,
he continues. The salmon of the north-west Pacific and the cod of the
Barents Sea are dwindling fast. 'In another two decades virtually no
substantial stocks of commercial fish will remain underexploited. . . .'
Moreover, when a species is over-utilised the balance of the whole
food-chain is upset. In other words, when large fish feed on smaller
which feed on still smaller, removing most of the smallest species
causes the population of the larger ones to fall as well.

People forget, also, that less than one per cent of fish caught comes
from the deep oceans, which are virtually barren. Fish come from
the shallow continental shelves, and hence are imperilled by the
effluent society. Water that is safe to swim in may be lethal to some
marine creatures. The committee appointed by the USA's National
Research Council to survey the subject confirms this view. It
reported: 'Menhaden, which traditionally has supported the largest
US fishery, is threatened by environmental pollution in its early life-
stages and by heavy fishing pressure later in life; it is another species
in need of wise management. Other species showing signs of serious
depletion are, for example, yellowtail flounder, herring, American
lobster, and haddock from the north-western Atlantic.' The famous
Grand Banks fisheries are in decline.

Regulation of catches and of fishing effort as a whole is essential,
says the committee, and failure to establish such controls 'could
bring about long-term declines in yield'. The committee also stresses
the pollution aspect, pointing out that pesticides, industrial wastes,
sewage, fertilisers, etc., do not only kill fish or block their powers of
reproduction, but may also weaken them so that they fall prey to
predators or succumb to diseases.

Minor steps which should obviously be taken include establishment of laboratories for diagnosing fish diseases, establishing a
disease-reporting centre, production of a suitable technical manual
—all simple things which have not been done.

'People have always perceived the sea as a limitless cornucopia,'
comments Hodge, 'a belief as fallacious as it is venerable.' Hence
the fancy gadgets of the technologists—the use of sonar, of electrical
fields to concentrate fish, of mercury lights, etc.—will make matters
worse, not better. Another proposal of technologists is to change

fishing methods by establishing fixed fishing platforms to which the fish will be attracted by these means, perhaps in such numbers that they can be pumped on board, rather than netted. Experiments have been run in the Gulf of Mexico which suggest profits might be six times as high as when fishing by normal methods. No allowance is made, of course, for the bankruptcy of fishermen elsewhere whose potential catches will be lured away. Fish can also be led, like sheep, by means of underwater lights from one fishing ground to another, opening up the prospect of a kind of marine cattle-rustling.

A far more constructive approach would be mariculture or fish-farming: the use of ponds, lakes, streams and even closed-off lochs and estuaries to raise fish. The same area that would yield a few hundred pounds of beef could produce a ton of fish or 100 tons of shellfish. The Japanese have been pushing this. The Chinese (who have been fish-farming since five centuries before Christ) have dotted the landscape with such farms and produce 1½m. tons this way. In Washington State an aquafarm is helping the impoverished Lummi Indians to become prosperous, while in Germany the Bavarian hydropower company is using sewage to enrich carp-ponds. Britain has just announced plans for its first large-scale trial of fish-farming, using warm water from the cooling system of Hunterston nuclear power station to foster the growth of the commercially valuable sole and turbot. The cost is now down to £500 a ton. In advanced countries labour costs are significant, but in the third world it is not labour but know-how which is the problem; and the right species must be obtained with which to start the system, for some will not tolerate the crowded conditions. However, pollution is the biggest threat to mariculture, and can affect temperature, salinity and oxygen content as well as purity. Shellfish are particularly sensitive.

While technomaniac forecasts of enough protein from the sea to feed a world population ten times the present may be discounted, it is reasonable to suppose that fish supplies could be doubled or trebled in the next 30 years. But to achieve that, we shall have to put a lot more effort into it.

4 Help

The developing countries need help. Perhaps the most pressing step is the creation of a world grain reserve, or at the very least, a coordinated system of national reserves, to offset the impact of bad harvests. But this is merely an emergency measure. What the poor world needs is money to buy the machine-tools and specialised equipment which will both provide the jobs for the urban populations and manufacture the essentials—waterpipes and electric cables, taps and switches and household goods—which will raise the standard of living from dire poverty.

For the third world lives in dire poverty, 'a poverty so extreme that it degrades the lives of individuals below the minimal norms of human decency', as Robert MacNamara, Chairman of the World Bank, recently put it. A poverty so extreme that 20–25 per cent die before the age of five. The absolute poor are not a tiny minority but comprise some 800 million people. Their average income is 30 cents a day.

A novel and constructive way of assessing the problem is this. For every 15 people in the developing world, one new child is born annually. So from the savings of the fifteen must come, in one year, all the capital that can ever be spent to feed, house, educate and care for that individual. (Their savings in the following year will be needed for a new mouth.) Harold Dunkerly, a British advisor to the World Bank, reckons that the average annual savings of these 15 people cannot exceed £360—insufficient to provide a place at school, still less a house to modern standards (£800) or the tools for a high-technology job (£600 to £2,400). We must lower our sights, therefore, and concentrate on the bare elementary requirements, such as water and sewerage (£40) and fitting up a traditional workplace (£160). Anything more can only come as a gift or loan from the rich nations.

World Bank experts have urged the rich nations to agree to give as much as one per cent of the gross national product (GNP) to helping the poor nations. But this was asking too much. At present they give, on average, about 0.6 per cent and have accepted the magnificent figure of 0.7 per cent as a target to aim at. You may think the richest nations should give more than the less rich. That is not at present the case. Americans often delude themselves that they give generous foreign aid. The truth is that they are almost the least generous of any developed nation, fifteenth on a list of sixteen—far outstripped by Norway or Denmark, for instance; exceeded even by Austria and Portugal. Here is the list showing economic aid given by developed countries as a percentage of GNP in 1975:

Norway	0.75
Netherlands	0.72
Sweden	0.71
Belgium	0.70
France	0.65
Denmark	0.61
Australia	0.60
Canada	0.52
Portugal	0.45

United Kingdom	0.40
Japan	0.40
Germany	0.36
Switzerland	0.32
Austria	0.25
United States	0.22
Italy	0.16

I propose that the target figure be raised to 5 per cent immediately.

The oil crisis has disastrously worsened the situation. A special World Bank report, issued in April 1974, calculated that third-world countries would need *additional* support, over and above the aid they already get, to the tune of $6,600m. in 1974 and as much as $9,000m. in 1975 to cover the increased cost of oil and raw materials. In particular, India, Sri Lanka and Bangladesh face economic disaster if not helped. Developing countries will be able to meet part of this demand by running down their reserves and by borrowing from the International Monetary Fund, but will still be $2,600m. short in 1974 and $6,800m. short in 1975.

Moreover, much of what the World Bank calls 'financial aid' has strings attached or is not in any sense charitable. Ordinary commercial loans which, if made to a developed country would not be called 'aid', compose almost half the aid referred to above. When allowance is made for this and similar double-talk, it is calculated that aid comes to only $2.5 billion out of the $13 billion claimed to be aid: or about 2 cents for every $10 of income in the rich countries.

And much of it is mis-spent on armaments, prestige symbols like jet airliners, luxury goods for the better-off, or in the interests of the lending country, as when a railway is built to bring out the ore from a mine, or a port is improved. The distribution of aid is crazy. A relatively wealthy country like Venezuela, with a national income close to Italy's, gets $6 per head of population, whereas India and Pakistan get $2 *per capita*. Liberia gets $21.50 and Egypt $0.50. Much just disappears in the hands of inflated bureaucracies—kleptocracies as they are now bitterly called.

And since lending countries often stipulate that what they give or lend shall be spent with them, aid becomes little more than a way of subsidising exports. An American official admitted that no less than 93 per cent of us financial aid is spent in the us. Poor countries thus become virtually protected markets for rich ones: a modern form of colonialisation. It is striking that the three countries which, perhaps, have received most help from rich 'uncles'—Liberia, the Philippines and Colombia—are all marked by balance-of-payments difficulties, high unemployment and social unrest. And since much aid consists of loans, on which interest has to be paid, the point is approaching at which countries will be paying back *more* in interest every year than they receive in aid. By 1977 (says Professor Tibor Mende), for every $100 received, Africa will be paying back $121, Latin America $130, East Asia $134!

Surely it is obvious that, if we really wish to help these poor countries, we must—and they must—study their actual needs and prepare specific plans to meet them, instead of dishing out money or providing Western gadgetry. To take but one example: in South America, only 3 per cent of professional academics have diplomas in agronomy, although more than 40 per cent of the population is in agriculture. In India, where two-thirds of the population works in agriculture, the figure is even lower: 1.2 per cent. The numbers in engineering and medicine are also tiny. (These figures, from the National Sample Survey of 1960–1 are now somewhat out of date, but the problem is not.)

The two questions which no one likes to face are: how far is the whole objective of industrialising the poor world in the image of the West possible, and how far is it desired or desirable? When the industrial revolution started in Britain, lack of transport created virtual monopolies: a man who set up a small factory to make some new device could sell it nearby with little or no competition. Today, the poor-world budding entrepreneur faces the competition of automated, efficiently run plants in the West. The capital requirements are astronomically higher. It has been reckoned that in 1800 you could buy the equipment needed to put a man to work for the equivalent of four months of his wages. In India today, it would be at least ten years of his wages—or, for an automated spinning mill, four centuries of them. Finally, food was plentiful in Britain, where agriculture was well developed. But underdeveloped countries now have monocultures in coffee, tea, sisal, etc., developed for the benefit of the rich countries, and must import food. To climb to current Western standards could take centuries or may even be impossible.

But there are signs that, despite a certain fascination with Western gadgetry, many undeveloped countries are reluctant to swallow Western culture, and wish to work out ways of retaining their own. To wish to eliminate poverty and starvation is not the same as to want 'development'—a thing Americans find particularly hard to comprehend. Either way, the answer is to stop trying to measure welfare in terms of Gross National Product. (Even in Western economies, we can see that a decline in welfare can manifest as an addition to the GNP.) For poor countries, a sane policy would include such policies as to stop moves which exaggerate urban-rural differences. Create market-centres in the country. Get money into the pockets of the poor.

Though 70 per cent of the poor world's population lives in the country, most of the aid goes to the cities, where about four times as much is spent, per head, on welfare than is spent in the country. A major effort must be made to help the small farmer, with his few acres. The productivity of such farms is low and shows little sign of rising. But it is not impossible, as Japan has shown: her small farms produce four times as much per acre as those of the third world. Small farmers need credit, water, advice, and institutions to promote productivity (such as agricultural colleges). They also need stable prices and the social and medical services which will enable them to function effectively.

Dr Sen, of the Food and Agriculture Organisation, has long argued that, to eliminate starvation, the central problem is to get money into the purses of the poor. What happens at present is that rich farmers grow richer, but the poor remain poor. The farmer who can profit is the one who owns his own land. Thus in many countries, notably South America, the central problem is land ownership. Land is held in vast *latifundia*, which are grazed, used for coffee growing, or just neglected. They could be farmed, but naturally the owners oppose the break-up of their estates. Leases, too, may be absurdly onerous: a peasant may have to give 50 to 60 per cent of his crop to his landlord. Overall, the million small farmers of the world own only 20 per cent of the agricultural land.

In short, radical social change is imperative. Poor countries will have to solve their own problems: find ways of limiting waste, corruption and privilege. What Western countries can do for them is to open markets to their exports, thus easing their balance of payments; cancel debts; stop offering package deals in which help is tied to industrial concessions; stop competing with their exports; push alternative technologies, suitable for poor countries; help with education. Professor Mende suggests that we should form non-government teams to tackle specific problems, financed by *ad hoc* funds, and that citizens, instead of contributing to an aid-pool through taxes, should support the fund of their choice. Thus there could be Development Funds for plant research, for building techniques, for portable energy sources, for small fertiliser plants, for agricultural education, and so on.

Above all, Western countries could stop intervening, stop thwarting the autonomy of these countries, stop using them for politico-military ends. But they are not likely to. The multi-nationals really want the poor world to develop in a lop-sided manner, with a rich sector which will absorb the kind of goods they want to export and a poor one to work in their mines and plants. Western banks want a 'favourable climate for investment'. Western governments refuse to sign the international commodity agreements they have jointly worked out, and are now the main salesmen of armaments—often to both sides. It is difficult to avoid the conclusion that the situation will deteriorate. Eventually there will be an explosive outburst of discontent. When these countries lose patience, they will no doubt start by attacking their own leaders and burning their own cities, though this will only make matters worse. We can see the signs already. Thus in Baluchistan last year more than 860 soldiers were killed in attempts to suppress riots and opposition movements. (Though this figure is 'official' it has not been released and parents have not been told of the deaths of their sons in an attempt to play down the situation.) Young men are arming themselves and forming resistance groups. According to the leader of the National Awami Party, 16,000 troops were being used to try to quell this revolt.

But eventually, the poor world will turn its envious eyes towards those who have so much. President Boumedienne of Algeria told reporter Vanya Walker-Leigh that unless the third world could combine with Europe to build a new world in which poverty and misery would be eliminated and in which human beings could find true fulfilment, 'no number of atom bombs will stop the tidal wave of billions of human beings who will one day break out of the poor south of the world into the relatively open spaces of the rich north in search of survival.'

That prospect provides another possible scenario for the future. Or again, even though mass violence may be avoided, shall we see a world of south-eastern despots dominating by sheer weight of numbers the more civilised but perhaps decaying cultures of the north and west?

In short, the world as a whole faces serious problems. But it is the fact that the developed nations are suffering from such severe internal stresses which makes it uncertain whether they can rise to the challenge. The sort of measures we could take to deal with the physical problems I have indicated as I went along. But the social and psychological problems of the West need more detailed treatment and so, in the two chapters which follow I shall try to summarise policies for coping with them. However, the ultimate problem, underlying all this, consist in the fixed attitudes and erroneous beliefs about the nature and objects of social change which distract us from taking the necessary steps and even impel us to go further astray. These I shall discuss in the final chapter.

PART VI

Suggestions

XVII

SOCIAL SUGGESTIONS

The climate has been changing in ways that bode ill
for the immediate future of world food supply.
—Reid A. Bryson and John E. Ross

1 Run for the Hills

A recent cartoon showed a man emerging from a room marked
Think Tank, clutching festoons of computer print-out, and advising
his colleagues: 'Run for the hills.'

The cartoonist correctly sensed the current mood, but the Think
Tank may be issuing its advice a bit late. Those who decide to batten
down the hatches until the storm is over had better move fast and
prepare for a long vigil. They should prepare a retreat, remote from
urbanisation, equip it with an independent power source, stock it
with medicines, how-to books and tools. Food will have to be home-
grown as far as possible and a study of eighteenth-century living
standards in Scotland, where oatmeal was the main article of diet,
might prove rewarding. (It is surprising what you can do with
oatmeal.) A year or two of rehearsal will help to reveal the problems
—like how do you grind the flour after you've grown the corn? The
sort of indispensable item one is apt to overlook is a packet of
needles—almost an impossible thing to make for oneself. Don't
forget to take yeast. Since fire-making is a tedious task when matches
have run out it will be necessary to maintain sacred fires, as of old,
from which one can rekindle one's own in emergency. Alternatively,
a magnifying glass would be a good investment.

Small groups are attempting such experiments in independent
living in many countries and a stream of useful books is emerging, so
I need not pursue the subject. I would however suggest that such
ventures be surrounded by a moat and a wall to discourage the less
farsighted when they swarm out of the towns looking for safety and

sustenance. I would also urge charitable trusts to finance rather larger-scale experiments on these lines.

However, this may prove an unreliable as well as an escapist formula for survival, since the government will probably commandeer all such economic units, or at the least confiscate their stores and equipment for their own use, even if the place is not wrecked by the envious or the criminal. Furthermore, war, a mini ice-age or a serious radiation disaster would put paid to any such plan. Better stay in business and fight for a Disaster-minimising Policy.

The top priority, as I have suggested, is to get rid of the short-sighted and pussyfooting governments under which most Western countries now suffer and raise the administrative system to a modest level of competence. For only governments, of some kind at some level, can carry out the reforms which are needed. Unless the management can be restored to competence, suggesting policies for avoiding chaos is simply a waste of time.

A SUBURBAN SURVIVAL COURSE

Two RAF instructors working in the Bavarian Alps have devised the ultimate answer to the fuel crisis: survival in the open in 54 degrees of frost if necessary without coal, electricity or very much else. . . . Their trade secrets—derived from sources ranging from Dartmoor poachers to the Apache Indians—have numerous applications to civilian life if strikes bring the apocalypse to suburbia. . . . With a reasonable stock of food in store (one moderate meal daily is all most people need) and a bathful of drinkable water, most of us should be able to survive comfortably for at least 30 days, if all power sources fail. After that it may be necessary to become more adventurous. . . .

The four principles of catching wild game are easily memorised. They are: Tangle, Dangle, Mangle and Strangle. . . .

Tony Geraghty, *Sunday Times*, 10 February 1974

On a national scale, it would obviously be wise to take every possible short-term precaution to protect the situation until longer-term plans can take effect. I am thinking here of such things as economising in fuel and resources, recycling wherever possible, developing alternative sources of energy, and so on. In the field of food production this would include establishing emergency grain reserves, pressing on with protein substitutes and mariculture, and switching to a less energy-intensive agriculture. These requirements are becoming well understood, although little has so far been done to put them into effect.

The problem must also be looked at on the world scale. Probably the industrialised countries should be moving towards a greater degree of self-sufficiency, rather than trying to boost world trade. To link yourself to a vast world trade machine is fine when the machine is spinning but simply propagates disaster when the machine begins to slow down.

And of course, on a world view, we should be doing far more drastic things to narrow the gap between the rich world and the poor, while trying to persuade the developing nations to avoid repeating Western mistakes. All this is well known. But let us not forget it is only a stop-gap, a plugging of the leaks. We still have to mend the sails.

2 Technosoc and the Metaproblem

Whichever line we pursue we seem to go round in circles. If we seek to meet the energy crisis by developing nuclear power we run into problems of heat pollution and radioactive waste disposal. We could grow more food if we had more energy. We could meet the oil shortage, to take a specific instance, by cultivating plants which could be distilled to give alcohol, which can substitute for petrol as a fuel— if it were not for the overriding need to grow plants for food. And so on.

When we find a group of problems such that solving one only intensifies another, we can infer the existence of an underlying problem: a metaproblem, a philosopher would call it. The emergent problems are only symptoms of a basic malfunction. The meta-problem in this case is, as we now begin to see increasingly clearly, the whole pattern of life associated with a technologically sophisticated society. We need a conveniently brief label for this life-style and I shall call it Technosoc.

Technosoc is the breeding-ground not simply of the physical problems of resource-exhaustion, pollution, etc., but *also* of the social problems of violence and decohesion. Even if it is possible, as some struthious optimists claim, to blunder on to ever greater material consumption by grinding up the entire surface of the planet to provide power and raw materials, it would *still* be necessary to abandon Technosoc for social reasons. Technosoc is blowing our society apart. That is the central message of this book.

We are beginning to understand that Technosoc currently presents a double threat. Not only does it disrupt the social patterns and idea patterns on which a stable society depends, but, because it innovates at such a high rate, it makes life unpredictable, renders projects obsolete long before the end of their design life, and makes social adaptation (which is tied to the generation interval of human reproduction) hopelessly difficult. It would be wise to reduce the innovation rate, but even if it were zero, a society organised for conspicuous consumption and rapid resource-use would still be socially unworkable.

Though the nature of the sickness has finally been diagnosed and the regimen prescribed, no one knows how to make the patient obey the doctor's orders. The profit-making machine seems incapable of modifying itself or evolving into a more socially effective form. Every day we read in the papers cases where the pursuit of individual profit results in general harm—over-fishing is a well-known example. Pollution and resource exhaustion are others, and show us that attempts by the state to restrain the pursuit of private profit are usually half-hearted, belated and incompletely effective. (As several studies have shown, regulatory agencies, such as the Federal Communications Commission in the US, or the Alkali Inspectorate in the UK, gradually become the protectors and advocates of the industries they are supposed to regulate.) In any case, a system of a lot of people trying to do one thing and a lot of people trying to restrain them from doing it is hardly impressive conceptually. It would be an awkward way to steer a car: to build in a bias to swerve to the left and constantly turn the steering wheel to the right.

In this sense, at least, the popular idea among the more rebellious that there is a 'system' responsible for all our ills which has to be overthrown contains a core of truth. Nor is it simply the fact that the pursuit of private profit leads to misuse of resources that justifies challenging the system. It is the system's need to stimulate new demands, to maximise the rate of obsolescence, so that the wheels of industry can keep turning, which is the real problem. In this need government, which wants to avoid unemployment, makes common cause with industry, which wants not only profits but expansion for prestige reasons. This is familiar stuff and I need not elaborate. I refer to it simply as the springboard for a consideration of alternatives.

Reducing hours of work progressively, as has often been suggested, would reduce resource-usage but would not solve the social problems. In a leisure society people would find the lack of purpose and the absence of social support far more painful than they do now. At least the workplace provides social contacts of a kind; improving pay provides a sense of purpose and achievement (this is probably the real motive behind a good deal of industrial strife) and, at least in some cases, provides opportunities for the exercise of skills. Another suggestion has been to divide the community into two groups, workers and drones, the latter living on a basic allowance paid by the state. This is, if possible, even less realistic. The devil finds work for idle hands to do!

However, in criticising the profit-making system, I by no means intend to argue for state-capitalism or Communism. This is just as concerned to maximise production as its counterpart, and the Russians have demonstrated all too clearly the persecution and oppression, and have failed to hide the inefficiency, which such a system spawns. (It is truly curious that Russia has repeatedly taken the very steps most likely to discourage other nations from turning to Communism: it is as if they wished to keep their position as a unique system unchallenged.) The Chinese version seems to be even less free.

As I have argued elsewhere, there is a third alternative: mixed motives.* In unsophisticated societies, activities are assessed not simply from an economic viewpoint, but simultaneously in human and in religious terms. Our society puts economic decisions in the hands of people who are divorced from or unaffected by the social and personal consequences. Naturally, they either rate them very low or ignore them. (I was taken by a recent suggestion that all judges and magistrates should spend 48 hours in prison before taking up their jobs, so that they should realise what they are sentencing people to. This is practised occasionally in the US, where newly-elected judges are stripped naked and hand over all their belongings just like other prisoners, and discover what it means to lose your identity. This admirable idea could be extended: social-service workers could spend a night with up to a hundred other people in the overcrowded dormitory of one of Britain's antiquated mental hospitals; the appropriate civil servants could spend a week living on public assistance; and 'chairmen of local welfare committees should be left alone in a house in an artificially disabled condition, deprived of a telephone or any other of the special facilities called for in the 1970 Chronically Sick and Disabled Persons Act and still not provided by many councils.')

To create a society of mixed motives, in which material gain is balanced at every point against social and personal values, we need a better system of accounting. It is the fact that we can put a price on some things but not on others which leads us to favour the former.

I see a ray of light in a recent initiative in Japan. At the request of the Prime Minister, a special committee was set up, under the chairmanship of Dr Miyohei Shinohara, to study 'Net National Welfare'. Its object was to construct a new index which would measure the extent to which the Japanese economy was meeting qualitative 'welfare' goals, and to propose changes in the whole national accounting system with this object.

According to a memorandum submitted by Japan to the OECD

* *Rethink: A Para-Primitive Solution* pp. 175–6.

(Organisation for European Cooperation and Development) the committee has focused on four main approaches, each quite startlingly novel for a body of this kind:

1 *GNP to be reclassified according to social goals.* At present GNP is simply a statement of who bought how much of what, but doesn't tell you for what reason. Napalm counts as an addition to GNP on just the same basis as antibiotics or food.

2 *GNP to be strengthened as a welfare index.* At present money spent as a result of traffic accidents, to check pollution or to care for those injured by it, or to provide travel to work over an unnecessarily long distance as a result of urban sprawl, all appears as an *addition* to the GNP though it has a *negative* value from the welfare viewpoint. Pollution can even appear as a positive factor when GNP is calculated. On the other hand if working hours are shortened, this appears as a negative factor in GNP although it is a positive factor in welfare, or may be.

3 *Change from a flow-economics to a stock-economics.* By 'stock' the committee means not merely stocks of goods, in the ordinary commercial sense, but trained personnel, e.g., doctors, teachers; social capital, e.g., houses, roads, parks; private stock, e.g., clothes, consumer durables; natural stock, e.g., clean air and water, beautiful landscapes; cultural stock, e.g., pictures, orchestras, communications media; and social institutional stock, e.g., social security systems. Quite a comprehensive list. Current economic statements spotlight what money has come in and what has been paid out; they are income-and-expenditure statements, not statements of assets. And building up assets, especially social assets, is what it is all about.

4 *Non-monetary approach to a welfare index.* Many important items in welfare are difficult to express in monetary terms: we can put a figure on the cost of medical care but not on the value of health. Much the same is true of nutritional standards, education, leisure, safety. . . . But if these cannot be expressed in money terms, could they not be expressed in some other form?

This remarkably original and ambitious proposal received very little comment in the European and American press or from economists, for that matter. But in Japan the Social and Economic Plan for 1967–75 which called for a doubling of income has been scrapped, and instead Japan substituted the aim of doubling NNW (Net National Welfare). In the rest of the world, plastic gnomes continue to count as additions to the standard of living, still defined as the GNP per head of population. In reality GNP is simply an index of the resources we have destroyed during the year. As Philip Brachi, from whose account I have derived these facts, epitomises it: it lumps together the goods and the bads, which are 'all the same in the eyes of British economists, whose descent from off-white ivory-style tower blocks to sully themselves in reality is eagerly awaited'.

However, a purely economic approach is only a partial answer; the Japanese initiative serves to open the subject up and reveal the mistakes, it does not tell how to correct them. The problem divides into two; changing society and changing people. In this chapter I discuss the first, in the next I discuss the second.

3 Social Policies

In Norway, although farming, fishing and certain other industries have become increasingly 'uneconomic' the Norwegians are happy to subsidise them in order to keep the remoter parts of the country populated and to preserve a certain way of life. It was because they feared that the rules of the Common Market would destroy these traditional activities and patterns that they voted against joining. At the moment they are deeply worried about the impact of North Sea oil.

In Scotland, in contrast, although local communities in the Shetlands, the Orkneys, and elsewhere are deeply worried about the break-up of their life, the central government regards this as expendable, and presses on with oil recovery regardless of its social consequences. Nor is the attitude of these island communities based on ignorance and backwardness. Most of those who live there have been, at one time or another, in centres of what we are pleased to call 'modern life' and have consciously rejected it, realising that a strong community with simple tastes has something to offer which compensates for the material difficulties.

The example of Norway shows that governments *can* set themselves against the disintegrating forces of Technosoc, even if they seldom do so. Let us for the moment assume that governments in general see the light: what could they then do? Much of what they would have to do should already be clear from the preceding discussions, but it may help to recapitulate some of the key points. In doing so, we must bear in mind the need to protect society against physical disruption and economic disruption as well as the need to restore its social cohesion.

The primary need would be to decentralise—not so much to decentralise population as to delegate power. At the same time, a decentralisation of the physical structure (for instance, electricity generation and distribution) would help to make the political decentralisation meaningful. A community does not have self-management if others can deprive it of its basic needs. Since he who controls the purse-strings has the power, it would also be necessary to give local communities more power to raise and spend money. A system of supervision to limit corruption and incompetence would have to be devised, but something more on the lines of an Ombudsman than on the lines of civil-service control.

Community life also depends on a reduction of personal mobility, and especially repeated changes of abode. Taxation on all such moves could be introduced without delay. Hopefully, oil shortage will limit personal mobility.

The creation of communities must be supplemented by giving them an internal structure, i.e., by restoring the functioning family and, as far as possible, recreating the extended family; and by tying communities together with what we have called intermediate structures. Concomitantly, appropriate rituals and ceremonies must be created. In addition, every effort should be made to destroy the money-based status system and re-create one based on functional contribution to society. A first step in this direction would be to reconstitute the 'patronage committees' which all too often tend to reward industrialists who have destroyed group structure, and which then seek to curry popular favour by rewarding rock-stars and footballers. Particularly objectionable is the 'Prime Minister's list'—other countries have equivalents. Prestige is too important to be left to the favour of prime ministers.

In making such changes, governments should seek the advice of anthropologists rather than economists, and anthropological studies should be warmly encouraged—especially studies in applied anthropology and social psychology. Research should also be prosecuted in maximising the efficiency of small-scale industry: as the Volvo company has demonstrated in Sweden, you can mass-produce a car perfectly efficiently without a conventional production-line. Some Volvo assembly plants only employ a few hundred people and are dispersed into different parts of the country. Small-scale industry does not have to be uncompetitive, as we are slowly beginning to discover.

In any such programme, the most difficult task would certainly be the dismantling of factions, and especially the super-factions of organised labour. As long as governments are under the influence of either one or other of these malignant growths, progress towards an organic social structure is likely to be negative. American writers, such as Galbraith, have advocated a policy of building 'countervailing power'—that is, building up a second powerful organisation to oppose the first. As the current battle between capital and labour warns us, two such monsters are not enough. The method only works if the rival interests are numerous. So we should build up other interest groups: perhaps consumers, the young, the professional classes, could be built into 'estates'. In the event of a religious revival, so could the church.

Finally, we need intensive education in the nature of cohesion at all ages. Practical experiments in self-government, on the lines of the Barns experiment,* would help people to understand some of the problems. The formation of small experimental communities could be encouraged. Some sense of historical continuity could be fostered.

Underlying such changes there would have to be a change of official attitude towards stimulating groups to help themselves. The notion of the state as universal parent would have to give way to the notion of mutual aid. The United States has always had glimpses of this conception, common to unsophisticated societies. The 'barn-raising' ceremonies of rural America echo the communal boat-launchings and tribal hunting expeditions of other small-scale communities. But this admirable concept has been swamped by the nineteenth-century idea of man as an atom or struggling individual.

Of course, such changes would offend many, and some of them would be labelled authoritarian. Any restriction of personal freedom tends to be labelled authoritarian, as if the choice were simply between totalitarianism and chaos. In reality the question is: how much chaos are we prepared to put up with? Certainly, a long process of education would be required before people would accept such changes. And we do not have a long time.

Everything depends on how far governments can be persuaded to see the need for something on these lines, since changes of this magnitude cannot be introduced without their consent and support. So the point at which reform must start is reform of the administration.

4 Reform of Governments

If it is unrealistic to expect such measures to be adopted, it is far more unrealistic to propose ways of pepping-up government, for who is to impose them? No one has power over governments, and they are highly tolerant of their own faults. Nevertheless, just to show what might be done, let's make some suggestions:

THIRTEEN THINGS TO MODERNISE GOVERNMENT

1   Selection of candidates on non-party lines by primary elections.
2   Use of single transferable vote (STV).
3   Much stronger upper house to supervise lower house.

* See page 113.

4   Extension of Ombudsman system; Ombudsmen to have inves-
     tigatory powers.
5   Supervision of working of system by committee of non-nationals.
6   Up-date administrative system and mechanics of the chambers.
7   Executive (cabinet) to be distinguished from the delegates.
8   Limit duration of membership of parliamentary body.
9   Preliminary examination for delegates and tuition in weak subjects.
10   Greatly reduce secrecy of administrative machine, and of govern-
     ment.
11   No new law to be passed without abrogation of an old one.
12   Massive research into the deficiencies of bureaucracies followed by
     appropriate action.
13   Introduce The Initiative. (Used in Switzerland and some us states,
     this is the right of a group of citizens to draft a law and have a
     vote taken on it.)

The primary need is for a supervisory system to crack down on
legislators. Far from building a supervisory machine to keep parliamentary delegates up to the mark, parliaments naturally try to
dismantle them. (For similar reasons, schoolboys would like to get
rid of schoolmasters.) Unfortunately parliaments tend to have a
wrong conception of their function; they tend to regard themselves
as law-making machines and to rate their own achievement by the
number of laws they succeed in passing. As a result, every country
becomes snowed under by laws which attempt to do what would be
better done by tradition. (As an old Indian told the anthropologist
Ruth Benedict: 'We never had any quarrels about hunting territories until there were laws about them.') Unfortunately few
delegates have taken the trouble to study the limited role of law in
achieving social cohesion. In any case, they have a vested interest
in law-making, of which they have a monopoly and, like most
monopolies, they abuse their privileged position.

Members of parliaments and senates are supposed to be a sample
of the public, speaking for those they represent, since the entire
public cannot be consulted every time. The party system destroys
this democratic intention, and the 'professionalisation' which comes
from prolonged membership of the legislative body steadily makes
the member less a representative. The internal battles of politics
become of more interest to him than the real issues. Current proposals that Members of Parliament should have no other source of
income than their parliamentary salary would make sense if their
term in the House were quite limited, but can only bind them further
to professionalism if not. The deprofessionalisation of members is a
top-priority reform. However, if representatives are to have less
opportunity to become knowledgeable they will need much more
briefing and support.

Particularly objectionable is the party system, and the growing tendency of each party to govern in the interest of one of the factions —capital and labour—at the expense of everybody else. But parliamentary faction can only be healed by healing the faction in society which it reflects. However we could start by changing the method of selecting candidates. Leaving the choice to groups of party enthusiasts biases the whole system and tends to exclude moderates and men of independent thought. The sensible plan whereby universities (in Britain) returned candidates should be restored.

A word may be needed about the single transferable vote, which has proved to work well in many European countries, including Northern Ireland, and in associations such as the British Medical Association. It breaks the deadlock by which people who are dissatisfied with existing parties nevertheless vote for one of them because they feel a vote for a new party would be wasted. It permits the voter to specify his second choice, and even a third or fourth. Something of this kind is essential to break up the rigidity of the present system.

These are simply ideas thrown off to show that the present system is not immutable or sacrosanct. Each country will have its own approach, and I would not presume to re-design my own, let alone anyone else's ruling system. All I am doing is to recommend the most urgent attention to the matter.

5 Sense of Helplessness

Despite rising living standards, a certain diffuse discontent is noticeable, chiefly among the young but also present less explicitly in other sections of society.

It has two components, I believe. First, we who live in mass societies feel a sense of helplessness. We feel that we are ciphers personally, and that we are powerless to influence the course of events. The stream of letters to the newspapers, the desire to appear briefly on television to make a point, membership of amenity and other pressure organisations, all bear witness to the individual's desire to take part in the settling of issues which seem to be important. As one woman writer to a newspaper put it: 'I don't expect my opinions to prevail but I do want to feel that they are taken into consideration.' This sense of helplessness is due, of course, partly to the size of the administrative grouping but equally to centralisation of decision-making and to the sweeping away of intermediate organisations and structures. To recall Dostoevsky again, it is not rational choice but independent choice that people really want.

The psychiatrist S. L. Halleck has pointed out that this feeling of helplessness is kept from consciousness by action, which gives an illusion of being in control, and is thus crucial in the genesis of criminal and violent behaviour, or as F. T. Melges and R. H. Harris put it: 'The feeling that one has little control over one's destiny may lead to attempts to restore oneself as an active agent.'

When social researchers asked people who had said they were dissatisfied with society why they did not take some positive action to remedy the position, about three in ten—in the case of Britain and the us—replied that they felt it was beyond their power to change things. The French and Swedes were more optimistic (some 17 per cent felt helpless) the Japanese far more pessimistic, with 73 per cent saying it was useless to try, though 9 out of 10 recognised an obligation.

The second factor is more fundamental: the inexplicable human need to find an overriding purpose in life. When one is cold, starving, homeless, the struggle to meet these wants provides a purpose capable of absorbing all one's energies. Once they have been satisfied, a divine discontent emerges, an existential despair. That is the real problem in the developed world today and naturally it hits hardest at the young who, guaranteed support at a university, and without yet being involved in the struggles of a profession, have time to contemplate their emptiness. The production-line worker may also feel that life is aimless, but at least he is earning money and moving to fulfil some of his ambitions. Sex and raising a family also provide interim goals. Hardest hit, perhaps, are those who have made a reasonable success, produced a family, and don't know what to do next. Jung said that many of his patients were men in their forties who had suddenly begun to ask themselves what life was for.

There are three classic ways of relieving such existential anxiety. One is to sink oneself in some project—political, charitable, artistic, or even the struggle for personal prestige and public honours. The second is to live for the moment, extracting the maximum pleasure from every sensory or emotional experience. The third is to prepare oneself for life in another world: in a word, to turn to religion. No doubt we need today a new religion—it would have to be a matrist, orgiastic one, modelled on the worship of Ishtar and Cybele. Many of the young seem to be hunting for something of the kind, but lack a suitable cult-figure. The restless searching which this discontentment gives rise to, the sense that one has somehow been cheated or disappointed of something, accounts for a part of the unrest and mobility we see today, and which was common in declining Rome. It explains the evanescent popularity of mystic religions, and of astrology, magic and occultism. It also explains the desire to believe in visitors from another world who will either tell us how to resolve all our problems and live happily ever after or who, possibly, will destroy us—in either case terminating our anxiety. It also accounts for Utopianism: the belief in a Golden Age if only we could advance to it—or retreat to it. Thus it provides an atmosphere in which more serious revolutionaries can flourish and find support, even if in the crunch their supposed sympathisers drop away.

But while some part of this existential dissatisfaction springs from external social conditions, some part of it comes from within. To be more precise, the personal and the social are inseparably interlocked. You cannot build a constructive society with destructive people, a peaceful society with violent people, or a civilised society with un-civilised people. A society is no better than its citizens. How far, then, is it possible to 'improve' people? This is the most crucial of all our problems, the most urgent of all our tasks.

XVIII

PERSONAL PROBLEMS

The crisis of violence is really the crisis of man.—M. F. Gilula and G. Daniels

1 Psychological Rescue

The one great area of possible progress which stands wide open to attack is that of reducing the forces which corrupt and distort personalities, producing violent, criminal and anti-social human beings. After more than half a century of sophisticated research, we now know more than enough to make a real impact, given the resources. Moreover, pilot schemes in several countries have shown that it is possible to rehabilitate the majority of such persons, including even some hardened and exceptionally disturbed criminals. There are many people of goodwill only too ready to begin the work, if only the obtuse individuals who run society could be persuaded to provide the funds and the necessary administrative cooperation.

Instead, the cry is for severer punishments, for longer prison sentences, for the return of flogging and for the death penalty. While such penalties give some members of the public a sense of satisfaction and justice done, there is ample evidence that they will do little or nothing to reduce the incidence of crime and delinquency. The figures are quite uncompromising. Boys who go to reform school are *more* likely to commit another crime than those who do not. Criminals who are flogged are *more* likely to become set in a life of crime than those who are not. Prisons are schools for crime. True, the death penalty prevents a man from committing a second murder, but it does not cut the murder rate. In the US, for example, those states which have the death penalty have higher murder rates than those which do not. Nor has South Africa, which uses the death penalty freely, been able to eliminate violence.

'We have to face the disagreeable paradox that experience of what are intended to be reformative institutions actually increases the

282

probability of future lapses into criminality,' says Barbara Wootton, in her book *Social Science and Social Pathology*; 'It has for example been shown that a previous residence in an approved school is one of the best predictors of recidivism among Borstal boys.' And the success rate of Borstals is steadily declining, in Britain.

On the other hand, there have been many rather successful essays in rehabilitation, if always on a small scale; their success little appreciated and never developed. Thus, not long ago, workers at the University of Kansas established a school for boys, aged 11–16, who had become problems at school. It was based on lines advocated by Professor B. F. Skinner, viz. on rewarding desirable behaviour rather than punishing bad. Boys who had been through this school recorded far better attendance-rates (truancy being regarded as a convenient index) than had problem boys who had been placed in institutions or put on probation. (The success rate was 90 per cent, against 9 per cent for those in institutions, 37 per cent for those on probation. Recidivism after one year was only 6 per cent, and the school cost far less to establish and run than the penal institutions.)

As far back as 1950, a similar experiment in New Jersey placed 20 boys in a permissive group atmosphere and compared them with boys at a traditional reformatory, nearby Annandale. One-year recidivism was 16.5 per cent against 48.9 per cent at Annandale; residence time was months rather than years, and the cost per capita was about one-third.

In a British experiment, launched by the Bishop of Lancaster and the Chief Constable of Lancashire in 1965, social workers have been able to cut child crime rates by one-third. Their object was to detect early signs of maladjustment, rather than to treat children only after they had emerged as persistent delinquents. 'The experiment showed that that technique was more likely to succeed than conventional methods. Punitive treatment, though successful in reducing offences in the short term, had long-term disadvantages. It tended to alienate the children and make them less able to cope adequately in the future,' according to the research officer on the project, Mr Tony Marshall of the Home Office Research Unit.

It is even possible to rehabilitate the most violent and hardened criminals, as the Danes showed at Herstedvester, where an experimental prison run on lines designed to restore a man's self-respect has drawn world-wide admiration from criminologists. Though psychotics were not accepted, the intake included sex-maniacs, alcoholics, pilferers, drifters and so on. Inmates are released on parole when it looks as if they can adjust to normal life and return if they fail, to be paroled again when more confident. After ten years only ten per cent of the original intake were still in detention. Staff requirements are high, looked at conventionally: 199 staff for 200 prisoners. But since detention-time is shorter than in ordinary prisons, the figures would look very different on a long-term view.

Nearly thirty years behind the Danes, Britain has started a similar experiment at Grendon Underwood. In another British experiment, prisoners have built their own prison, at a saving of £2.5 million, earning money in so doing.

These few instances must serve to convey the flavour of the numerous encouraging experiments in rehabilitation which are being tried in several countries. But, unhappily, the bulk of prisons remain soul-destroying. The idea that a man can be rehabilitated by locking him up in a cell with two or three other criminals is so ludicrous that it is hard to understand why the system has not long been swept away. Every country complains its prisons are over-crowded—Britain is spending £60 million expanding its prisons. Yet one-third of the occupants are people who have not yet come to trial, two-thirds of whom will not receive a prison sentence anyway. The whole position is nothing less than a public scandal.

Even more desirable, of course, is to prevent young people from becoming criminals in the first place.

2 Adolescent Outlets

Dr Mia Kellmer Pringle, Director of Britain's National Children's Bureau, has admirably summarised the needs which, if thwarted, lead to violence. 'They are,' she says, 'the need for love and security; for new experiences; for praise and recognition; and for responsibility.' And she comments: 'These needs have to be met from the very beginning of life and continue to require fulfilment—to a greater or lesser extent—until the end of life. If any one of these basic needs remains unmet—or inadequately met—then one of two reactions follows: flight or fight, attack or withdrawal.'

When we look at a group of young men standing about on a street corner or aimlessly playing the slot-machines in what is laugh-ingly called an 'amusement arcade' we certainly see people who have no responsibility, who are not gaining recognition, and are not facing new experiences. We should therefore not be at all surprised if they show signs of apathetic or violent behaviour.

However, I would add to Dr Pringle's list two items, at least as regards boys: the need to rise to a challenge and the need for a sense of purpose.

In contrast with unemployed or under-employed urban youth, the young man in an unsophisticated society who, having demon-strated his courage and self-control in initiation ceremonies, becomes a 'young brave' and sets off to do battle for his tribe or to return with the scalp of an enemy, is clearly meeting all of these needs. How, in civilised society, can we find adequate substitutes, short of war? The youths who arrange a gang-fight or a burglary are, unconsciously, making a very sensible attempt to meet their instinctive needs. Such enterprises enable them to prove their courage and skill, provide them for the time being with an all-absorbing purpose, create responsibilities and provide them with new experiences.

How can we find something more constructive than gang-fights and burglaries which will have the same effect? Some small-scale attempts have been made and have proved very successful—such as the Outward Bound camps and Adventure Schools in Britain, or the camping trips organised by social-service groups in the US and Canada.* Instructors at such camps bear vivid witness to the transforming effect of a challenging environment on those who attend.

Alas, these efforts only deal with a tiny fraction of the problem. When it is recalled that nearly a quarter of all serious crime and more than forty per cent of burglaries and robberies, in Britain, are committed by those under 17, the social cost of ignoring the problem can be guessed at—and the figures for other industrialised countries are not much different.

Moreover, while adventure camps add something to the lives of children of school age, the real problem is the young person who has left school, and especially if he or she is unemployed, or in a frustrating job which offers no challenge. Worthwhile careers are what is needed. This is well shown by the success of 'Uncareers', launched by Ann Link and a fellow-student at Birmingham University in 1971. Within a few weeks, the first edition of their *Directory of Alternative Work* had been sold out and a new edition of 2,000 copies was under way, assembled ten pages at a time in a bed-sitting-room. Now it sells 6,000 copies a year. Among the openings it lists are night shelters for down-and-outs, village communities for mentally-handicapped adults, democratically run factories, homes for battered wives, and so on. Ann Link and her husband get some 3,000 enquiries a year; they report that the demand for 'alternative work' is increasing. At least two British universities now make efforts to help students find 'alternative work', though most careers officers view it as a short-term experience rather than a way of life.

Community Service Volunteers (it grew out of an organisation known as Voluntary Service Overseas) has been finding projects for volunteers for twelve years: a 12-month stint in a Borstal, a children's

---

* As this book goes to press, it is announced that an Outward Bound school is closing down for lack of funds!

home, a gypsy camp, or with immigrant children; and among the volunteers have been immigrants, ex-offenders, and even blind persons. Some local authorities have been quick to see the advantages. 'The London Borough of Camden, for instance, early on saw the saving, in cash and emotional misery, in taking two girl volunteers to look after three small boys when their mother was in hospital on and off for two years, and the only alternative was to put the children into care. Islington now has 27 volunteers scattered round the borough in various jobs. Volunteers get board and lodging and £3 a week pocket money, paid by a variety of means, and administered by csv', reports Caroline Moorehead. 'In 1965 the police forces saw the value of this type of service for their cadets, and many of them now make three months community service a compulsory part of training. Chief Inspector John Harrison of Hampshire, believes that three months on the other side of the fence, inside mental hospitals and with Borstal boys, does immeasurable good. He is prepared to risk the fact that several of the cadets take to community service so strongly that they leave the force and stay on in it once their three-month stint is over.'

Regrettably, industry has not yet done much to help: it could lend lathe operators to training centres for the subnormal, for instance. An organisation called Action Resource Centre has been set up to act as a clearing-house for such cooperative efforts, and is already training fifty young West Indians in building skills with the aid of craftsmen and an industrial coordinator lent by industry. Business management schools might well include a stint of this kind in their training. Retired people could also help.

Unsophisticated societies are, almost universally, insistent on marking the transition from childhood to manhood very clearly by public ceremonies. In childhood, one is dependent and has no responsibilities except to cooperate with those who have the responsibility of supporting and protecting you. In manhood, one stands on one's own feet, accepting responsibility for one's own actions and also a responsibility towards society. A part of the unrest of young people today comes from the blurring of this transition in our society. On leaving school, are you automatically an adult? Then society should want you and make clear what it expects from you. In agricultural societies your help is wanted in the fields at the earliest possible age. Our society too must have jobs, whether social-service or industrial, waiting for every adolescent. And the privileges and obligations of manhood, including such things as jury service, military service, the right to vote, the obligation to work, etc., should accrue at the same moment. I would go so far as to say that some outward sign—badge, style of clothing, hair-style or what you like—should make the change obvious so that others know what behaviour to expect and what to demand.

Boredom, to which I referred in Chapter V, is the consequence of having no purpose, of having 'nothing to do'. Obviously, unemployment compounds this sense of futility. The young person on the threshold of life—perhaps after a period of travel and experiment —wants something which not only brings in money but advances his whole life. He needs not simply money or promotion, but the need to be part of a movement bigger than himself, to be working for some really worthwhile end, and in so doing to realise himself. This was the attraction of the Hitler Jugend and the Brown Shirts to the mass unemployed young of Weimar Germany. Similarly today, the high unemployment rates of young US blacks represent a social risk which no government in its senses would ignore. If unemployment rises in Europe or Japan as a result of a world slump, the risk of totalitarianism will become acute. Even now we can see that to join an activist political group provides, in an otherwise boring existence, the needed sense of purpose, the responsibility, the praise and recognition and the new experiences to which Dr Pringle referred. Student protest fulfils a similar function.

When society offers you no role, you feel alienated from it, rejected. Your response is: 'The hell with society, if it does not want me, I do not want it.' This feeling could be present even in a person with a job, if that job seemed futile and unchallenging, if one is only wanted as a robot. To the unemployed, it is far more intense. As the psychiatrist S. L. Halleck observes: 'Adolescent delinquency drops when the adolescent can associate himself with a meaningful struggle.'

Coupled with this goes a sense of helplessness, of 'inability to influence the course of one's own life or of the world'. This reaction of helplessness evokes a feeling of depression. Committing a crime relieves this sense of helplessness: one is doing something positive, which is enabling one to progress towards one's goals—both in the financial sense and in the psychological. (Where parents kept a child dependent and helpless, such feelings are enhanced.)

However, behind the adolescent stands the child. In the first months of life patterns are established and wounds inflicted which, in some cases, can distort personality too severely for measures such as I have just described to have any effect. To improve the quality of 'parenting'—something more than 'parental care'—is the *fons et origo* of the whole social problem.

3 Family Backgrounds

We have all the psychological knowledge needed to mount a major attack on the family conditions which make for embittered and distorted personalities, and hence for crime and anti-social behaviour. (It is typical that 74 per cent of the confirmed criminals in Herstedvester had come not from secure families but from child-care institutions.) Literally thousands of studies of disturbed and delinquent children have been made in many countries—to say nothing of studies of adults—and the consensus of the findings is pretty clear. If there is one area where we are in a position to mount a major effort, this is it. 'If we stopped all research into children for five years and just applied what we know already, we might begin to get somewhere,' is how Dr Pringle puts it.

A quarter of a century ago, the Gluecks, path-breakers in this field, found (for lower-class children, later confirmed by Bandura and Walters for middle-class children) that 'aggressive, anti-social persons emerged from an environment characterised by parental rejection, familial discord, punitive discipline and inconsistency'. Thus it is not 'broken homes'—as is often asserted—which constitute the main problem; it is unbroken homes where love and an ordered environment are absent. The homes of many often well-intentioned professional people of high intelligence fail in these respects, frequently because the parents are absent at moments when the children particularly need them, especially at mealtimes. Food being a symbol of affection, it is not enough to ensure that food is available: the caring and the sharing are an essential part of the deal. Even more important is bedtime, when the experience of the day is reviewed and absorbed and reassurance is given.

In another long and careful study of 174 non-delinquent boys, devoted to discovering the origins of aggressiveness, it was found that the more aggressive boys had punitive parents who employed threats, while lack of affection was even more important. Only five per cent of the aggressive boys had parents both of whom were affectionate; only five per cent of the non-aggressive boys had not.

Sears, Maccoby and Levin (1957) interviewed 379 New England mothers and found that aggression in small children was associated with 'parental permissiveness for aggression, the use of physically punitive discipline, and maternal lack of self-esteem'. They concluded that 'the desire and intent to hurt others' was learned in infancy. ('Learned' may not be the most appropriate word, for it has been shown that monkeys reared in total isolation become aggressive. Either way, however, it seems clear that lack of affection contributes to the formation of the aggressive personality.)

Reversing the approach, Perry London studied altruistic people, whom he termed 'rescuers'. He found that almost all of them had strong identifications with their parents, who were themselves good models of moral conduct. The influence of the father was particularly important.* In a British study, delinquent boys, when questioned, said that they felt their father loved them less than did their mother, adding that he ought to love them *more* than she did. In contrast, non-delinquent boys felt that both their parents loved them equally, and that this was as it should be.

A particularly interesting study was that of Bacon, Child and Barry (1963) who studied a wide range of societies around the world and found that criminal behaviour in adult life was associated with:

1 a mother–child household (i.e., absent father), hence inadequate opportunities in early life for identification with the father
2 mother and child sleeping in the same room or bed, creating a strong dependent relationship on the mother
3 abrupt, punitive socialisation and pushing into independence, producing emotional disturbance in the child

They considered that this kind of childhood experience would produce persistent attitudes of rivalry, distrust and hostility which would probably continue into adult life. In fact, they found evidence of a suspicious, almost paranoid attitude in adult life. (Abrupt thrusting into independence seemed to favour theft as against violence and disturbed personal relationships.)

Numerous other reports might be cited, but it is not my object here to make a full-scale analysis of aggression. I only want to establish the point that, if society wishes to reduce the level of aggression, it has to devote a maximum effort to helping these defective families. To begin with, many parents do not know the bald psychological facts. For instance, no child under the age of about seven should be left by its parents for more than forty-eight hours, and for lower ages proportionately less. Yet educated parents not infrequently take vacations lasting two weeks or more, leaving their children with a nurse or with friends. Moreover, infants should be habituated to parental absence by a gradual stepping-up of the absence time.

The problem is partly a social one: parents who work far from their home, commuting, cannot easily be back in time to feed their children and put them to bed. (I come to the social aspect later in this chapter.) But, this aside, there is certainly a need to educate

* It is an interesting detail that Wolfenstein, after making a study of the psychology of Lenin, Trotsky and Gandhi, noted that each had unusually ambivalent relations with his father. Trotsky particularly had a need to humiliate his father and resented his father's attentions to his mother. Lenin resented his father's absences and felt guilt when his father died.

parents. Keith Joseph, as Minister for Health in 1973, announced that a small-scale effort would be made to break 'the cycle of deprivation' in which bad parents produce children who themselves become bad parents and so on indefinitely. No doubt this small beginning will be criticised as 'interference'. The parents who most need guidance will be the last to listen to the advice. Parents who are themselves psychologically disturbed, moreover, will not alter much just because they receive advice; their problem lies much deeper. Nevertheless, we must do what we can, wherever we can.

In Washington, Professor Cortés has proposed identifying a sample of families who seem particularly at risk, giving half of them the maximum of help and support, and seeing whether, after ten years or so, the proportion of disturbed and delinquent offspring is any lower in the group which received help.

It is now possible to identify potential delinquents with about 90 per cent success at about age 8, using information about the family and (oddly enough, as it might seem) the physical build of the child—muscular boys seem more inclined to work off their problems in physical activity, where the more cerebral type internalises his problems and becomes 'neurotic'.

The belief that parents know, instinctively, how to bring up children dies hard. But just as parents have to be told how to provide an adequate diet, whereas it used to be assumed this was something every mother knew by right, so with child upbringing. It is not instinct but copying others who do it right which transmits rearing practices, and in modern society there are no models, in many cases. In the mud hut or around the fire, the young mother could see what other mothers did and ask advice; in the modern house or apartment such cultural transmission fails. (Research has, as a matter of fact, shown that mothers in a single American community differ widely in their methods of weaning, house-training, discipline, etc., while generally believing that they are doing it like everybody else.)

Courts and social workers are nearly always in agreement about how the young delinquent should be treated, declares E. S. Higgins, Chairman of the Society of London Directors of Social Service, 'But the facilities just do not exist in sufficient quantity or in the right quality. There are insufficient staff to do the job, and current rates of pay for this particularly onerous and often physically dangerous work are quite unrealistic.'

4 Death of the Family?

Perhaps the most serious of all the myths currently being propagated is that the family, as an institution, is obsolete. This argument derives, it would seem, from the idea that it is the family which socialises—which induces the child into its culture and which establishes the idea of obedience to older and wiser authorities. Hence, to bring about the revolution, get rid of the family. Though supposedly derived from popular psychological writers, like Theodore Reik, this is actually much older. The Russians tried to abolish the family for similar reasons immediately after the revolution and soon found that bringing up children in institutional groups simply created wildly asocial individuals who could not be fitted into any society. The policy was soon reversed.

Indeed, the family is a microcosm of society and in a much more complex way than the revolutionaries have realised. When the family is disintegrated, society is disintegrated. The story of Western decline could almost be told in terms of how we have gradually undermined the family. One must start by distinguishing the nuclear family of parents and their children from the extended family which includes other relatives. In pre-industrial society, the extended family is usually within walking distance of the nucleus, and children grow up seeing most of their relations regularly, while family reunions periodically bring the extended family together. The arrangement is more secure and workable than the nuclear family as we know it today, since if a parent falls ill there are relatives to step in and help, and so on. Moreover, anthropology shows that the family can take various forms: in many societies children are brought up by mother and her brother; in others the biological mother and her sisters are jointly mother to all their offspring. Polygamy, polyandry and group marriage produce yet other family patterns, all more or less successful. There is nothing sacred about the family as we know it. But this is a totally different thing from saying it should be abolished.

The essentials are that models be provided with whom the child has an emotional link, with whom he or she can identify, and who provide security and an ordered environment. If these conditions are absent, the result is neurosis, failure of conscience-formation, and ego-disturbance. Families also transmit the culture, teaching the child, by imitation as well as overtly, social skills and tabus, rituals, values, techniques and attitudes. They may do this well or badly, the tabus may be irrational, the attitudes undesirable, but anything is better than nothing.

The experience of the kibbutzim shows that children need extended contact with their biological parents; nurses and teachers, however pleasant, are not enough. They also, it seems, need private property and kibbutz children are now generally allowed their own toys—formerly all toys were communal.

Dr Urie Bronfenbrenner, on the basis of extensive studies of child upbringing in half a dozen different countries, stresses the close relationship between parental involvement with children and social behaviour. The only country where the children were even more willing to engage in anti-social behaviour than in the US was England. 'England is the only country in our sample which shows a level of parental involvement lower than our own with both parents —and especially fathers—showing less affection, offering less companionship, and intervening less frequently in the lives of their children.' This is confirmed by R. G. Andry, at St Thomas' Hospital, London, who noted that the delinquents whom he studied wanted to see more of their parents and thought that they should receive more praise for achievement, especially from their fathers. In point of fact, these fathers saw less of their sons than did the fathers of non-delinquents and shared things with them less.* Similar results are reported from the US. As Irenaeus Eibl-Eibesfeldt, the ethnologist, remarks in his important study *Love and Hate*, 'Our trust in our fellow-man starts in the family.' From this 'basic trust' evolves our general capacity for social commitment.

Hence communal movements directed against the family as the source of repression are extremely dangerous. 'What is overlooked is the fact that this artificial suppression of strong personal bonds is simply creating experiences of deprivation,' says Eibl-Eibesfeldt. 'And this is not because human beings everywhere have been wrongly programmed by their education but *because we come into the world already programmed in this way*' (my italics). If the child is denied these experiences, its personality will be distorted. 'Such people will never enter into strong relationships; they will be withdrawn into themselves.'

In some communes attempts are made to arrive at collective consciousness by pooling money, by polygamous relationships, even by eating from one dish. They theorise that the child should not turn to its parents by preference but should have a bond with several parent-figures; that it should have no toys of its own, because this encourages a love of possessions. Actually, refusal of all possessions frustrates: it is only through having possessions that one can learn to share.

These communards do not reward achievement, believing that striving for achievement is a source of aggression. They permit no aloofness: a child who wanders off by himself is brought back and subjected to analysis—though a need for quiet and meditation is

---

* There were of course other factors, not discussed here: thus delinquents had been breast fed less than non-delinquents; and they believed that their mothers had been too lenient with them.

common to all human beings. So far does the passion for mutuality go that in some communes even the lavatory doors are removed.

Above all, the family is to be abolished as the bulwark of authority: so no praise or blame is allowed, and denial or display of love must not be used to educate children. But to win praise by achievement is a basic human need, on which the development of self-respect is based. Thus these methods of upbringing, far from being 'advanced', are regressive in the extreme and will surely produce highly disturbed adults in due course. The conjugal life which the communards dismiss as bourgeois exists, as Eibl-Eibesfeldt demonstrates, in all primitive societies and is not bourgeois at all. As he rightly says, every form of extreme upbringing is fundamentally intolerant and therefore repressive.

Alas, technological society is breaking up the family pretty effectively without the help of the communards. Any government which wishes to restore a modicum of social cohesion should bend its efforts to restoring the family—by changing the conditions which take fathers and mothers away from their children, by education and social help for parents who are ignorant or in psychiatric difficulties themselves, and by nesting their housing development plans into the reconstitution of larger groupings above the family level (the assessment groups of which I have already written).

When these matters are better understood we shall no longer see large firms, or government departments, moving employees to new posts every two or three years—as is standard practice in some large corporations. Children will not be deprived of their chance to become members of a community—or parents either, for that matter.

As it is, the forces which disrupt the family are growing stronger, the disruption worse. The social situation is therefore bound to deteriorate. Eibl-Eibesfeldt takes this seriously enough to say: 'The odds would seem to be against our being equal in the long run to the needs of mass society.'

5 Conclusion

This is not a textbook on crime and delinquency, and I shall not attempt a comprehensive summary of all the factors involved, nor all the measures to be taken. Just to mention one which is not widely known: it has recently been shown that many violent and asocial persons have suffered minor brain damage at birth—probably because the oxygen supply to the brain was briefly reduced. (The adult brain suffers irreversible damage if the oxygen supply is cut off for even a couple of minutes.) This brain damage can be detected, as a rule, by abnormalities in the brain-waves monitored by the electroencephalograph. It would be an obvious preventive measure therefore to monitor all children, or at the least, all those who showed signs of behaviour disturbance. Those found to have physio-logical deficits could then be given special supervision. When old enough to understand, they could be given insight into their condi-tion, which might help them to control it. For instance, they could be supplied with sedative drugs to be taken when they felt an attack of rage impending. Naturally this would not cover every case and there are difficult ethical problems in dealing with these human time-bombs.

There are other individuals who suffer from 'stimulus hunger'. Life seems flat and boring to them unless they are very highly stimulated. Hence they seek thrills—driving a motor-cycle very fast, robbing a bank, attacking a machine-gun nest with hand-grenades, such things give them a sense of well-being, of 'really living', and they function well in such situations, a fact which those of us who would be scared in such situations find hard to appreciate. Efforts might be made to direct such people into appropriate activities (capping oil wells, the Marines, construction work?) rather than let them drift into jobs which bore them, or maintain themselves by crime.

Nor do I overlook the influence of the social setting—crime and delinquency are high in housing estates where no social structure exists. Nor of cultural factors—violence can be a way of proving manhood, or a traditional pattern, as in the feud. Again, there are triggering effects: the sight of violence or even of instruments of violence can release violent impulses in persons who normally manage to restrain themselves. Margaret Mead has stressed the need to provide rituals which relieve guilt and discharge aggression. Other writers have pointed out that conditions such as noise and over-crowding stimulate aggression. Work with animals suggests that whenever strangers are introduced to a stable group they upset the social balance—the pecking order—and fighting ensues.

The point is simply that we now have a mass of information about the causes of aggression and of asocial behaviour generally. In relation to the size of the problem, we make far, far too little use of it. Seen from the future, our present happy-go-lucky attitude to psychological and social distress will seem as blindly inept as the medieval attitude to plague and infection seems to us.

Naturally, I am not claiming that *all* pathology can be avoided, however hard we try. Chance plays too great a part: a child may lose a parent by death, to take only the most obvious example. In some people there may be inherited weaknesses, an inability to resist stress, making neurosis probable. But the existence of a few well-ordered and peaceful societies elsewhere shows that we could hope for something a good deal better than we have.

People rightly fear attempts to 're-model personality' and fear that such methods could be misused, by design or even by accident. It depends on how you conceive of the human psyche. If it is simply a *tabula rasa* case on which so many reflexes can be imprinted by the methods of Professor Skinner, then attempts to produce a better individual by conditioning (as he proposes) could indeed be risky. But if personality is conceived of as having a normal development just as the body has, then all we need try to do is to ensure that it is well nourished and exercised, not exposed to excessive strains, given rest, and so on, and it will achieve its natural harmony and perfection. It is this normative course alone that I am advocating. I fear the dangers of 'personality re-modelling' and 'thought control' as much as anyone.

Finally, let us look at social cohesion in a long perspective.

XIX

PERSPECTIVES

Myth fulfils in primitive culture an indispensable function; it expresses, enhances and codifies belief; it safeguards and enforces morality; it vouches for the efficiency of ritual and contains practical rules for the guidance of man. Myth is thus a vital ingredient of human civilisation . . .—Bronislaw Malinowski

1 Mythic Thinking

The nub of it is this: if western civilisation is to avoid a decline into chaos, it must set about restoring an organic social structure. In the two preceding chapters I have tried to show the lines on which this could be achieved. This leaves us with the metaproblem: if the courses of action are clear, why don't we pursue them? Why do we drift ever deeper into turbulence?

Briefly, because we are bogged down in various fixed ideas which we hold with irrational intensity, and which obstruct our ability to judge. When widely held, such irrational beliefs are technically known as myths. (The word myth does not imply that such beliefs are necessarily false; it simply means that they provide justifications for behaviour.) Much emotion is locked up in myths and anyone who challenges them or even criticises them is liable to be exposed to obloquy or penalties. A familiar example is found in Communism, which Communists may not criticise under pain of penalties, just as was once the case with Christian doctrine.

There are many minor myths in our society, some of which are beginning to lose their force—for instance, that what's good for business is necessarily good for society, that technology can solve the problems created by technology, or that everyone envies the American way of life. My concern is not with these but rather with such emphatically held beliefs as that liberty and spontaneity are overriding values. They are indeed desirable, but so are their opposites: order and discipline. The problem is to find the right balance.

Currently another powerful myth is flourishing: that equality is an absolute value and that all subordination and hierarchy are diabolic. It is as much as one's life is worth to say anything in favour of inequality. Indeed, many people now find it hard to accept the existence of qualitative differences between individuals. Here too, however, the real problem is to find the right compromise between the admirable idea of quality and other equally valid but less fashionable ones, such as the recognition of merit—which is also a deeply-rooted human need.

One of the more deceptive of these myths is the belief that Utopia is *possible*. Many young people genuinely believe that with very little effort the world could be made a far better place and that only a malicious conspiracy of vested interests prevents this situation coming about. They have been encouraged in this belief by the technomaniacs who, for more than fifty years, have been asserting that 'there is no reason why anyone should live in want any longer'. But the truth is that, just *because* human beings are so erratic, diverse and irrational, it is extremely difficult to bring about even quite minor and obvious reforms. The sad truth is that a perfect society depends upon the existence of perfect people and people are not perfect.

Thus the Utopian delusion springs from the most radical of all the currently held myths; to wit, that man is inherently good and is only made bad by the corruptness of his society. Ergo, put society right, then men will become perfect, and everyone will live happily ever after. This belief is, of course, the polar opposite of the Puritan belief that man is bad and can only be induced to refrain from sin by punishments now and hereafter.

In reality, neither view is correct. Man is neither good nor bad; he just follows learned or instinctive patterns of behaviour which may be 'good' or 'bad' depending on the context of his act and the aims and values of the observer. To the extent that every man has a natural tendency to put his own interests first, and hence to harm the interests of others, he has to learn a measure of restraint if he is to live in association with others. Men who wholly fail to learn to regulate themselves can, from a social viewpoint, be regarded as 'bad' and those who do practice self-regulation can be seen as 'good'. In short, though individuals can be sometimes assessed as good or bad, man as a species cannot.

The point may sound academic but it is not. Many social issues which arouse strong feelings hinge on today's romantic belief in man's inherent 'goodness'. The myth of man's inherent perfection is linked to the current distaste for authority and worship of spontaneity. For if man is naturally good, let him follow his instincts, do his own thing, trust his impulses, and all will be well. The weakness of this position is shown by considering the man whose impulse is to torture children or something equally undesirable.

This dichotomy also permeates attitudes to class. The conservative, seeing men as unequal in abilities and in 'goodness' thinks it reasonable that society should find ways to give the most important jobs to the most able and conscientious people, hence that there should be a social scale and differential rewards. The radical, seeing all men as equally good, plumps for equality, although (somewhat illogically) he accuses those who happen to be in power of being 'bad' and/or incompetent.

However, it is the political implications of this myth which I want to emphasise here. If we think man is, or could be, perfect, we naturally devote all our efforts to improving society—thus reversing the error of the medieval church, which concentrated on improving people's behaviour. The fact is, we have to attend to both—particularly to those social patterns which influence behaviour and which I have already discussed. Today we understress the need to reform man and overstress the need to reform society.

Thus in education we no longer seek (as Wesley advocated) to break the child's will, to instruct it, or to motivate it by punishment. Most educators believe that the child should be given the optimum environment for the development of its potentialities, and rewarded for achievement rather than punished for failure. Like a flower, the pupil will know just what inputs he needs, can decide his own curriculum, and will unfold his own perfection. This view, which seems to be widely held, is every bit as ridiculous as its Puritan opposite. The truth lies between. The pupil needs both instruction and opportunities for constructive activity, both punishment and reward, a measure of discipline and a measure of freedom.*

The philosophy of the permissive upbringing undermines the whole mechanism by which the individual is socialised. And having brought up children permissively, we are amazed to find that we have created a permissive society!

There are many other myths, and one that seems to me especially harmful: the belief in centralisation and standardisation. For some strange reason, many people are bothered by anomalies and variations. Like the general who wants to see his men identically

* To make such remarks is of course highly dangerous, and I shall no doubt receive angry letters. When in an earlier book I advocated a middle course between too much discipline and too little, I was promptly accused by one popular critic (a lady of aggressive character) of wanting to bring back flogging. Such violent responses reveal the irrationality of these beliefs.

dressed standing in a mathematically straight line, the civil servant regards 'uniformity of practice' as of overriding importance. But in real life every case is different, and local feeling about how even comparable cases should be handled varies greatly. Life is already too standardised and needs more variety and flexibility, not less. Decisions should be delegated even if this leads to inconsistency. It is easy to defend consistency on grounds of justice; it is another aspect of the preoccupation with equality. And equality begins to be seen as identity. Here again we have to compromise: equality is fine, but so is variety. Consistency is fine, but so is flexibility. We must keep our sense of proportion.

2 Trahison des clercs

Today mythic thinking is encouraged by precisely those who should do most to expose it: for lack of a better word, intellectuals. Read *Le Trahison des clercs*: the betrayal of (that is, by) the intellectuals, written by the French philosopher Julien Benda fifty years ago but just as relevant today. Benda considered that intellectuals should keep themselves free from political or other bias and state the facts as honestly as they could. By *'clercs'*, he meant any highly educated person.

Lack of bias is particularly important in those who teach the younger generation. Today, it is often argued that religious instruction should not be dogmatic: that the alternatives should be displayed, with their strengths and weaknesses exposed, and that the customer should make up his own mind. If this is true for religion it is certainly true for politics, which has today taken the place of religion for many people.

Today, nevertheless, many teachers—particularly young university lecturers—try, quite consciously, to sell a political viewpoint. Ironically enough, students themselves even demand that a lecturer should be 'committed'. Those who complain that orthodox instruction is riddled with unconscious right-wing and *status quo* assumptions are precisely those who seek to import what is worse, a deliberate and conscious bias. Furthermore, they decline to listen to any contrary arguments. (This illustrates the defect of letting students determine their own curriculum.) The extremes of class bias which can permeate teaching in England, to the point of making nonsense of it, have an irrational, not to say paranoid, character. One lecturer told me that to have any determinate method of spelling was simply a middle-class ploy to make things more difficult for the lower class! (His assumption that the lower class is naturally less able to spell than the middle class is rather revealing.)

Political preconceptions are freely imported into the social sciences which—of all disciplines—should be most free of them. The intellectual bias of a writer like the late C. Wright Mills, whose work has been very influential with students, is just as socially dangerous as the possibly unconscious right-wing bias of, say, David Riesman. Both these writers assert their views dogmatically; both cannot be right. I mention these particular writers because the contradiction in their positions has been closely analysed by William Kornhauser in an article: ' "Power Elite" or "Veto Groups"?' He concludes that no one can say which of them is right until some disciplined research has been done. That is, their assertions are not scientific but polemic. This, to be sure, is a mild example. It is when professional sociologists advocate vandalism that one's toes curl.

Still more disgraceful, morally, are the defences of violence produced by those who should know better, such as Jean-Paul Sartre, about which I wrote earlier, or the philosophical double-talk and semantic ambiguity of a writer like Herbert Marcuse. (I am not here referring to his conclusions as such, but to the philosophically devious presentation, which fools the naïve. The dangerous nature of these intellectual games is shown by Professor Adorno's indignant remark, when students broke up his lecture, to the effect: 'When I told them to defy authority, I didn't expect them to take it literally!')

It is difficult to know how to prevent teaching bias. No one wants censorship, however discreet. At the same time, we should not expect a school or university to continue employing a geography teacher who taught that the world was, or even might be, flat. It is reasonable to demand that, in matters which are controversial, a teacher should seek to be neutral.

However, the real iniquity of the intellectual left is deliberately to have misrepresented the nature of the very real problems confronting us to the public in general, and so to have made their solution more difficult, if not impossible. The iniquity of Herbert Marcuse *et al.* is that they give intellectual respectability to an urge to hate and destroy which can only wreck society—and this is the ultimate reason for taking a pessimistic view of the future.

Misrepresentation extends even to the way in which language is used: thus the poor are commonly referred to as 'deprived'. But 'to deprive' means to take away something which one had. It is not the case that the poor have less than they had: even the poorest today are richer than the poor of a century or two ago. Moreover, the word 'deprive' implies the existence of a depriver, a villain—where in fact the rich are today contributing more, not less, to the well-being of the poor. In general, the sense of being oppressed is cultivated today: people, at every level, are encouraged to feel cheated. Envy, once considered a deadly sin, is fostered. Society cannot work on this basis.

It is less likely to solve its problems on a basis of hatred, not more.

None of this means that the present situation is satisfactory. My point is simply that the very difficult problems of balancing rival, mutually exclusive demands, is made more difficult by mis-representing them and by encouraging an outbreak of chaos which can only make *everyone* worse off.

Also socially dangerous is the readiness with which some scientists, on the basis of their standing as scientists, make pronouncements in fields which they have not studied. (Remember Robert Oppenheimer, the nuclear bomb man, on how to bring up children?) Precisely because they are so dedicated to the mysteries of science, they are worse-than-average advisers on ordinary affairs. Indeed, many scientists choose science precisely because it is free of the emotional and value problems which they feel ill-equipped to handle. A world run by scientists would be completely unliveable.

The situation is worse when social scientists venture into real life. Take a look at the work of Professor David McClelland who has devoted his life to studying what motivates people to high achieve-ment. His recommendations on how to bring up children so that they will all go out and compete fiercely and create an even more jungle-like society than the US already is, and his bland confidence that other countries should follow the American pattern, fill one with deep alarm.* The conjunction of childishly naïve socio-political thinking with technical expertise, such as is here demon-strated, is one of the major dangers threatening our society. Yet society as a whole, instead of indicating disapproval, bestows public rewards on these well-meaning but fundamentally dangerous men.

The same is true of the technomaniacs, about whom I wrote in *Rethink*. A wiser society than ours would tell them firmly that their schoolboy vision of the future, full of gadgetry and devoid of humanity, is simply not wanted; and that their belief that what *can* be done *should* be done betrays a dangerous immaturity of mind. Once again, the problem is one of arrogance.

Particularly disgraceful are those professional optimists (as one might call them) who, while claiming a superior scientific detach-ment, deploy arguments which they must know to be invalid in order to reassure people that all is well. A common example is the statement, constantly repeated, that we need not worry about the population problem as birth-rates have begun to fall. The essential fact that death rates are falling even faster than birth rates is usually

---

* A world-wide survey of different cultures revealed that where achievement is stressed in educating children the society tends to be aggressively preoccupied by idea of military glory and to prefer the use of force, including torture, to achieve its ends. Thus McClelland's prescription would probably make a world war more likely.

unmentioned. Every demographer knows that birth rates are falling
—they have been doing so for over a century in some countries—
but the population continues to rise nevertheless.

The one common feature of all this pontificating is its arrogance—
but arrogance unfortunately seems to be a general disease of our time.

3 The Swollen Ego

The world seems to be undergoing an arrogance explosion. In my
youth, we worried about 'inferiority complexes'. Today, many
people seem to have an unjustified sense of superiority. On every
hand, we see people laying down the law about what should be done,
often on a basis of total ignorance. The letter columns of the newspapers bear daily witness to this marvellous certitude. Arrogance is
also visible in the assurance with which people demand this or that
concession as their 'right', and in their total reluctance to pay
deference to those who have demonstrated their ability while expecting to be treated with great consideration themselves.

This is a form of ego-mania, linked with the desire to 'be someone'
to which I have already referred. But its immediate origin is in the
excessively supporting and encouraging environment now given to
many children, in reaction from the excessively discouraging and
putting-down treatment common sixty years ago. Though no doubt
more fun for the individual, it does not make the prospects of
achieving a balanced and cohesive society very promising.

Above all, arrogance underlies the actions of the politicians who
so confidently, as we have noted earlier, overrule the expressed
wishes of the public, and it informs the civil servants who believe
they know what is best for the public and employ a veil of secrecy
to avoid consultation. Most arrogant of all is the assumption that
you have the right to destroy the innocent (for instance by bombing)
in pursuit of your aims.

The counterpart of complete confidence in oneself is total cynicism
about everyone else. Everyone is thought of either as venal or stupid.
Psychologists know that there are two kinds of individual: those who
blame themselves when things don't work out, and those who
blame others. They call them intro-punitive and extra-punitive.
Today we are witnessing a wave of extra-punitiveness. A less polite
word for it might be paranoia: the belief that all one's problems are
due to the persecutory behaviour of others is paranoid. This is
recognised in the current American witticism: 'Just because you're
paranoid doesn't mean they won't get you.'

I believe it is literally true that we live in a paranoid world: there
have of course been paranoid atmospheres before, but seldom on

anything like the present scale. The psychological origins of paranoia are, as Freud first explained to us, to be found in a disturbed relationship with the father. Society is sick because people are sick. Not the reverse.

Even if you find this overstated, you must admit that we find it hard to achieve maturity. Far too many people are childishly dependent, narcissistically self-satisfied, unable to postpone satisfaction or to stand frustration. At the same time, society is if anything too mature—too rigid, even senile.

4 Social Sclerosis

In England, cars and other traffic keep to the left. To change over to the Continental and American practice of driving on the right, though desirable, would be so expensive and confusing that it has been rejected as impracticable. When a similar change was decreed in India, where cars are fewer and traffic lights comparatively rare, the bullocks declined to change their habits, and the country had to abandon the effort.

That illustrates how difficult it is, once you wear a groove, to get out of it. In the same way, Western society has established habits and set up institutions which are hard to change, but which are steadily becoming less appropriate. One could say that society becomes sclerosed; that it ages in the pejorative sense of becoming more rigid, less adaptable and increasingly obsolete. This process has not received much attention, but has recently been explored by Professor E. Orowan of Massachusetts Institute of Technology in his book *The Aging of Societies*.

The channels of advancement in society tend to become tradition-bound. Without the recognised 'qualifications' it is difficult to enter the majority of elite posts, yet the qualifications themselves are largely irrelevant. A knowledge of case-law is thought more important than an understanding of equity. Few of the dominant elite understand the major innovative ideas which have transformed our conception of government, such as general systems theory or information theory, let alone the great physical concepts such as entropy, quantum mechanics or relativity. Even less do they pay heed to what social psychology can tell us.

The flexible society provides 'back staircases' by which people whose mode of thinking is original and creative can find their way to levels where their thinking can be applied. If in 1829 a certain putative clergyman named Charles Darwin had not been given a microscope and led to study natural history it seems improbable that he would have advanced an idea-scheme so unorthodox as the

Origin of Species. Modern society is busy closing off backstairs and asks for a ticket of admission from those who apply by the front.

These are some of the factors which explain the demand, increasingly heard in Britain, France, Germany and elsewhere for a 'shake-up'. It is a demand heard at many social levels, and underlies the growing support for national-secession groups. It is, in fact, a muted moderate equivalent to the extremist's desire for bloody revolt. It is a request for a gentle mini-revolution. (On the face of it, in an era of massive and continuous change, such a demand might seem perverse. Some people would say that what we need is time to settle down and count the pieces.)

The focus of this discontent is 'the dominant elite'. As I argued in an earlier chapter, the dominant elite is basically out of touch with reality, both in the sense that its model of society is obsolete and because its conception of 'success'—of what is required—is unrealistic. It is unresponsive to the underlying demands behind popularly voiced demands, sometimes because it lacks empathy, sometimes because it simply disagrees. Even when it does listen and agree, its response is far too slow and usually inappropriate or inadequate.*

The reasons for this sclerosis of elites are the high age-level of elites and still more the length of time they have been in existence. In a world in which half the population is under 30, a government with an average age of 55, or a senior civil service with an average age of 60 is living in the past. As Roger Garaudy has argued, when we allow for the exponential rate of development, the mid-point of history was about fifty years ago. For instance, the world, now approaching a population of 4 billion, reached 2 billion in 1925. In terms of world energy consumption, the half-way point was as recent as 1966! Thus anybody born before the end of the war (including of course myself) is liable, unless he makes exceptional efforts to update his thinking, to be living in the past.

Elites, alas, are self-perpetuating, since they only accept those who satisfy their requirements, i.e., candidates who resemble themselves and show no signs of wishing to 'make trouble'—that is, make inconvenient changes which threaten the status of those in positions of power and esteem by rendering their knowledge and methods obsolete.

Indeed the dominant elite has a horror of innovators and knows no more crushing judgment than to say someone is 'too clever by half'. This recherché anti-intellectualism undermines the confidence

---

* The fact is that the dominant elite has lost its charm, as Toynbee puts it; but perhaps a stronger word is needed. That much-misused word *charisma* (which means 'a special grace or talent') identifies what elites need and no longer have. Hence, the rest of society is reluctant to follow them.

of innovators, who too often end by settling for a sinecure within the system. Hence our loss of vim.

The French have an admirable word for the kind of academic who tries to protect his own position by running down the achievements of younger rivals who might render him obsolete. They call him a *cuistre*. The *cuistre* opposes the promotion of original thinkers to professorships and their election to the *Académie Française* until they have lost their originality and have become as sterile as themselves. The great Pasteur is the classic example of an innovator who was always rejected by the *cuistres*. But it is not only in the academic world, I fear, that *cuistres* are to be found.

It may be, then, that our society is approaching old age; that it is suffering from a hardening of the arteries which nothing will really reverse. Even if we scout deterministic theories of history it may still be true that societies age. In this state they can perhaps survive a long time if isolated from all external pressure, as happened in China under the Han dynasty. But no such isolation protects our Western society today.

5 The Evitable Future

Where are you from? People feel themselves united in a community when they share common tastes, beliefs, experiences, friends, and when they have invested emotions in common symbols, rituals, landscapes or endeavours. In the US, where a largely immigrant population is devoid of such common coinage, it is usual to start by asking a stranger where he is from? If you can then say that you know the place, or, better still, know people living there, common ground is established. In smaller and older communities, such as the Scottish Highlands, you can usually find common ancestry—if not indeed cousinhood.

So, in a larger sense, a whole country is unified by its culture, by a preference for certain ways of cooking, shaving, dressing, by ritual occasions (Christmas, Ramadan, Yom Kippur) and, quite often, by common religious beliefs. Finally, culture in the intellectual sense can be unifying. I may meet a total stranger, who might differ from me in most or all of the above respects, but provided we can communicate at all, I can develop a relationship with him if it turns out that he has read many of the books I have read, heard the same kind of music, seen the same kinds of art, and—most important of all— is familiar with the same basic ideas in philosophy and the sciences. Until recently there was a common culture shared by all educated Europeans and Americans, as well as many educated people in other countries. Thanks mainly to modern ideas of education, with their stress on the future, and to a popular belief that the past has nothing relevant to teach us, that common bond is fast vanishing. The split came first between science and the humanities (the two cultures which Snow made widely known) but today there are many who pass as educated who, thanks to early and excessive specialisation, have little share in either of the two cultures.

Worse still, there are many who no longer even have the ambition to become 'cultured'. The very word has taken on a derogatory implication: and is taken to mean culture snobbery rather than culture. To be sure, it is increasingly difficult to attain a broad culture, as the ideas of science become more complex and the back-log of art and philosophy grows longer. Besides, today a purely European culture is too narrow: one must try to know something of the whole world. But it is not the difficulty of the task which is the main obstacle; it is the progressive abandonment of the whole concept and intention. Now we hear reports of candidates for non-manual posts who cannot write, cannot spell and cannot calculate.

The question is: what is 'worth knowing'? To read that candidates for entry to the British Civil Service; aged 16, had no idea of what a monopoly is ('where men live together' ventured one) or what the Stock Exchange is ('a place where bookies gambol') and that some youths leave school at sixteen without having heard of Jesus Christ, brings out the magnitude of the problem. If we want a more cohesive society, we should make a serious attempt to meet this lack. You cannot have a cohesive society without a coherent culture.

Looking at human society in the longest possible perspective, I am struck most of all by the absence of any unifying principle, aim or 'world-view'. The medieval world found a measure of unity in the concepts of piety, obedience, order. The Renaissance sought harmony with man as the measure. What do we seek today? We know too little about world-views and how they are arrived at and discussion of the subject is dismissed by most people as remote and academic philosophising.

Perhaps we should take the question more seriously. History suggests that in periods of spiritual confusion, if a new unifying principle offers itself, people turn to it with explosive rapidity. We have prepared the materials for such an explosion right now.

Failing some such startling turn of events, I find it difficult to believe that Western culture will find a compromise between freedom and disorder or develop the social insights which will restore cohesion in such a way as to make it influential rather than merely powerful in a physical sense, in a perspective of some hundreds of years. On a shorter time-scale—say, in the lifetime of those now young—there seem to be three probable outcomes: dictatorship of the right, dictatorship of the left, or a crypto-dictatorship in a world much like today but more so.

The mixed-economy countries are in an unworkable situation: people can change jobs freely, strike for higher wages, save as much or as little as they like. In these circumstances socialist planning cannot work, but neither can capitalism, beset as it is by regulation and changes of government policy. Either the system must move forward to communism, or retreat to something nearer free enterprise. In the present climate of opinion, a retreat seems unlikely.

The American historian Crane Brinton, after examining four major revolutions, concluded that five factors seemed to precede a revolution:

1 Society was economically on the upgrade.
2 There were bitter class antagonisms.
3 The ruling class had lost confidence in its traditions and individuals were going over to the attacking groups.
4 The government machinery was inefficient.
5 The intellectuals had transferred their allegiances away from the powers that be. (He thought the third particularly important.)

All these conditions obtain in Britain and in Italy today, and in many other countries too, for that matter. An age of revolutions is, it seems, probably very near.

As against these gloomy anticipations, there are still Old Struthonians who persuade themselves that the present convulsion is merely a mighty hiccough, after which everything will fall into a new and far better pattern. If I understand the argument (where there is an argument—often this position is based on an irrational optimism) the mere fact that old assumptions are being challenged, that the young envisage a better world and furthermore regard it as attainable, is something so new as to be reason for optimism in itself. And up to a point it is. But the road to hell, as they used to say, is paved with good intentions. What depresses me is the absence of any detailed planning or problem-solving, the idealistic belief that somehow men of goodwill, without instruction or forethought, will create a workable solution, and the massive failure to look realistically at the obstacles, and make plans to deal with them. The idealist believes that everyone else, if not ruined by age or greed, is as well-intentioned as himself. But if disrupted families continue to spawn perverted individuals the world will continue much as before. Just as the colonial nations believed that, once the imperialist powers were thrown out, a new world would dawn—but found that corruption and even tyranny left things much as before, and sometimes worse—so now the optimistic left believes that it is only necessary to throw out the present rulers for everything to correct itself.

The key fact is: a change of style is imperative. Inventiveness, enthusiasm and good intentions are not enough. Misapplied, they just carry us further on the wrong course. We have to change from a fragmented to an organic social pattern. Otherwise we are headed for chaos.

I have tried, as best I can, to foresee the future and to suggest policies which might avoid or at least weaken the impact of its dangers. But though we *could* do a great deal, it seems unlikely— mankind being what it is—that we shall actually achieve very much. This is the basis of my pessimism: not the external threat but the internal weakness. However, a truly pessimistic person would not even trouble to write a book about it.

As I draw to a conclusion, I ask myself whether I have overstated the problems or underestimated man's ability and determination to solve them. In gathering so much discouraging material it is possible to become discouraged oneself. But when I have made generous allowance for good luck, ingenuity and serendipity, I am left with the fact that we have changed from a traditional world to a rational one, in which nothing is taken for granted. Poverty and injustice can be ignored when they seem natural and inevitable. They no longer do. That is the key fact. Consequently we now try to 'manage' what before happened by chance. And since management is inevitably incompetent and certainly cannot please everyone, we are bound to live in a world of protest, anger, wasteful mismatches, and resentments. Anthropologists speak of the transition from tradition to rationality, but of course man is very imperfectly rational: emotion, prejudice and superstitution are far more prominent in his behaviour.

Moreover the assumption that progress is inevitable is no longer tenable. Those who cling to this belief resent the warnings of the pessimists which threaten their sense of personal security: this is why pessimistic forecasts are so hotly denied. But it is not simply material progress which is in doubt: it is the feeling that moral idealism has lost its power, that force and expediency are triumphing, which is so disturbing.

On the positive side, however, we have far more factual knowledge than did, say, declining Rome; and our aspirations are certainly nobler. We have far greater resources of energy, both in the physical and in the human sense. Have we also the courage and the flexibility of outlook and the unselfishness to put them to good account? Could we prove to be the first civilisation in the course of history to maintain itself at a high level indefinitely? It is an objective worthy of our arrogance if only we would rise to it.

APPENDIX

In 1948 it occurred to me that many historical changes could be understood in terms of the introjection of father and mother figures, as I noted in *Conditions of Happiness* (1949). Anthropologists have observed that many primitive societies fall into one of two groups: either they have a sky-father religion, a restrictive morality and a low status for women; or they have an earth-mother religion, a permissive morality and a high status for women. Since deities are projections of the unconscious, it seemed plausible that the first group was based on a predominance of the father projection, and the second on a predominantly mother-introjection. I termed these two patterns 'patrist' and 'matrist'.

In *Sex in History* (1954) I showed that several other facets of behaviour were connected with these patterns: thus patrists are preoccupied with homosexuality, matrists with incest. Patrists prefer dark, formal clothing; matrists don't. Patrists are good at disciplined, thought-out forms of art, such as architecture; matrists are best at extempore music and dancing. Moreover, patrists set up hierarchic political structures, matrists democratic or egalitarian ones. Patrists worry about crimes against property and social disorder; matrists worry about people going sick and hungry. There are also curious details: thus patrists prefer smooth textures, matrists shaggy ones. And so on.

It was immediately clear that this distinction not only accounted for the differences between some primitive societies (if primitive is the word) but could also be applied to historical changes in western civilisation. The Middle Ages were evidently a patrist period, in contrast with the Celtic culture it swamped. Or again the Victorians were patrists in contrast with the freedom of the Age of Reason. The rise of Christianity itself was a triumph of the father figure over the pagan mother deities of early Mediterranean civilisation.

Today we, in the West, are clearly far advanced in a matrist swing away from Victorian patrism—perhaps almost due for a reversal of the trend.

Naturally, parental introjection is not the only psychological factor at work in society, by a long chalk. In *The Angel Makers* (1958) which analyses the origins of Victorianism and Puritanism, I note at least two others, of which the distinction between 'hard-ego' and 'soft-ego' is particularly important; and in *Rethink* (1973) I discussed the relevance of this last distinction to the present day.

Two comments must be added. First, there is no suggestion that society swings between these extremes like a pendulum. Sometimes it switches quickly, sometimes it remains frozen in one pattern. Second, the most productive and successful cultures are those which, like the Greek culture, for a time find a point of balance. Patrist discipline must harness matrist creativity for a culture to become great. To regain that balance is our problem today.

SOURCE NOTES

I have not attempted to give every one of the hundreds of newspaper items referred to in the text, but have tried to give all those where figures were cited or the views of named individuals quoted. I have also included all articles containing original material where it was important that due credit be given to the writer concerned, either for his presentation of facts or for his opinions. I have also included some background material and sources of facts amplifying or confirming points I have made.

PART I FUTURE IMPERFECT

I POSSIBLE FUTURES

6   Maurice Strong quoted: *The Times*, 6/6/74: 'World is heading once more for Doomsday'.
6   Alexander King quoted: 'Another Kind of Growth' (David Davies lecture, David Davies Memorial Inst., London, 1972), p. 20.
7–8 Theodore Gordon's prediction: 'Some Crises that will determine the World of 1994' (Report 137.01.16), AAAS Symposium on the World of 1994, 27/2/74.
8   Hasan Ozbekhan's prediction: *Futures* (1969), *1*, p. 478.
7–8 Harrison Brown's views: in Tiselius and Nilsson (1970), pp. 351–2.
9   nuclear blackmail: John Platt, 'The World Transformation and what must be done', in Coelho and Rubinstein (1972), p. 175.
9   Platt's 1969 opinion: 'What we Must Do', *Science* (1969), *166*, p. 1115.
10 Platt's 1973 opinion: Book reviews, *Science* (1973), *180*, p. 580.
10 Kahn 'educated incapacity': Kahn and Bruce-Briggs (1972), pp. 80–2.
11 Kahn 'some acceleration . . .': ibid. p. 42.
11 Kahn 'long-term future': BBC-TV programme, 'The Future goes Boom' 3/4/74.
12 Kahn 'Caribbean danger spot': Kahn and Bruce-Briggs, p. 75.
12 Kahn 'world food surplus': ibid. p. 154.

12   Kahn 'crisis in 1985': ibid. Ch. 8.
12   Kahn 'counter-culture has peaked': ibid. Ch. 4.
13– Alternative images of future: P. Hall, 'Urban Europe 2000', *Futures* (1973),
14   *5*, pp. 449–56; A. J. Jansen and S. Faith, 'Agriculture in Europe 2000',
     Futures (1973), *5*, pp. 438–48.
14   Scenario of the Unacceptable: *L'Express*, 5/11/73, p. 61, 'Alain Decaux
     raconte L'Avenir'.

II Expecting the Unexpected

18   genetic engineering risks: *Science* (1973), *181*, p. 1114, 'Guidelines for DNA
     Hybrid Molecules' (letter); *Science* (1974), *185*, p. 332, N. Wade, 'Genetic
     Manipulation: Temporary Embargo proposed on Research' and com-
     ments in *Nature* (1974), *250*, pp. 278–80, 'NIH Backing for NAS Ban'.
18– Lederberg: biological risks: 'The Perfection of Man' in Tiselius and Nilsson
20   (1970), pp. 36–9.
20   J. Vallentyne cited: 'Freshwater Supplies and Pollution: Effect of Demo-
     phoric Explosion' in N. Polunin (ed) (1972), p. 195ff.
20– adulteration of food: Ben Feingold, 'Adverse Reactions to Food Additives',
21   Man/Food Conference, London, 20/9/73.
21   Ehrlich's *Ecocatastrophe*: reprinted in A. Toffler (ed) (1972), pp. 13–26.
21– carbon dioxide in oceans: A. W. Fairhall, 'Accumulation of Fossil CO_2 in
22   the Atmosphere and the Sea', *Nature* (1973), *245*, pp. 20–22.
22   ozone and ultra-violet layer: Professor Reid Bryson summarised the story
     in a statement reproduced in Polunin (ibid.), p. 150; Harvard team,
     Science News (1974), *105*, p. 160; Harold Johnstone, *Science* (1971), *173*,
     pp. 317–22, and *Science News* (1973), *103*, p. 101; congressional com-
     mittee's conclusions, W. J. Burroughs, *Environmental Bulletin* (1973), No. 18;
     for the critical view, P. Goldsmith, *et al.*, *Nature* (1973), *244*, pp. 545–51;
     Science News (1972), *102*, p. 262, 'NAS Panel finds Johnstone's conclusions
     credible'.
23   ozone: the effect of aerosols: M. J. Molina and F. S. Rowland, 'Strato-
     spheric Sink for chlorofluoromethanes: chlorine atom catalysed destruction
     of ozone', *Nature* (1974), *249*, p. 810; for Ciccione's work, *Sunday Times*,
     3/11/74, Bryan Silcock 'Aerosols "threaten atmosphere" '.
24– ice surge: NAS/NRC/NAE *News Report* (1974), *24*(6), pp. 1, 8; J. T. Hollin,
25   *Nature* (1964), *202*, p. 1099; van den Heuvel, 'Ice Shelf Theory', *Nature*
     (1965), *210*, pp. 363–5.
25–26 Galtung: war unlikely; Jungk and Galtung (1969), p. 12
26   Bernard Feld cited: Pearce Wright. Scientists put odds at three to one on a
     nuclear weapon being used in a conflict before 1984. (Note: the headline
     is in error: the odds quoted were one to three.)
26   Chinese think war unavoidable: D. Bonavia. Chinese leaders sure that third
     world war is unavoidable, *The Times*, 16/10/74.
27   Boulding cited: The Social System and the Energy Crisis, *Science* (1974),
     184, p. 257.
28   arctic ice-spill: This possibility has been analysed by W. J. Campbell and
     S. Martin: Oil and Ice in the Arctic Ocean, *Science* (1973), *181*: 56.

PART II INTERNAL WEAKNESS

III GROWING ANARCHY

35– the growth of terrorism: I have drawn on Colin Legum, 'What is Terrorism?',
37   *Observer*, 26/11/72, and unsigned articles in *The Economist*, 1/6/74 ('The
        Companies in the Guerrillas' Sights'), and 5/1/74 ('Your Neighbourhood
        Terrorist').
37   El-Zitouna citation; methods: B. Crozier (1960); for terrorist methods see
        R. Thompson (1966).
38   June 22 movement; Schmucker: F. Kemna, 'Death of a Nightingale',
        Encounter, Sept. 1974, *43*(3), p. 60.
38   training of subversives: J. Barron (1974); I. Greig (1973); A. Terry, 'Arabs
        Terror Squad trained by Russians', *Sunday Times*, 16/6/74; J. Hoagland,
        'Under Black September's Cover', *Guardian*, 19/3/73.
38   Qaddafi quoted: Libya helps IRA: *New York Times*, 21/4/73.
40   Black Liberation Army manual: *The Economist*, 1/6/74 (as above).
41   Peter Hamilton: women guerrillas, personal communication.
43– Philosophies of violence: See M. Cranston (ed) (1970), especially the con-
45   tributions concerning Fanon, Sartre, Marcuse; and the works of these
        writers.
45– violence and Christianity: J. Ellul (1970); also *The Times*, 14/5/74, 'Canon
46   urges Christian backing for violence'.
46   violence and anarchism: M. Lerner, 'Anarchism and the American Counter-
        culture', in D. E. Apter and J. Joll (eds), 1971.
47   aims of the New Left: R. Neville (1970); lecturer at Vincennes University,
        The Times, 18/6/69.
47– Japanese Red Army: *Observer*, 22/9/74, 'An Army inspired by divine
48   violence'; *The Times*, 7/2/74, 'A Red Army's Philosophy of Death', etc.
50   Amnesty International Report: *New York Herald-Tribune*, 27/11/73; and for
        use of halperidol, *The Times*, 19/2/74, 'Plea for Soviet dissenter dying in
        mental hospital'.
50   torture equipment deal: Pakistan: *The Times*, 18/7/72, ' "Torture equip-
        ment" deal stopped'.
50– CIA activities: Marchetti and Marks (1974); L. Stern, 'The CIA Uncovered',
51   *Japan Times Weekly*, 10/8/74, reprinted from *Washington Post*.
51   Jewish execution squad: *Observer*, 5/8/73, P. Deeley, 'How the Wrath of
        God came to Ahmed'.
51   Brazilian death squadrons: *Observer*, 17/6/73, 'Death Squadron in Brazil's
        Terror Wave'; see also *The Times*, 9/5/74, 'Shackles that preserve Brazil's
        image of tranquillity'; and for Uruguay, *The Times*, 17/6/74, 'Jurists
        condemn torture in Uruguay'.

IV VULNERABLE WORLD

54   air traffic control: The British Civil Aviation Authority is working towards
        complete automation of air traffic control, all civil flightplan data being
        handled by a multi-computer complex at West Drayton.

54 GPO telephone towers: R. I. Moxon, 'Problems of Tower Design', *P.O. Telecom. J.* (1970–1), *22*(4), p. 117.

55 Arthur Hawkins quoted: CEGB *Newsletter* (1973), No. 90.

56 threat to oil rigs: H. Stanhope: *The Times*, 14/5/74, 'Balancing the Books...'.

58– home-made nuclear device: *Undercurrents* (Summer 1972), not paginated;

59 *The Times*, 24/11/73, 'Arabs urged to make atom bombs'; J. Tinker, 'Making an atomic bomb...', *New Scientist* (1973), *57*, p. 473.

59 O'Toole, basement bombers: *Japan Times Weekly*, 29/6/74, reprinted from *Washington Post*.

60–63 Vacca's thesis: R. Vacca (1971), Introduction; also p. 52.

62 maximum city size: K. Leibbrand, 'City Planning and Traffic Engineering', *Traffic Quarterly* (1968), *22*(4), p. 595.

63 Barrington Moore's prediction: Moore (1972), p. 47, also see p. 151.

V TIDES OF RESENTMENT

For a close-up view of the problem and useful analysis and suggestions I would particularly recommend reading James Patrick's *A Glasgow Gang Observed* (1973).

67 a recent US survey: *The Times*, 15/1/74, 'One in three victim of crime in US cities'; *The Times*, 10/10/73, 'Violent crime is on increase in US suburbs'; etc.

68 striking American truck-drivers: *Sunday Times*, 10/2/74, Stephen Aris, 'US lorry strike brings violence and petrol panic'.

68 violence of strike pickets: *The Times*, 5/10/73, 'Terrifying display of violence by "flying pickets" at building sites, prosecution says'; *Sunday Times*, 7/10/73, T. Rocca, 'Building strike's flying pickets in the dock'; *The Times*, 29/1/74, 'Angry pickets "impossible to arrest"'.

69 interruption of Aida opera: *The Times*, 1/8/74.

70–71 crimes of violence in UK: N. Fowler (1973), pp. 6–8.

71–72 crimes of violence in US: *Time*, 23/10/72, 'Street Crime: Who's Winning?'

72 Eisenhower commission cited: *Sunday Times Magazine*, 27/6/71, 'Washington: District of Crime'.

73 stabbing of George Riddell: *The Times*, 28/9/73, 'Murder by boy aged 15 "only for pleasure"'.

73–74 US school violence: *The Times*, 14/1/73, Stephen Aris 'New York's Schools of Violence'; and US delinquency literature generally.

74 British school violence: *The Times*, 13/12/71, 'Myths and Realities of School violence'; *The Times*, 19/12/72, 'Enquiry into "stabbings and extortions"'; *Observer*, 28/10/73, 'The 10-year-old who led 23 robberies'; *Sunday Times*, 21/11/71, 'Violence in our schools: the grim reality' etc.; L. F. Lowenstein (1972), found that some 29 per cent of secondary schools reported having problems of violence.

74 increased violence by girls: *The Times*, 24/8/72, 'Bigger part claimed for women in crimes of violence'; *Daily Telegraph*, 17/1/74, 'Schoolgirl Gangs' Reign of Terror'; *Time*, 16/10/72, 'The Girl Gangs etc.'; *The Times*, 25/7/74, P. Evans, 'Big increase in crimes by girls under age of 14'.

74 European school violence: *The Times*, 15/12/71, 'Europe's variety of violence in schools'.

74 Union of Women Teachers: Mrs Norrie Shelton, *The Times*, 29/8/72.

74 Institute of Research Techniques survey: *The Times*, 24/9/73, 'Boys admit Razor Attacks, Beatings up and Stabbings'.

75–76   vandalism: spray paint episode: C. Ward (1973), p. 277; A. Wilson, 'One way to stop vandalism', *Observer Magazine*, 24/6/73, pp. 16–17, 19–21.

77   vandalism: railway accidents: *The Times*, 29/12/72, '214 railway accidents caused by hooliganism'; and annual Railway Accidents reports, from 1970.

78   vandalism in nature reserve: *The Times*, 13/9/72 (letter).

78   Stan Cohen quoted: C. Ward (1973), and see 'Who are the Vandals?', *New Society* (1968), *324*, pp. 872–8.

78   Ashdown Forest fires: ibid. pp. 300–301, citing 'Tomorrow's Countryside', by Garth Christian.

79   Arthur Miller quoted: 'The Bored and the Violent' in S. Endleman (ed) (1968), p. 270f. See also J. Patrick (1973), pp. 80, 124.

79   James Patrick cited: ibid. p. 136, and for Miller's comment.

80–81   Marseille club for boys: Elton Mayo (1969), p. 65.

82   defence of self-image: H. Toch (1969), p. 137f.

82   Dr Kellmer Pringle cited: 'Violence and Vandalism' (roneoed) no date.

82   frustrated 19-year-old quoted: W. H. Allchin (1970).

82   stimulus hunger: See George F. Solomon, 'Psychodynamic Aspects . . .' in D. N. Daniels *et al.* (1970), for a summary.

82–83   confession of psychopath: in T. E. Geddes and J. O. Long (1970) and compare the man executed for eating a child in Wertham (1949), pp. 66–7.

VI   Sources of Cohesion

86   Harry Minton: Minton, 'Blind Man's Buff', *Observer Magazine*, 16/12/73, p. 63.

88   'Representative men': C. W. Mills (1963), Ch. 6.

88–89   Jeremy Seabrook cited: J. Seabrook (1973), p. 30.

90   shoplifting, American: *The Times*, 22/12/71, 'One shopper out of 15 in American stores is a thief'.

90–91   shoplifting, British: *The Times*, 11/12/73, 'Shoplifting by 5-year-olds'; *Shoplifting and Thefts by Shop Staff:* report by a working party on internal shop security, HMSO (1972).

91   shoplifting, European: Lisa Schmidt, 'Lead us not into Temptation', *Europa* (December 1973), p. 32.

92   true crime rates: *New York Times*, 27/4/73, 'Study finds Crime Rates far Higher Than Reports'.

92   Gerry Mars cited: in S. Cohen, 'Living with Crime', *New Society*, *26*(579), p. 330 (1973).

92   British indictable crime rates: N. Fowler (1973).

93   US arson figures: *Seattle J. of Commerce* (Nov. 1973), cited in *SRI News Items*, No. 18 (1974), p. 6.

93   UK arson figures: *Financial Times*, 18/4/74, 'Fire Protection Survey'; *Sunday Times*, 11/8/74, 'Arson at School'.

93   theft and rape on express trains: *The Times*, 2/9/74, ' "Rape and Theft" on Istanbul train'.

94   book thefts: Howard Nixon quoted: G. Smith, 'The Fine Book Thieves', *Sunday Times*, 17/6/73.

95   young advised to steal books: *Antistudent*, unpaginated.

95   ways of changing the system: *Y-Front*, No. 4 (1974), p. 9.

96   Michael Lerner quoted: 'Anarchism and the American counter-culture', in D. E. Apter and J. Joll (1971), p. 34ff.

98   C. Frankel on 'irrationalism': *Science* (1974), *180*, p. 1927, 'The nature and sources of "irrationalism"'.

99   altruism: in J. Macaulay and L. Berkowitz (eds), 1970.

100 Clancy Sigal cited: in S. Lipset (1966), ch. 5.

101 Japanese crime rates: PHP Magazine (May 1974), *5*(5); *Japan Times Weekly*, 24/11/73, 'Crime in Japan'.

PART III   FLASHBACK

VII   THE ROMAN WARNING

For details of the Roman economy I have drawn on Bury (1923), Dill (1910), Finley (1973), A. H. M. Jones (1964), Walbank (1969) and of course Rostovtzeff (1926).

108 corporate state: Walbank (1969), Ch. 5.

110-111   Rostovtzeff cited: Rostovtzeff (1926), p. 487.

111 mimesis: Toynbee (ed. Somervell) (1947), p. 275ff.

112 Empire not hated by barbarians: Dill (1910), p. 291.

113 community for evacuated children: Wills (1945).

114 challenge and response: Toynbee (1947), especially Ch. 5.

114 Edwyn Bevan quoted: in Toynbee (1947), p. 363.

VIII   FROM CHAOS TO TYRANNY

For a general treatment of social structure and its relationship to cohesion it is essential to read W. Kornhauser, *The Politics of Mass Society* (1960 and subsequent editions) and R. A. Nisbet (1953) especially p. 277.

120 medieval corporate society: Trevelyan (1953), p. 239.

120 de Tocqueville (1954), pp. 9-11.

121 Durkheim on anomia, etc. (1951); also Durkheim (1958), pp. 62-3.

122 Lederer quoted: Lederer (1940), pp. 86-7.

124 Toynbee on universal states: Toynbee (1947), pp. 383-4 and 422-3.

124 P. Elton Mayo quoted: Mayo (1969), p. 132.

PART IV   DANGER ZONES

IX   UNGOVERNABILITY

130 Italian unions dictate policy: D. Willey, 'We run economy or we strike, say unions', *Observer*, 9/6/74.

134 journalists' union demand: see also P. Hazelhurst, 'Warning on trade unions' threat to free press', *The Times*, 15/5/74.

135   hospital patients endangered: *The Times*, 25/7/74.
136   Ross and Hartmann's prediction: B. C. Roberts, 'The Strike Syndrome',
        cited in *Europa*, Jan/Feb 1974.
137– communist influence in unions: ISC Report, *Sources of Conflict in British*
139   *Industry*, pp. 28–32.
138   M. McGahey threatens Heath: *Observer*, 31/3/74.
140   Gen. Goldsmith quoted: *Brassey's Annual* (1973), pp. 206–20, 'Emergencies
        and Home Defence'.
140   right wing movements: Open File, *Guardian*, 17/6/74; Malcolm Brown, 'The
        Apostles of free enterprise', *The Times*, 11/4/73.
141   Brig. Kitson quoted: Kitson (1972), p. 80. He considers that the 'second
        half of the seventies is going to see large-scale insurgency giving way to
        civil disorder accompanied by sabotage and terrorism especially in urban
        areas'.
142   A. Wilson. Storm looms over riot gas book, *Observer*, 6/4/75.
143   Biggs Davison quoted: Defence Studies Seminar at RUSI, 4/4/73, 'The Role
        of the Armed Forces in Peacekeeping in the 1970s'.
144   AEU staff strike against AEU: 'Clerical strike affects Mr Scanlon's union', *The
        Times*, 30/10/74.

Note: the various references to specific industrial actions were taken from *The Times* between September 1973 and July 1974 but have not been listed individually.

X FINANCIAL DISASTER

Articles on inflation in all its aspects have been too numerous to cite, but I would like to mention one: E. J. Mishan, 'The New Inflation', *Encounter* (1974), *42*(5), p. 12.

147   Economics of the Real World: P. Donaldson (1973).
149   Healey's warning: 'Political solvent of inflation', *The Times*, 28/3/74.
149   Burn's warning: *Sunday Times*, 4/8/74, Robert Samuelson, 'The man who
        keeps you short of cash'.
152   redistribution of high incomes: *The Economist*, 16/3/74, p. 76, 'You didn't
        know you had such a broad back'; Alan Day, 'Who earns what', *Observer*,
        27/1/74.
155   public opinion poll: See also J. S. Duesenberry (*Income, Saving and the Theory
        of Consumer Behaviour*) (1952), for the theory that the satisfaction a person
        obtains from his expenditure is a function, not of the absolute level of his
        expenditure, but of the ratio of his current expenditure to that of other
        people.
161   breakdown in UK by 1980: Peter Jay, 'How inflation threatens British
        democracy with its last chance before extinction', *The Times*, 1/7/74.

XI CHARMLESS ELITE

163–164   S. Haseler quoted: *The Times*, 27/7/74 (letter).
164   Drucker quoted: Drucker (1969), p. viii and (1959), Ch. 7.

164 charmless elites: Toynbee, pp. 245–6 and 309ff.
164– criticisms of British governments: *The Times*, 30/4/74, 'Public Losing
165   Confidence in most of the leading British institutions'; *The Times*, 19/2/74,
      Penny Symon: 'TV coverage leads to despair and disillusionment', etc.
164 Mark Abrams' survey: *Social Trends*, No. 4 (1973), 'Subjective Social
      Indicators', especially Table X.
164 Dick Taverne quoted: Taverne (1974), p. 94.
166 Ronald Butt quoted: *Sunday Times*, 11/11/73, 'Will the 2-party system survive
      the protest vote?'
166 Wedgwood Benn's views: W. Benn (1970).
166 Roy Jenkins quoted: *The Times*, 28/12/73, Chalfont, 'Leading a political
      crusade down the middle of the road'.
166 criticism of US governments: *Time*, 31/12/73, p. 25; Kidron (1968), p. 106;
      Campbell and Converse (1972), Ch. 8.
167 community action as response: J. Cunningham, 'Current Issues in Com-
      munity Work', *Guardian*, 20/9/73.
172 Mayo quoted: Mayo (1969), p. 132.
172 Leo Abse quoted: Abse (1973), p. 49.
173 government secrecy: Drucker (1959), Ch. 7; A. Thompson (1970), and for
      a good example, *Ecologist* (1973), *3*(2), p. 47, R. Allen, 'Open Government
      or Open Contempt?', p. 64; G. Searle, 'The Secrets of Snowdonia', and
      p. 41, G. Foley, 'Chrysler buys Leicester'. Government secrecy has also
      been criticised in *Nature* (1974), *247*, p. 1, 'Government by Stealth and
      Secrecy'.
174 bureaucracy's expanding role: M. Weber (1956), p. 128, etc.
175 footnote: MPS' empty discussions: *The Times*, 26/7/73, Michael Ratcliffe,
      'The "Ring" of MPS'.
175 Moonman quoted: 'Give your MP a little tolerance', *The Times*, 16/10/74.
      See also B. Magee, *The Times*, 6/1/75.
176 'massacre of the innocents': cf. *The Times*, 8/2/74, '83 bills are lost . . .'.
177 slide into totalitarianism in US: S. Andreski (1973), pp. 102–9.
177 Hamilton quoted: Hamilton (1972), p. 10.
178 right-wing groups in Britain: *The Times*, 11/4/73, Malcolm Brown, 'The
      apostles of free enterprise'; *Observer*, 27/1/74, David Keys, 'New Right
      Wing Group'; *The Times*, 29/7/74, Christopher Walker, 'Privately pre-
      paring for the worst'; *Observer*, 23/6/74, David Martin, 'Mystery men
      behind the Club of Ten'; *Observer*, 18/8/74, Robert Chesshyre, *et al.*,
      'Britain's reluctant colonels'; *Guardian*, 17/6/74, Open File.
178 *The Times*, 2/2/74, ' "Nasty move" to right is feared by Mr Short', etc.;
      popular swing to right feared: *The Times*, 25/1/74, Chalfont, 'How silent
      majority could be pushed past limit of patience'.
178 Italian right-wing groups: *Financial Times*, 6/8/74, Robert Graham, 'Fascist
      group says we bombed Bologna train'; *The Times*, 31/1/74, 'Bomb attacks
      in Milan blamed on neo-Fascists'; *Financial Times*, 6/8/74, Robert Graham,
      'Hunting for villains on the Right'; *Sunday Telegraph*, 27/10/74, Leslie
      Childe, 'Spectre of Coup in Italy', etc.
179 Arendt on fascist methods: Arendt (1970), Ch. 11.

PART V PRACTICAL PROBLEMS

XII Scarcer?

183 National Assn. of Mfrgr's Poster: reproduced in *Newsweek*, 19/11/73, p. 120.
185 Lester Brown quoted: 'Population and Affluence' (1973), *Population Bulletin*, *29*(2).
185 John Morgan cited: Andrew Staines, 'Digesting the raw materials threat', *New Scientist* (1974), *61*, p. 609.
185 John Tunney attacks optimists: J. V. Tunney, 'Resources: Echoes of "Ecodoom" ', *Washington Post*, reprinted *Japan Times Weekly*, 24/8/74.
185 resource shortage prospect denied: *The Economist*, 29/6/74; *New Statesman*, 27/10/73.
186 bauxite producers unite: *The Times*, 8/3/74, 'Guinea call for bauxite producers to unite'.
186 Mobutu cited: copper cartel: *The Times*, 15/1/74, 'Zaire call to raise raw material prices'; *Observer*, 14/4/74, Anthony Sampson, 'Third World set to form new price ring'.
187 Brookings Institute summing-up: cf. Bergsten, *Japan Times Weekly*, 9/2/74, p. 12.
187 Japanese study group plans rejig: *Observer*, 15/5/73, Mark Frankland: 'Japan's recipe for disaster'.
187 us mineral import figures: Carroll Kilpatrick, 'The Minerals Shortage', *Washington Post* Reprinted *Japan Times Weekly*, 9/2/74. p. 12.
188 Sherman Clark's estimates: Clark, 'Energy and Resource Economics', *Investments in Tomorrow* (Summer 1972), *4*, p. 2.
188 Martin Sherwood cited: M. Sherwood, 'Chemicals and the Oil Crisis', *New Scientist* (1973), *60*, pp. 777–8.
189 helium from hydrogen: W. Murdoch (1972), p. 81.
190 lifetimes of some metal reserves: ibid. p. 73 (table).
191 demand estimates too conservative: K. Warren (1973), Ch. 12.
191– Professor Alexander cited: W. O. Alexander, 'Metals and Non-metallic
192   Materials', in *Futures* (1969), *1*(6), pp. 500–509.
192 optimism about wealth from sea: Charles Foley, 'Mr Hughes' amazing sinking barge', *Observer*, 28/10/73.
192 Ritchie Calder cited: ibid.
192–193 Preston Cloud's warning: W. Murdoch (1971), p. 87.
193 John Mero's estimate: G. Alexander, 'Get your Flippers', *Los Angeles Times*, reprinted *Japan Times Weekly*, 12/1/74.
194 built-in obsolescence: V. Packard (1971), Chapters 5 to 8 inclusive.
195 energy consumed in making a car: T. Johnson, 'Hydrogen Hysteria', citing *Bull. Atom. Scientists* (May 1972), in *New Scientist* (1972), *56*, p. 410.
195 recycling of steel: James Cannon, 'Steel: the recyclable material', *Environment* (1973), *15*(9), p. 11.
196 cost of industrial corrosion: T. P. Hoar, 'Corrosion of metals: its cost and cure', address, Royal Society, 7/2/74.

XIII Climatic Threat

The basic source for climatic information is H. H. Lamb: *Climate: Present, Past and Future* (1972) and I have drawn on it at several points.

197   evidence of a cooling trend: G. J. Kukla and R. K. Matthews, 'When will the present interglacial end?', *Science* (1972), *178*, 190–1; K. Frazier, 'Earth's Cooling Climate', *Science News* (1969), *96*, p. 458.

197–   meteorological opinion: H. H. Lamb, 'Whither Climate Now?', *Nature*
198   (1973), *245*, p. 433; Pearce Wright, 'Scientists believe dry spell could be start of 30-year trend', *The Times*, 26/3/73.

198   Sverdlovsk: *Nature* (1973), *244*, p. 395.

198   400 icebergs: Bryan Silcock, *Sunday Times*, 9/7/72, 'Arctic Heatwave and British Blues'.

198   new climatic regime: J. Namias, 'Seasonal Interactions between the North Pacific Ocean and the Atmosphere during the 1960s', *Mon. Weather Rev.* (1969), *97*, p. 173.

199   Baffin Island observations: R. S. Bradley and G. H. Miller, 'Recent Freezing Level Changes and Climatic Deterioration in the Canadian Arctic Archipelago', *Nature* (1973), *243*, p. 398.

199–200   satellite observation of snowcover: *Environmental Bulletin* (July 1973), p. 20.

199   MIT computer analysis: V. P. Starr and A. H. Oort, 'Five Year Climatic Trend for the Northern Hemisphere', *Nature* (1973), *242*, p. 310.

200   oxygen isotope studies: W. Dansgaard *et al.*, *Science* (1969), *166*, p. 377, 'One Thousand Centuries of Climatic Record . . .'; W. Dansgaard, *et al.*, 'Glacier Oxygen-18 content and Pleistocene Ocean Temperatures', *Science* (1969), *166*, p. 499.

201   symposium at Brown University: G. J. Kukla and R. K. Matthews, ibid.

201   Emiliani quoted: C. Emiliani, 'Quaternary paleotemperatures and the duration of the high-temperature intervals', *Science* (1972), *178*, p. 398.

201–   Manley's work: G. Manley, *Geographical J.* (1951), *117*, p. 43, 'The Range
202   of Variation of the British Climate'; *Arch. f. Met. Geophys.* (1958), B.9, p. 413, Vienna, 'Temperature trends in England 1698–1957'.

202   sunspot cycles: J. W. King, 'Solar Radiation Changes and the Weather', *Nature* (1973), *245*, p. 443. In correspondence Dr King says he has 'no reason to suppose that a descending sequence of four sunspot peaks can now be expected or that such a sequence would be associated with a worsening climate for the remainder of the millennium'. It will be instructive to see whether such 'scientific caution' is justified.

202   magnetic field of earth and climate: G. Wollin, *et al.*, 'Magnetic Intensity and Climatic Changes 1925–70', *Nature* (1973), *242*, p. 34; J. W. King, 'Weather and the Earth's Magnetic Field', *Nature* (1974), *247*, p. 131.

203   proposed 179-year cycle: J. Gribbin, 'Planetary Alignment, Solar Activity and Climatic Change', *Nature* (1973), *246*, p. 453.

203   effect of particulates: R. Bryson, Climatic modification by air pollution in N. Pounin (ed.), 1970; S. I. Rasool and S. H. Schneider, 'Atmospheric carbon dioxide and aerosols: effects of large increase on global climate', *Science* (1971), *173*, p. 138; W. Hamilton and T. A. Seliga, 'Atmospheric Turbidity and Surface Temperature on the Polar Ice Sheets', *Nature* (1972), *235*, p. 320; L. Machta reported by W. J. Burroughs in DTI Reports (UK Scientific Mission), 1973/6.

204   volcanic dust: H. H. Lamb (1972), pp. 410–436.

204 global monitoring: L. A. Purrett, 'Analysing the Atmosphere', *Science News* (1972), *102*, p. 60; G. D. Robinson, 'Global Environmental Monitoring', *Technology Review* (1971), *73*(7), p. 18.

205 Budyko's calculation: *Tellus* (1969), *21*, p. 611. See also J. S. Sawyer, *Nature* (1972), *229*, p. 23.

205 Fletcher quoted: and AIDJEX experiment: L. A. Purrett, 'The shifting world of Arctic sea ice', *Science News* (1971), *100*, p. 80.

206 Mitchell quoted: *Science News* (1969), *96*, p. 458.

207 consequences for food supply: D. Winstanley, *et al.*, 'Climatic Changes and the World Food Supply', *Environment Canada* (roneoed), 1974; G. C. Johnson and L. P. Smith (1965).

207 consequences for fisheries: A Longhurst, *et al.*, 'Instability of Ocean Populations', *New Scientist* (1972), *54*, p. 500.

207 energy supply implications: D. Pimentel, *et al.*, 'Food Production and the Energy Crisis', *Science* (1973), *182*, p. 443; J. R. Stansfield, 'Fuel in British Agriculture', Nat. Inst. Agric. Engineering, 1974; A. J. Low, 'Modern food production and fossil fuels', *Nutrition and Food Science* (July 1974), p. 36.

207 alteration in rainfall distribution: D. Winstanley, 'Recent Rainfall Trends in Africa, the Middle East and India', *Nature* (1973), *243*, p. 464; ibid. 'Rainfall Patterns and General Atmospheric Circulation', *Nature* (1973), *245*, p. 190.

210 Bryson cited: R. Bryson, 'Drought in Sahelia: who or what is to blame?', *Ecologist* (1973), *3*(10), p. 366.

211 resettlement as solution: H. Church, 'Resettlement seems to be the only way of beating continued drought', *The Times*, 10/9/74.

211 counter measures: I. Peschansky, 'Breaking the Russian Ice', *New Scientist* (1969), *41*, p. 574; also *New Scientist* (1968), *37*, p. 404 and *38*, p. 290.

XIV ENERGETIC MEASURES

213 no fuel shortage; Professor Cambel: In Bronwell (1970), pp. 165–83.

213 increasing energy use: the best source is probably J. Darmstadter, 'Energy Consumption Trends and Patterns', in S. H. Schurr (ed) (1972), but there are many estimates.

215 7m. tons of oil a day worldwide: based on J. L. Crabb, 'Oil', *Geos* (Winter 1974), p. 5. Other estimates are slightly lower.

215 calculation of oil reserves: I have drawn heavily on King Hubbert, Ch. 8, in NAS/NRC Committee on Resources and Man (1969), on the whole energy problem, but I did not have access to L. Rocks and R. P. Runyon (1973) which is probably more up to date. Of course, there have been countless newspaper articles and articles in technical journals. The energy issue of *Science* (1974), *184*, No. 4134, and A. B. Lovins (1973), are valuable in their different ways.

218 Athabasca tar sands: see *The Times*, 4/10/74, 'Tar sand mining—the hard way to get oil'; W. L. Dack, 'Athabasca Tar Sands', *Geos* (Summer 1974), p. 5.

218 shale oil: see King Hubbard, ibid., pp. 198–200; G. N. Dineen and G. L. Cook, 'Oil shale and the Energy Crisis', *Technology Review* (1974), *76*, p. 26.

218 Occidental Oil announcement: *The Times*, 24/11/73, 'New method makes getting oil from shale economic . . .'.

219 natural gas reserves: *Investments in Tomorrow* (Spring 1973), No. 7, p. 2, John P. Henry Jr., 'Plug Technology into the Energy Shortage'.

219   growth of US electricity usage: *Science* (1973), *180*, pp. 155–62, G. A. Lincoln, 'Energy Conservation'.

219   Japan's fuel consumption: Report of International Ad Hoc Committee on Air Pollution, OECD, Paris 1973.

219   uranium supply, Faulkner: in King Hubbert, pp. 223–4.

219   uranium supply, Anthony Gray: *Nuclear Engineering International* (1973), *18*(203), p. 280.

220   AEC forecast: cited V. V. Abajian and A. M. Fishman in *Physics Today* (1973), *36*(8), p. 23; also *Nature* (1973), *245*, p. 348, 'Uranium Resources' for British supplies.

220   breeder reactors, plutonium produced: according to T. O'Toole in the *Washington Post* (reprinted *Japan Times Weekly*, 6/7/74, p. 2), the figure is as high as 200,000 bombs.

221   At Ranstad in Sweden: D. Gabor in Jungk and Galtung (1969), p. 160.

223   uranium from sea-water: *J. Brit. Nuclear Energy Soc.*, April 1967, and personal communication.

223   D. R. W. Marley cited: *Nuclear Engineering International* (1973), *18*(20), p. 124.

223   background radiation: recent measurements suggest that background radiation is much lower than thought—about 40 mrem/yr. So the officially acceptable exposure of 170 mrem/yr ought to be cut by 75 per cent anyway.

224   Alvin Weinberg cited: *Science* (1972), *177*, p. 27, 'Social Institutions and Nuclear Energy'.

224   krypton and tritium: J. O. Blomeke, *et al.*, 'Managing Radioactive Wastes', *Physics Today* (1973), *26*(8), pp. 36–42; A Martin, 'Management of Radioactive Wastes', *Nuclear Engineering International* (1973), *18*, p. 124.

225   John Edsall's letter: *Science* (1972), *178*, p. 933.

225   Geesaman cited: D. P. Geesaman, 'Plutonium and the Energy Decision' in *The Energy Crisis* (ed. R. S. Lewis and B. I. Spinrad, 1972), pp. 58–9.

226   fusion energy: R. F. Post, 'Prospects for fusion power', *Physics Today* (April 1973), *26*(4), p. 30.

227   Don Steiner's calculation: 'Radiological Impact of Fusion', *New Scientist* (1972), *52*, p. 168.

228   risks of fast breeder reactor: I have not discussed the risk of a reactor explosion, which is not negligible. See Sheldon Novick, 'Nuclear Breeders', *Environment* (1974), *16*(6), p. 6.

228   hydrogen economy: W. E. Winsche, *et al.*, 'Hydrogen: its future role in the Nation's Energy Economy', *Science* (1973), *180*, p. 25, and, for a critical view, T. Johnson, 'Hydrogen Hysteria', *New Scientist* (1972), *56*, p. 410.

230   Francis Bacon cited: F. Bacon and T. Fry, 'When there's no more oil and gas . . .', *New Scientist* (1972), *55*, p. 285.

230   Bockris cited: J. O'M. Bockris, 'A Hydrogen Economy', *Science* (1972), *176*, p. 1323.

231   energy wastage; C. Berg cited: C. A. Berg, 'Energy Conservation through effective Utilisation', *Science* (1973), *181*, p. 128.

232   solar energy sources: A. B. Meinel and M. P. Meinel, 'Solar Energy', *Physics Today* (February 1972), p. 44; M. Wolf, 'Solar Energy Utilization by Physical Methods', *Science* (1974), *184*, p. 382, and M. Calvin, 'Solar Energy by Photosynthesis', *Science* (1974), *184*, p. 375.

232   temperature differences in oceans: C. Zener, 'Solar Sea Power', *Physics Today* (1973), *26*(1), p. 48; W. D. Metz, 'Temperature Gradients: Solar Power from the Sea', *Science* (1973), *180*, p. 1266.

233 electricity from waste: for some difficulties see D. Wilcox, 'Fuel from City
      Trash', *Environment* (1973), *15*(7), p. 36.
233 US distribution of research funds: R. Gillette, 'Energy R. & D.: Under
      Pressure a National Policy takes Form', *Science* (1973), *182*, p. 888.

XV CROWDED

For an impression of what the population problem means in practical terms see
Dom Moraes, *A Matter of People* (1974).

235 Jakarta's overcrowding: P. Norman, 'Jakarta—dying from within', *Sunday
      Times Magazine*, 31/3/74, p. 32.
235 growth rate of cities: table from 'The World's Crisis Points', *Sunday Times
      Magazine*, 31/3/74, p. 24.
236 Papaiannou's forecast: C. Doxiadis, 'Cities of the Future', in A. B. Bronwell
      (ed), 1970; J. G. Papaiannou, 'Some Highlights for AD 2000', in R. Jungk
      and J. Galtung (1969), p. 230.
236 Calcutta: P. Wilsher, 'The Breaking Point', *Sunday Times Magazine*, 31/3/74,
      p. 27; Ajit Roy, 'The Problem', *Seminar* (1973), *163*, p. 10.
236 Dunkerley; upgrading slums: at Oxford Conference on Exploding Cities,
      1974, *Sunday Times Magazine*, 31/3/74.
237 Lubell cited: his *Slums are for People*, cited Wilsher, ibid.
238 Detroit as murder capital: S. Aris, 'Detroit—ring of no confidence', *Sunday
      Times Magazine*, ibid.
238 British cities in decline: T. Dawe, *et al.*, 'Why British Cities are seizing up',
      Sunday Times, 21/10/73; T. Jones, 'People are leaving Britain's big cities',
      The Times, 7/8/74.
238 London facing collapse: Alan Day, 'Is London facing collapse?', *Observer*
      4/11/73.
238 Gallup Poll; rural preference: also for comparative costs: *Science News* (1973),
      103, p. 309.
239 Calhoun; crowded mice infertile: M. Pines, 'How the Social Organisation
      of Animal Communities can Lead to a Population Crisis . . .', Nat. Inst.
      Mental Health: Mental Health Program Reports—5; Urbsdoc 200 (1971).
239 R. Meier's urban fantasy: R. Meier, 'Material Resources', in Jungk and
      Galtung (eds), p. 110.
240 Tata's optimism: J. R. D. Tata, 'A Strategy for Human Survival', in
      Tiselius and Nilsson (1970).
241 opposition to population control: T. E. Smith (ed), 1973.
241 Tara Ali Baig cited: New Legislation, *Seminar* (1974), *175*, p. 12.
242 Khanna study and opposition: see J. B. Wyon and J. E. Gordon (1971), and
      Bina Agrawal's review of B. Berelson (ed), *Family Planning Programs* (1969),
      in *Seminar* (1974), *175*, p. 33. Agrawal also cites Mahmood Mamdani, *The
      Myth of Population Control* (1972).
242 Java's attempt to cope: J. Tinker, 'Java birth-control battlefield', *New
      Scientist* (1974), *61*, p. 483.
243 population of England and Wales: Registrar General's Quarterly Reports
      (1973).
243 population control in China: Han Suyin, 'Family Planning: the Chinese
      Experiment', UNICEF (Aug. 1974), 21–5.
244 Bangladesh population outlook: 'Bangladesh condemned?' *Ecologist* (1973),
      3(6), p. 201. The UN Report referred to was 'given extremely limited
      circulation' because of its alarming nature.

246 disadvantages of tourism: G. Young, *Tourism: Blessing or Blight?* (1973); see also J. Young, 'Ochlothanasia comes to the National Parks', *The Times*, 12/7/74.

246 air-traffic growth estimates: British Overseas Airways Corporation (privately communicated).

249 Gerald Leach's study: *The Times*, 11/1/74 (letter).

249 energy and agriculture: D. Pimentel, *et al.*, 'Food Production and the Energy Crisis', *Science* (1973), *182*, p. 443.

XVI FAMINE

There have been numerous reviews of the food situation; among the best are Lester B. Brown, *Population and Affluence: Growing Pressures on World Food Resources* (1973), and N. Wade, 'World Food Situation: Pessimism comes back into Vogue', *Science* (1973), *181*, pp. 634–8.

252 meat analogues: *Farmers Weekly*, Synthetic Food Supplement; A. W. Holmes and C. Burke, 'Simulated Meat Foods', *BNF Information Bulletin*, No. 6 (July 1971), p. 57; also 'The Switch from Meat', *Sunday Times*, 14/4/74.

255 Japanese food habit changes: N. Pirie, 'The Direction of Beneficial Nutritional Change', *Ecology of Food & Nutrition* (1972), *1*, p. 279.

255 W. David Hopper cited: 'New Directions in Development' (an address to the board of governors of the International Development Research Centre, of which he is President, on 25/3/74) in *The IDRC Reports* (June 1974), *3*(2), p. 4, especially p. 8 and p. 11.

256 Indian hydroelectric plants shut down: *Time*, 29/4/74.

256 Addeke Boerma cited: V. Walker-Leigh, 'Obstacles to feeding the World's Hungry', *The Times*, 6/5/73; and *The Times*, 8/10/74, 'FAO Director says millions face starvation'.

256 death from starvation: Among many reports in 1974 see 'Death by starvation faces millions', *The Times*, 30/9/74; 'Ethiopia's plea went unheeded', *Observer*, 4/11/73; 'Indians reduced to eating leaves', *The Times*, 2/10/74, etc.

256 world food production: *The State of Food and Agriculture*, FAO, Rome 1973.

257 fertilizer shortage: M. Westlake, 'Is the Green Revolution foundering?', *The Times*, 6/5/73; and Hopper, ibid.

258 Lester Brown quoted: *Science* (1973), *180*, p. 373, 'Rising Food Prices: Who's Responsible?'.

259 overfishing of oceans: Carle O. Hodge, 'Farming the Oceans', *Technology Review* (1973), *75*(7), p. 73; NAS/NRC/NAE *News Report* (Nov. 1973), xxiii(9) 2–3; 'leading fish to an automated harvest', *Ocean Industry* (April 1971), p. 65; and Lester Brown, ibid.

261 fish-farming: For a knowledgeable review see J. I. W. Anderson, 'The Aquacultural Revolution' (roneoed), 1974.

262 McNamara cited: address to the Board of Governors of the World Bank, Nairobi, Sept. 1973.

262 Dunkerley's estimate of capital needs: in P. Wilsher, 'What Hope for the Shanty Towns?', *Sunday Times*, 7/4/74.

262 economic aid as per cent of GNP: McNamara, ibid.

263 special World Bank report: 'World aid: $6,600m. is needed', Paul Lewis in *Financial Times*, 16/4/74.

264   economic aid, realities of: Mende (1973), passim.
266   Boumedienne cited: V. Walker-Leigh, 'Obstacles to feeding the world's hungry', *The Times*, 6/5/73.

PART VI   SUGGESTIONS

XVII   SOCIAL SUGGESTIONS

273   practical experience for politicians: the idea and the comment from *Observer*, 30/6/74.
273   Net National Welfare concept, Japan: P. Brachi, 'Japan's GNP—Going, going, gone', *Ecologist* (1972), *2*(9), p. 26.
275   Norway preserves rural lifestyle: *Economist*, 7/9/74, *252*, p. 75.
277   single transferable vote: successfully used in Northern Ireland in 1973, with the result that 85 per cent of those who voted are represented by a person of their choice, whereas before, a party with 51 per cent of the votes won 11 of the 12 seats. See Lakeman (1975).
279   sense of helplessness: Halleck (1967), pp. 125, 174, 190.
280   poll on sense of political impotence: *PHP Magazine* (April 1974), p. 68.

XVIII   PERSONAL PROBLEMS

282–283   Barbara Wootton cited: op. cit., p. 69.
283   Achievement Place: R. J. Trotter, 'Behaviour Modification', *Science News* (1973), *103*, p. 260.
283   Highfields, New Jersey: H. Ashley Weeks (1958).
283   British experiments: *The Times*, 3/11/73, Social workers relive juvenile crime; see also, *The Times*, 23/8/74, 'Community Service Orders to be made nationwide'.
283   Danish experiment, Herstedvester: G. K. Sturup (1968). A prison for women on similar lines was opened in 1970 at Hämeenlina, north of Helsinki.
284   needs of children, Dr M. K. Pringle: *Violence and Vandalism*, Assn. of Chief Police Officers of England, Wales and Northern Ireland (roneoed), 1972.
285   Uncareers: *The Times*, 5/6/71, M. Cooper: 'Careers for people who do not want a career'.
285   Community Service Volunteers: R. Chesshyre, 'Sentenced to serve', *Observer Magazine*, 17/2/74; *The Times*, 20/3/74, P. Moorehead: Matching work to the idea of social service.
287   Halleck cited: S. L. Halleck (1967), p. 125.
288   Dr Pringle cited: *Observer Review*, 9/6/74, p. 28; Whitehorn: Don't just research: Do something.
288   Bandura and Walters enquiry confirms Glueck and Glueck study: A. Bandura and R. H. Walters (1959); S. Glueck and E. Glueck (1950).
288   174 non-delinquents studied: see W. McCord, J. McCord and R. Howard, 'Familial Correlates of Aggression in Non-delinquent Children', in Megargee and Hokanson (1970), pp. 41ff.
288   370 New England mothers studied: R. R. Sears, E. E. Maccoby and H. Levin (1957).

289 altruists studied: P. London, 'The Rescuers', in J. Macaulay and L. Berkowitz (1970), p. 247.

289 British study: R. G. Andry (1971).

289 adult criminality, world wide study: M. Bacon, I. L. Child and H. Barry (1963), 'A Cross-Cultural Study of Correlates of Crime', *J. Abn. & Soc. Psychol.*, 66, p. 291.

289 Lenin, Trotsky, Gandhi: E. V. Wolfenstein (1967).

290 Professor Cortés's proposal: J. B. Cortés and F. M. Gatti (1972).

292 English children worst: U. Bronfenbrenner (1971) and see Andry (1971).

292 importance of family: I. Eibl-Eibesfeldt (1971), pp. 229 and 234.

293 physiology and aggression: K. E. Moyer, 'The Physiology of Aggression' in J. L. Singer (1971); B. E. Eleftheriou and J. P. Scott (1971).

294 stimulus hunger: F. Solomon 'Psychodynamic Aspects of Aggression', in D. N. Daniels, M. F. Gilula and F. M. Ochberg (1970); see also H. C. Quay, *Amer. J. Psychiat.* (1965), *122*, p. 180.

294 guilt-relieving rituals: M. Mead, 'Some Anthropological Considerations concerning Guilt', in R. C. Johnson, P. R. Dočeski and O. H. Mowrer (1972).

XIX PERSPECTIVES

300 Kornhauser: W. Kornhauser, ' "Power Elite" or "Veto Groups"?' in R. Bendix and S. M. Lipset (1967), p. 210.

LIST OF SOURCES

The following is a list of the books mentioned in the Reference Notes, giving title and publisher, together with the date of the edition actually used. It is not a bibliography, nor does it represent all the works consulted. It does not include references to newspapers and periodicals as these are given in full in the notes.

ANON The New Technology of Repression: lessons from Ireland. (BSSRS Paper 2) British Society for Social Responsibility in Science, London. 1974.

ABSE, Leo *Private Member*. Macdonald, London. 1973.

ALLCHIN, W. H. *Young People: problems of adaptation to a fragmented society*. Guild of Pastoral Psychology, London. 1970.

ANDERSON, J. I. W. *The Aquacultural Revolution*. ICI, Bedford. 1974 (roneoed).

ANDRESKI, Stanislav *Prospects of a Revolution in the USA*. Stacey, London. 1973.

ANDRY, R. G. *Delinquency and Parental Pathology*. Staples Press, London. 1971.

APTER, David E. and JOLL, James (eds) *Anarchism Today*. Macmillan, London. 1971.

ARENDT, Hannah *On Violence*. Allen Lane, London. 1970.

BANDURA, A. and WALTERS, R. H. *Adolescent Aggression*. Ronald Press, New York. 1959.

BARRON, John *KGB: the secret work of Soviet secret service agents*. Hodder & Stoughton, London. 1974.

BECKWITH, Burnham *The Next 500 Years*. Exposition-University Book, Jericho, New York. 1967.

BENDIX, R. and LIPSET, S. M. (eds) *Class, Status and Power*. Routledge & Kegan Paul, London. 1967.

BENN, Anthony W. *The New Politics: a socialist reconnaissance*. (Fabian Tract 402) Fabian Society, London. 1970.

BERNSTEIN, M. *Regulating Business by Independent Commissions*. Princeton University Press, Princeton, N.J. 1972.

BOOKCHIN, Murray *Listen, Marxist!* Times Change Press, New York. 1971.

BRINTON, Crane *The Anatomy of Revolution*. Vintage Books, Englewood Cliffs, N.J. 1965.

BRITISH CENTRAL STATISTICAL OFFICE Social Trends, No. 4. HMSO. 1973.

BRONFENBRENNER, Urie *Two Worlds of Childhood: USA and USSR*. Allen & Unwin, London. 1972.

BRONWELL, A. B. (ed) *Science and Technology in the World of the Future*. Wiley-Interscience, New York. 1970.

327

BROWN, Lester   *United Nations, World without Borders.* Random House, New York. 1972.

BRUNNER, John   *The Jagged Orbit.* Arrow Books, London. 1972.

BURY, J. B.   *A History of the Later Roman Empire* (2 vols). Macmillan, London. 1923.

CAMPBELL, A. and CONVERSE, P. (eds)   *The Human Meaning of Social Change.* Russell Sage Foundation, New York. 1972.

CHEVALIER, L.   *Labouring Classes and Dangerous Classes in Paris in the first half of the nineteenth century.* Routledge & Kegan Paul, London. 1973.

COELHO, G. V. and RUBINSTEIN, E. A.   *Social Change and Human Behaviour.* National Institute of Mental Health, Bethesda, Md. 1972.

COMMITTEE ON RESOURCES AND MAN   *Resources and Man: a study and recommendations.* W. H. Freeman, San Francisco. 1969.

CORTÉS, J. B. and GATTI, F. M.   *Delinquency and Crime: a biopsychosocial approach.* Seminar Press, New York & London. 1972.

COUSINS, Jane   *Turkey: torture and political persecution.* Pluto Press, London. 1973.

CRANSTON, M.   *The New Left.* Bodley Head, London. 1970.

CROZIER, Brian   *The Rebels: a study of post-war insurrections.* Chatto & Windus, London. 1960.

DANIELS, D. N., GILULA, M. F. and OCHBERG, F. M. (eds)   *Violence and the Struggle for Existence.* Little, Brown, Boston. 1970.

DE TOCQUEVILLE, Alexis   *Democracy in America.* Vintage Books, New York. 1954.

DILL, Samuel   *Roman Society in the last Century of the Western Empire.* Macmillan, London. 1910.

DONALDSON, Peter   *Economics of the Real World.* Penguin Books, Harmondsworth. 1973.

DRUCKER, Peter F.   *Age of Discontinuity.* Heinemann. 1969.

DRUCKER, Peter F.   *The Landmarks of Tomorrow.* Heinemann, London. 1959.

DUESENBERRY, J. S.   *Income, Saving and the Theory of Consumer Behavior.* Harvard Univ. Press, Cambridge, Mass. 1952.

DURKHEIM, Emile   *Professional Ethics and Civic Morals.* The Free Press, Glencoe, Ill. 1958. *Suicide.* The Free Press, Glencoe. 1951.

EIBL-EIBLESFELDT, I.   *Love and Hate.* Methuen, London. 1971.

ELEFTHERIOU, B. E. and SCOTT, J. P. (eds)   *The Physiology of Aggression and Defeat.* Plenum Press, New York. 1971.

ELLUL, Jacques   *Violence: reflections from a Christian perspective.* SCM Press, London. 1970.

ENDLEMAN, S. (ed)   *Violence in the Streets.* Quadrangle Books, Chicago. 1968.

FINLEY, M. I.   *The Ancient Economy.* Chatto & Windus, London. 1974.

FOWLER, Norman   *The Cost of Crime.* (CPC 521). Conservative Political Centre, London. 1973.

GALBRAITH, J.   *American Capitalism: the concept of countervailing power.* Houghton Mifflin, Boston. 1952.

GARAUDY, R.   *L'Alternative.* Laffont, Paris. 1972.

GEDDES, T. E. and LONG, J. O.   *Killer: a journal of murder.* Macmillan, London and New York. 1970.

GLUECK, S. and GLUECK, E.   *Unraveling Juvenile Delinquency.* Commonwealth Fund, New York. 1950.

GORDON, Theodore H.   'Some Crises which will determine the World of 1944.' AAAS Symposium, San Francisco. 1974 (roneoed).

HALLECK, S. L.   *Psychiatry and the Dilemmas of Crime.* Harper & Row, New York. 1967.

HAMILTON, Peter *Computer Security*. Cassell/Associated Business Programmes, London. 1972.

JOHNSON, G. C. and SMITH, L. P. (eds) *The Biological Significance of Climatic Changes in Britain*. Symposium 14 of the Institute of Biology. Academic Press, London & New York. 1965.

JOHNSON, R. C., DOKEČKI, P. R. and MOWRER, O. H. *Conscience, Contract and Social Reality*. Holt, Rinehart and Winston, New York. 1972.

JONES, A. H. M. *The Later Roman Empire*, 284–602. Blackwell, Oxford. 1964.

JUNGK, R. and GALTUNG, J. (eds) *Mankind 2000*. Allen & Unwin, London. 1969.

KAHN, H. and BRUCE-BRIGGS, B. *Things to Come: thinking about the seventies and eighties*. Macmillan, New York. 1972.

KORNHAUSER, William *Politics of Mass Society*. Routledge & Kegan Paul, London. 1960.

LAKEMAN, Enid *How Democracies Vote*. Faber and Faber, London. 1975.

LAMB, H. H. *Climate: Present, Past and Future*. Methuen, London. 1972.

LEDERER, E. *State of the Masses*. W. W. Norton, New York. 1940.

LEWIS, R. S. and SPINRAD, B. I. in *The Energy Crisis* L. E. Rocks and R. Runyon, Crown Press, New York. 1972.

LOVINS, Amory B. *World Energy Strategies: facts, issues and options*. Earth Resources Research Ltd, London. 1973.

LOWENSTEIN, L. F. *Violence in Schools and its Treatment*. National Association of Schoolmasters, Hemel Hempstead. 1972.

MACAULAY, J. and BERKOWITZ, L. (eds) *Altruism and Helping Behavior*. Academic Press, London & New York. 1970.

McMULLEN, Ramsay *Enemies of the Roman Order*. Harvard University Press, Cambridge, Mass. 1967.

MARCHETTI, Victor and MARKS, John *The CIA and the Cult of Intelligence*. Jonathan Cape, London. 1974.

MATTHEWS, W. H., KELLOG, W. and ROBINSON, G. D. (eds) *Man's Impact on the Climate*. MIT Press, Cambridge, Mass. 1971.

MAYO, Patricia Elton *The Making of a Criminal*. Weidenfeld & Nicolson, London. 1969.

MEGARGEE, E. I. and HOKANSON, J. E. (eds) *The Dynamics of Aggression: individual, group and international analyses*. Harper & Row, New York. 1970.

MENDE, Tibor *From Aid to Re-Colonisation: lessons of a failure*. Harrap, London. 1973.

MILLS, Charles Wright *Power, Politics and People*. O.U.P., New York. 1963.

MOORE, Jr, Barrington *Reflections on the Causes of Human Misery*. Allen Lane, The Penguin Press, Harmondsworth. 1972.

MORAES, Dom *A Matter of People*. Andre Deutsch, London. 1974.

MURDOCH, William W. (ed) *Environment: Resources, Pollution and Society*. Sinauer Associates, Stamford, Conn. 1971.

NEUMANN, Franz *The Democratic and the Authoritarian State*. The Free Press, Glencoe, Ill. 1957.

NEUMANN, Sigmund *Permanent Revolution: the total state in a world at war*. Harper Bros., New York. 1942.

NEVILLE, Richard *Playpower*. Paladin Books, London. 1970.

NEWMAN, Oscar *Defensible Space*. Architectural Press, London. 1973.

NISBET, R. A. *The Quest for Community*. Oxford University Press, London. 1953.

PACKARD, Vance *The Waste Makers*. Penguin Books, Harmondsworth. 1971.

POLUNIN, N. (ed) *The Environmental Future*. Macmillan, London. 1972.

REDFORD, E. M. *Administration of National Economic Control*. Macmillan, New York. 1952.

ROSTOVTZEFF, M. *The Social and Economic History of the Roman Empire*. Clarendon Press, Oxford. 1926.

SCHURR, S. H. (ed) *Energy Consumption Trends and Patterns*. Johns Hopkins Press, Baltimore, Md. 1972.

SEABROOK, Jeremy *City Close up*. Pelican Books, Harmondsworth. 1973.

SEARS, R. R., MACCOBY, B. and LEVIN, N. *Patterns of Child Rearing*. Harper Bros., New York. 1957.

SINGER, J. L. (ed) *The Control of Aggression and Violence: cognitive and physiological factors*. Academic Press, New York. 1971.

SMITH, T. E. (ed) *The Politics of Family Planning in the Third World*. Allen & Unwin, London. 1973.

SPETH, J. G., TAMPLIN, A. R. and COCHRAN, T. B. *The Plutonium Decision*. National Resources Defense Council, Washington D.C. 1974.

STETLER, Russell (ed) *Palestine: the Arab–Israeli conflict*. Ramparts Press, San Francisco. 1972.

STURUP, G. K. *Treating the 'Untreatable': chronic criminals at Herstedvester*. Johns Hopkins Press, Baltimore, Md. 1968.

TAVERNE, Dick *The Future of the Left: Lincoln and After*. Jonathan Cape, London. 1974.

THOMPSON, Antony A. *Big Brother in Britain Today*. Michael Joseph, London. 1970.

THOMPSON, Robert *Defeating Communist Insurgency*. Chatto & Windus, London. 1966.

TISELIUS, A. and NILSSON, S. (eds) *The Place of Values in a World of Facts: proceedings of the 14th Nobel symposium, Stockholm 1969*. Wiley, New York. 1970.

TOCH, Hans *The Social Psychology of Social Movements*. Methuen, London. 1971.

TOFFLER, Alvin (ed) *The Futurists*. Random House, New York. 1972.

TOYNBEE, Arnold *A Study of History* (abridged by D. C. Somervell). Oxford University Press, London & New York. 1947.

TREVELYAN, G. M. *History of England*, Vol. I, Longmans Green. 1943.

VACCA, Roberto *Il Medioevo Prossimo Venturo*. Mondadori, Milan. 1971.

WAELDER, Robert *Progress and Revolution: a study of the issues of our age*. International Universities Press, New York. 1967.

WALBANK, F. W. *The Awful Revolution*. Liverpool University Press, 1969.

WARD, Colin (ed) *Vandalism*. The Architectural Press, London. 1973.

WARREN, Kenneth *Mineral Resources*. Penguin Books, Harmondsworth. 1973.

WEBER, Max *Wirtschaft und Gesellschaft*. J. C. B. Mohr, Tübingen. 1956.

WEEKS, H. Ashley *et al*. *Youthful Offenders at Highfields: an evaluation*. University of Michigan, Ann Arbor, Mich. 1958.

WERTHAM, Fredric *The Show of Violence*. Gollancz, London. 1949.

WILLRICH, Mason and TAYLOR, Theodore B. *Nuclear Theft: Risks and Safeguards*. Ballinger, Cambridge, Mass. 1974.

WILLS, W. D. *The Barns Experiment*. Allen & Unwin, London. 1945.

WOLFENSTEIN, E. V. *The Revolutionary Personality*. Princeton University Press, Princeton, N.J. 1967.

WOOTTON, Barbara *Social Science and Social Pathology*. Allen & Unwin, London. 1959.

YOUNG, George *Tourism: Blessing or Blight?*. Penguin Books, Harmondsworth. 1973.

INDEX

331